THE STANDARDS EDGE:

Dynamic Tension

2004

THE STANDARDS EDGE:

Dynamic Tension

2004

EDITED BY SHERRIE BOLIN

© 2004 Bolin Communications

EDITOR: Sherrie Bolin
President and CEO
Bolin Communications
Phone: +1 (510) 655-2293
email: sherrie@sbolin.com
http://www.bolincommunications.com

ISBN 0-9748648-1-1

Printed by Sheridan Books
Ann Arbor, MI

Printed in the United States of America

Contents

Section 5 Cross-Industry Impact 271

Preface and Acknowledgements

The Standards Edge: Dynamic Tension is the second in the series entitled The Standards Edge. As with the last book, this effort was produced in support of a conference on standardization and its content was expanded to provide a more comprehensive view of standardization today. This year the conference, entitled "Innovation and Legislation: Standardization in Conflict" was supported by Sun Microsystems, JEDEC, Georgetown University, Global Inventures, Samsung, Oracle, and America Online (AOL). The growing number and diversity of the sponsors serve as evidence of the increasing importance of standardization and its impact on the marketplace.

The Standards Edge series is designed to tackle the latest technological and standards issues and their impact on business. The original book in this series currently serves as a valuable resource to industry, government organizations, standards setting organizations, and academic institutions around the world. Future editions in this series will provide in-depth coverage of specific topics relevant to standardization and the information and communications technology industry. Feedback, suggestions, and requests for additional copies may be sent directly to the editor by sending email to sherrie@sbolin.com.

The Standards Edge: Dynamic Tension would not have been possible without the help of several organizations and individuals. First and foremost, I would like to thank Sun Microsystems, Inc. for providing the research grant—and the hands off approach—that made this book possible. Global Inventures also deserves thanks for contributing funding to the production of this book.

Each of the authors in this book has earned my sincerest gratitude and commendation. All are leaders in their respective fields and, as such, are under the extensive time pressures that leadership entails. Regardless of these pressures, they made the time to carefully craft their articles, ensuring that the knowledge they impart is accurate and relevant. To each of these authors, I give my wholehearted thanks for making this book a success.

A hearty thanks goes out to Lynda Banks, who designed the cover and layout of the book. If you find it easy to read and pleasing to the eye, it is thanks to her unparalleled expertise in graphic design. Laura Shelley undertook the indexing of this volume with great enthusiasm, and I extend a special thanks to her for sharing her expertise and incredible gift for organization.

Finally, I would never have undertaken or completed this endeavor if I had not benefited from the wisdom and experience of my parents. So considerable thanks goes out to them: To my mother, who taught me that creativity and visionary thinking require your feet to leave the ground and to my father, who taught me how to keep my feet on the ground long enough to make my visions a reality.

Introduction

SHERRIE BOLIN

Editor

The pit loomed just a foot away, gaping, almost mocking her as she was forced towards it. She fought desperately, digging in her heels, clambering madly to keep from sliding. The burning started in her calves, moving up her legs, searing pains traveling through her back to the very tips of her fingers. The pit beckoned her closer, seemingly moving the ground beneath her. Her grip on the rope was slipping. She could hear the others of the group scrambling behind her—a seemingly disparate cacophony of moans, screams, and pleas rushing in waves over her body, throwing her further off balance. "Hold," commanded one, "Grip down," pleaded another. She tried, but her energy—and her will—had dissipated, evaporating into the sweat soaked air. Her toes were peeking over the edge of the pit—she would be the first to succumb, to flail into the pit, and be covered by its noxious contents. "Loosen your grip." "Loosen!" came the order. Her body reacted before her mind—relinquishing her grip and letting the forces take over. And they did—for a moment—her upper body now tottering over the pit. But the incredible force from the other side was gone! "Now pull," roared another. With every remaining bit of energy that she could summon, she gripped down on the rope and dug her heels in. This time striving not to maintain but to move. Now, the force from the other side was less, the pulling easier, and they pulled back with one single stroke, dragging the other team into the pit. The crowd yelled, screamed, embraced them with their applause. Once again her team had triumphed in the annual tug-of-war championship.

Dynamic Tension. It's everywhere. From the games we play as children to those we play as adults. But as adults, the stakes are higher, the rules fuzzier, and the game itself keeps changing. What hasn't changed is the need to strategize and act in new and different ways. The team in the scenario above did what you are never supposed to do in tug-of-war: let go. By doing so, they threw their competition out of balance—a balance that was directly dependent on both teams pulling with fairly equal force—and prevailed.

Standardization is itself a similar strategy, a business tool. It is a loosening of the rope a bit to throw the traditional business world off balance. In doing so, it expands markets, increases market uptake, and spurs innovation. The process itself can be viewed as a temporary breaking of that dynamic tension between competitive companies, as they come together to agree on specifications from which future products will emerge.

But it would be a mistake to say that standardization removes tension. Rather, it creates and channels it. Attend a single standards conference and you will be confronted with passions, heated arguments, and strong opinions that would rival the most contentious football game. And while process rules may be the norm and the air may be saturated with the echoing of acronym after acronym, make no mistake about it—agreements incubated here can and do change entire industries. But the tension goes beyond individual participants. In standardization today dynamic tension exists between different countries, rival companies, vendors and users, national and international standards bodies, standards developing organizations and consortia, industry and government, and even between competing standards. Without that tension, there are no standards. And standards, make no mistake about it, are what it is all . about. Sometimes one side wins and sometimes another side prevails. Sometimes different sides team up together. Things may change but one principle remains the same: dynamic tension is essential. Without it, the business world would lose its motivation, its edge, and its drive for innovation. Governments would have little reason to work together on issues such as trade. And consumers would have few incentives to adopt new technologies in a desire to move ahead in their own industries.

The question is: How do we maintain that precarious balance that enables this dynamic tension? How do we keep the rope from becoming so tight that it prevents companies from moving at all? And how do we keep it from getting so loose that industries, in effect, hang themselves? If we construct too many rules, business will stagnate as companies are prevented from implementing innovative strategies. Remove all the rules, and chaos, or at least some blatant anticompetitive practices, will result. Perhaps that is the ultimate purpose of standardization—as a management tool. A tool that allows countries, industries, and companies to manage that precarious but necessary dynamic tension that fuels economic growth. A tool that enables companies to balance the tension between user requirements and product constraints, between competition and cooperation, and between innovation and market readiness. A tool that allows governments to balance the needs between domestic industries and global concerns, between regulations and free market dynamics, and between public and private interests.

This book examines standardization as a powerful management tool for dynamic tension from different points of view: the system as a whole, government, legal, vendors, and consumers. In each section, implementable strategies are provided to leverage standardization and strengthen its impact.

The book begins with the section entitled "Strengthening the System," which takes a high level view of the standardization system and its challenges. Moving beyond the tired arguments of standards developing organizations versus consortia, this section presents challenges and solutions to make the overall standardization industry stronger. And this, ultimately, is the goal as a stronger system will serve the needs of its members and other stakeholders more rapidly and effectively.

Building on the ideas presented in Section One, the next section, "Government Influence," takes a close look at where government is and should be involved in standardization. From facilitating and inhibiting international trade to fostering competition to protecting public interests, governments around the world are increasingly relying on standardization to solve global and national challenges. The way those challenges are solved will have a direct impact on your business and on your ability to do business.

Intellectual Property Rights issues continue to rise to the top of legislative and industry agendas. With Rambus still in the legal process and the added complications of the Eolas lawsuit, the dynamic tension here is clearly reaching a crescendo. Are standards setting organizations, industry, or government prepared to address these issues? This section examines alternative solutions that move beyond or capitalize on the more traditional Reasonable and Non-Discriminatory (RAND) and Royalty Free (RF) solutions.

How do companies take all of this information and directly apply it to their business, customers, and industry? The section entitled "Strategic Standardization" delivers directly applicable advice on how to craft and implement a standardization strategy. While the last edition of *The Standards Edge* provided strategic advice on external standardization activities, this section mainly focuses on developing standardization strategies and incorporating them into internal business processes.

Information and communications technology (ICT) standards don't just impact ICT's largest vendors. In fact, the effects of decisions made in Standards Setting Organizations (SSOs) around the world ripple through the business processes and profits of numerous industries from finance to biotechnology to agricultural equipment suppliers. They also impact the options available to the users and drive major government policies because of their public good content. The section, "Cross-Industry Impact," examines how various industries are not only reacting to, but also driving, ICT standardization.

Standardization provides a powerful tool for managing the dynamic tension that is essential to the health of the global economy. Their voluntary nature and emphasis on collaboration enable this tension to be managed in a way that encourages and stimulates free market trade and growth. Whether you will or will not be engaged in a tug-of-war game similar to that described at the beginning of this "Introduction" is not the question—you most undoubtedly will and probably already are. The true question is: When the rope has been pulled taut and *your* toes are tottering precariously on the edge of the pit, will you have the knowledge and strategy to ultimately triumph? In other words, will you have *The Standards Edge*?

Section 1

Strengthening the System

"We must, indeed, all hang together or, most assuredly, we shall all hang separately." Although these words were spoken by Benjamin Franklin at the signing of the Declaration of Independence, they are still applicable today—especially to the world of standardization. A year after the publication of the first edition of this book debates still rage about whether standards developing organizations (SDOs) or consortia are the better choice. Standards setting bodies continue to develop competing standards—often created by the same participants in different organizations. Consumers—and CEOs—continue to hide at the very mention of the word *standards* or at least quickly relegate a standards issue back to the world of engineers. The fragmented world of standardization is becoming increasingly confusing to navigate, and that confusion will keep its activities—and its value—a hidden secret of the select few who have made standardization their career.

This is not to say that standardization has not evolved in the last year. It has. A number of SDOs are offering alternative services to speed up the standardization process. Some consortia are submitting their completed standards for fast acceptance by SDOs, especially the international bodies of ITU, IEC, and ISO.[1] While

competing standards are damaging the intent of standardization by bringing about the very incompatibility they were designed to resolve, at least it shows that some SSOs are starting to think like a business—albeit not one with the best long term strategy.

Although this fragmentation might be a necessary stage in the effort to create a stronger, more responsive standardization system, it may also serve to undermine it all together if those who financially support the system don't recognize its value. In general, standards participation and SSO revenues have continued to decline. Although the economy can certainly take part of the blame, I believe that it comes down to two factors: perception and effectiveness.

In regards to perception, the first and foremost standards battle that must be fought is that of establishing and communicating its value. If it is not valued, then it will not survive. Since the measurement of a good standard is the number of implementations, then shouldn't the measurement of the value of standards be the same— the number of companies using it, the number of corporate strategies that include standards, the number of CEOs that can even define the word? Standardization needs to move beyond the argument over SDOs vs. consortia. The differences are becoming slightly blurred and, in the end, users don't care where their standards come from anymore than they care where their electricity comes from. The only thing they care about is whether products work the way they are supposed to. Instead, SSOs need to band together and take a "Got Milk? ®" approach to promote the value of standardization. Consider that ten years after the inception of the "Got Milk? ®" ad campaign, studies show that 95% of Americans still recall the slogan, it has spawned a multimillion dollar licensing property, and it successfully defended milk's share of the beverage consumption market in California and elsewhere. [2] If they want to survive, standards setting organizations need to do the same. They must band together to communicate the value of standardization to those who matter most— CEOs and other executive management that ultimately determine how corporate funds are distributed. Extending this communication out to the consumers, who can in turn put pressure on vendors, should also be considered.

Addressing efficiency and market relevance requires a high level look at the system in general. This section starts out with an examination of standardization as an ecology that must balance economic, social, and technical interests. Read the article by Rob Gingell, Sun Microsystems Fellow and Vice President, to gain a better understanding of this system and learn about a set of principles that can be used to effectively guide the utilization of standards. Dr. Linda Garcia of Georgetown University visits this issue from a different angle, approaching standardization as an organizational field. Given the competition currently raging between and within SSOs, read this article to discover why the government is being called on to set standards for standards setters. In addition, Ken Krechmer, International Center for Standards Research at the University of Colorado, explains why the standardization system that served the Industrial Age must evolve to effectively serve the Information Age.

While some view standardization as the antithesis of innovation, it in fact stimulates it.[3] Read Carl Cargill's article to discover how standardization not only encourages innovation, but provides a safe place for it to incubate, and discover why the standardization system, unless government and academia become involved, could ultimately fail. Houlin Zhao, Director of the Telecommunication Standardization Bureau (TSB), International Telecommunication Union (ITU), proposes a method for resolving some of the fragmentation in the standardization system in his article "Cooperation in the Age of Chance," while John Hill describes a plan to strengthen the system that is already being implemented.

Finally, NTT DoCoMo's James Kempf provides a practical article for "Getting to 'Yes' with the IETF." It is included here for two reasons: (1) To outline a system that many standards participants consider to be effective, and (2) To demonstrate how other SSOs might explain their processes to potential members.

The current standardization system can and should be strengthened. While the dynamic tension between the many entities involved in this system seems to be dangerously high right now, there are steps that can be taken to resolve the underlying issues or at least develop different, but compatible, solutions. This section provides a look into those challenges and some very possible solutions— but only if those who impact standardization work together to strengthen the system. After all, you don't want to leave yourselves hanging…

Notes

[1] ITU—International Telecommunication Union; IEC—International Electrotechnical Commission; ISO—International Organization for Standardization

[2] "Got Milk?"®: See http://www.gotmilk.com/news/news_018.html; and "Kaiser found that for every dollar a dairy farmer spends toward the milk marketing effort, the dairy farmer was rewarded with $3.40 in profits on average over the last 11 years," based on a study conducted by Cornell University; Kaiser, Henry. "Got milk? Apparently, you do.", Cornell University Science News; December 1997, see http://www.news.cornell.edu/releases/Dec97/GotMilk.bpf.html

[3] IDC, 2001, "Standardization: The Secret to IT Leverage," p.2

1

Standards as Economic Ecology: A System in Tension

ROB GINGELL
Sun Microsystems, Inc.

Abstract: *Within the Information and Communications Technology (ICT) industry, the art and practice of standardization can be viewed as an ecology of economic, social, and technical interests. Like many ecologies, a variety of stable situations may be possible, though not all such situations will be viewed as beneficial by all of the interests. An excessive force by any one interest may destabilize and potentially kill the whole ecosystem, though what constitutes excessive will vary over the life cycles of the various interests involved, which may alternately be in conflict or in support of one another. What is "right" may rarely be an absolute but rather something that provides the suitable stability for the state of the ecology's evolution.*

Standards as Economic Artifact

The existence of a standard can be viewed as an artifact of economy: an agreement among some community that the object of the standard has been sufficiently explored for the community to no longer accept the risks and costs associated with further innovation in the area. In its happiest conditions, such a community unanimously arrives at this conclusion thus obviating any conflict such a decision might pose for one or more of the parties. However, communities are often formed among parties whose relationship involves some aspect of

competing needs: those selling products desiring to maximize the revenue obtained and those purchasing products desiring to obtain their value at the lowest cost being the usual condition.

This innate conflict often leads to some compromises that cause one to inquire as to exactly whose economic interests are being protected with the establishment and maintenance of any given standard. In "Phase Relationships in the Standardization Process," James Gosling offered a cynical view of how the standards process could become perverted by the economic consideration of innovators attempting to avoid the risk of the marketplace.[1] By ensuring that the creation of a standard guaranteed a requirement for their investment, risk was moderated. The Information and Communications Technology (ICT) industry has been particularly exposed to such concerns over its technologically short life, motivated by technologies of relatively short market lifetimes.

When considered over a longer period than the initial introduction of an innovation, however,the additional complexity reveals behaviors that are not only phase related, but also life cycle related. In this case, behaviors that at first appear to be in static opposition with one another can also be viewed as phase relationships that vary with time. For the purposes of an ecology-based exploration of the art and practice of standardization in the ICT industry, we will consider the economic interests of three parties: consumers, suppliers, and government. We will then discuss those interests in standards covering technologies vs. products and examine how those interests form tensions that can either be managed to create a successful ecology that prospers or mismanaged to create a doomed ecology.

In this discussion we view a "standard" as representing a specification that admits of potentially multiple conforming implementations on which competition for those implementations occurs in domains outside of the space of the standard. One way of viewing standards is that they create localized homogeneity within a community, thus enabling the creation of an ecology where factors other than those described by the standard may be successfully varied and still retain harmony within the community.

Consumer Interests in Standards

Consumers use standards as a way of establishing choice among potentially several suppliers of a consumer need. The existence of choice promotes competition and innovation in areas outside of that expressed by the standard and, over time, is expected to deliver increasing value to the consumer, including lower prices and higher quality.

Over the short history of the ICT industry, we have seen a progression from the status of the early industry in the 1950s through the 1970s, which was dominated by vendor "lock-in" of customers. Customers often chose the product (a computer) first and then all other decisions were slaved to that decision. This meant that changing the vendor of the fundamental purchase was extremely costly and done only under conditions of extreme need.

In the 1980s, the notion of "open systems" was marketed, which included the concept that a customer would base their dependencies not on a product but on a series of interfaces that could be common to many products. This would permit the customer to have a choice of many potential suppliers. The industry of systems conforming to the UNIX® System[2] was the most significant illustration of this in the 1980s. However, UNIX® specifications mainly covered the technologies used to construct a system, and not so much the products resulting from those technologies. It thus enabled the economic boon of programmer portability but not the interchangeability of the products resulting from those programmers' efforts—each product involved a distinct combination of the specification with other artifacts that was unique to each vendor.

"Open systems" provided customers with greater freedom but still not the boon expected from the pervasive use of standards that typified the practice of open systems. Now, at the beginning of the 21st century, behaviors, practices, and capabilities have evolved sufficiently so that it is becoming feasible for customers to enjoy a level of competition that reverses the conditions of the early ICT industry and use standards to

> *"...it is becoming feasible for customers to enjoy a level of competition that reverses the conditions of the early ICT industry and use standards to "lock-in" vendors...."*

"lock-in" vendors rather than the other way around. The emergence of the Internet[3] as a foundation technology coupled with the arrival of portable product technologies such as Java™ (trademark of Sun Microsystems, Inc.),[4] have enabled ICT product consumers to base their purchasing decisions on their own application choices and use the standards upon which those choices depend to specify products that they will buy.

For consumers, such a reversal in the status quo would seem to present the attaining of an ideal situation—and indeed such is the case for dependencies captured by standards that are static. These same consumers, however, generate new problems that they request suppliers solve, seek advantages against the parties with whom they are themselves competitors, and attempt to drive ever-greater efficiencies. At certain times and places, innovation that occurs only outside the standard is not adequate—the standard becomes a millstone rather than an enabler.

Supplier Interest in Standards

Supplier interests in the abstract are to gain revenue from consumers in order to enable business growth and to fulfill customer needs in preference to their competitors. Initially resistant to standards as a device that eliminated "lock-in," suppliers have evolved to use standards as a means of reducing the risk associated with innovative activities by employing standards as a means to guarantee at least a modicum of economic success. Extreme usages of standards practices in pursuit of this goal led to the sarcasm evident in in the 1980s[1] and to the present day.

Yet, supplier interests are not completely divorced from those of the consumer. Often a supplier interest reflects an installed base of capabilities that employ a prior or different base than the subject of a standard. Customer investments are not only beneficial to the installed base of the supplier(s), but also represent a genuine customer investment whose (economic) interests should be protected. The experiences of the so-called "Y2K problem" revealed that quite a number of investments in the ICT arena are extremely long-lived, even though the technologies of the moment seem to have a fleeting lifetime.

Today, more enlightened suppliers view standards as a means to both satisfy customer

---

"...more enlightened suppliers view standards as a means to both satisfy customer need and as a potential roadmap to innovation."

---

need and as a potential roadmap to innovation. The "freedom of constraints" is a reflection that knowledge of where innovation is and is not possible is more liberating than it is constrain-

ing in many circumstances—but not in all. A paradox emerges when products, standards, and customer needs become overly constrained.

Consider the case of a "successful" standard: by providing a common set of products from which to choose, a standard enables a consumer to make the best choices for their needs among the available suppliers. So long as the customer's need is reflected in the standards on which they depend, the standard provides them this economic advantage.

It is a rare customer or marketplace that does not present evolving needs. If it is necessary for the new needs to be codified in a standard prior to their acceptance by any customer, then the industry is presented with the problem that innovation can only be introduced through a standards process. This gives rise to the absurd situations described in Gosling (1990)[1] and, in the worst case, to laughable circumstances leading to phrases such as "design by committee," which usually label soulless and ineffective contributions to the state of the art. The marketplace can be viewed as stagnant or ineffective.

If standardization is most effectively done as the codification of an existing practice, then there must be an existing practice and experience to codify. Innovators thus most often need to lead a standard by introducing innovations into the marketplace as a precursor to standarization. The resulting use and growth in dependency upon the innovation provides the impetus to standardize that innovation, especially if attempts at market differentiation appear to be causing divergence—too much innovation is as bad as too little..

If the innovation on which the marketplace depends gets too far ahead of the standard, the marketplace is viewed as a fragmented base of products in chaos. A "successful" standard can be viewed as one in which the base of the standard is within an "acceptable" distance of differentiating innovation that occurs within the marketplace—too far behind and the market is chaotic—not far enough behind and the marketplace is stagnant, slow, uncompetitive, and bureaucratic. Keeping that tension maintained is the first indication that the system of standards that establishes a community may have an ecology-like series of tensions.

Government Interests in Standards

A third entity in this system of relationships is government. A standard is itself a form of localized governance for a community, but in this case we're considering a social government such as that associated with a nation.

Governments uphold the interests of consumers with respect to the investments and national treasure that are expended upon ICT industry products. They also have interests in seeing indigenous industry prosper in a global economy, as well as public interests such as safety, security, and the maintenance of commerce. Government interest in standardization is often reflected in regulatory activities such as those that define minimum standards for food, medicines, and other life essentials. The increasing embedded use of ICT products in all parts of society will lead to a growing interest on the part of national and local governments in the use of standards that codify the most sensitive attributes of public interest.

While constraints may enable some elements of innovative freedom, a mismanaged or over-specified standardization ecology may well prove to be a dead one—starved of innovation or the ability to differentiate, it will move to a position of non-competitive stagnation. Jefferson's admonition that a "government which governs least, governs best" would seem to apply—the question is, what constitutes the most effective least governance? How would a government, or any party interested in applying the art and practice of standards, know when to say *when?*

The answer lies in the careful husbandry of a collection of interdependent relationships and economic interests, a portion of which have been captured thus far. The experience with the Internet, UNIX, and Java marketplaces has led to the observation of a set of principles that would seem to inform a sound management of the ecology surrounding a standard or set of standards.

Like any ecology, the overabundance of any one of the elements may lead to a destabilization or even collapse of the ecology, but also like an ecology, all of the elements are always independently evolving too. The principles that guide the management of a standards ecology are not absolutes but rather a system of parameters, the values of which must be established for the ecology and the community it serves.

Management (and Use) of a Standards Ecology

Successful users of an ICT standard will recognize that few things about the industry are indefinitely durable. A constant state of evolution exists such that any given framework of standards will have a lifetime much shorter than

---

"...the issue is not to prevent change but to maximize the economic efficiencies in what changes occur when."

---

the careers of any of the parties involved—the issue is not to prevent change but to maximize the economic efficiencies in what changes occur when. A set of principle parameters are identified below that can be used to guide the effective utilization of standards.

1. A standard delineates a point of homogeneity, enabling heterogeneity, change, and unbridled innovation in other areas.

We establish a standard for something so that we may have a point of reference from which to vary something else. It may be the set of applications we wish to enrichen and evolve on top of a stable base, as in the standards associated with many programming platforms. It may be to enable diversity in underlying technologies, as in the standards associated with the Internet that have permitted an explosion and convergence of communications technology upon the otherwise constant "IP protocol" that enables the Internet to exist.

New points of homogeneity appear in order to enable variation elsewhere or to serve the fact that the existing network of constants and variations has run its course and can deliver no further useful innovation. For most of the 1980s, several forms of network architectures existed in wide usage—what was common was often their cabled infrastructure, using Ethernet or some other comparable signalling system. In the ISO model of networking, we enjoyed localized homogeneity at the "Data Link" level of the network.

With the 1990s and the convergence of all networking and communications onto the Internet, we're in an era in which homogeneity has appeared at one level higher in the ISO networking model—at the Network Layer. This has enabled the creation of a variety of new signalling and wiring infrastructures (including un-wired infrastructures) as well as an explosion of systems models at layers "above" level three in the model.

It is worth noting that the assertion of a new homogeneity (at level three of networking) relieved a previous, localized assertion of homogeneity at a lower level. It could be argued that this was due to a market force—unification across everything that could exist was possible at level three where it was not possible except in a localized fashion at level two.

An ecology is thus characterized by the ability to enumerate the items that are constant and also the items that will vary. An inability to fully characterize the ecology along these lines will leave you exposed to mismatches in expectations between what can vary and what can not.

2. *A standard is a specification to which an artifact conforms—not an artifact implementation.*

As previously noted, a standard is necessarily a specification (and ideally paired with a set of tests of that specification) that is independent from any artifact claiming to implement the standard.

If this were not true, and a given artifact was in fact the standard, it would not be possible to change the implementation of the artifact without risking (probably unexpected) change to all the other things dependent upon the changed artifact. Indeed, the supplier of the changed artifact probably has no way of avoiding such side effects given the unspecified nature of what the dependencies could have been.

Standards that are solely artifacts are the vestigial remnants of the early days of the ICT industry in which suppliers used that status to "lock-in" their customers and, thus, unbalances the ecology to the detriment of the consumer and government entities. The ecology either collapses due to supplier non-responsiveness or is assaulted by legal or legislative action.

Consider the example of the VAX/VMS marketplace of the mid-1980s. Digital Equipment Corporation's VAX product line was, for most elements of the industry, considered "the product to beat." It was in many respects a marketplace standard for those segments of the market it served. It was managed by its supplier so that (mostly) only that supplier could offer changes or enhancements to the product set, making Digital effectively an innovation bottleneck. For customers who would not wait, their departure from the product line represented an irreversable loss of customer loyalty.

Successful standards ecologies are characterized only by standards expressed as specifications.

3. *A standard is more important for how it is consumed vs. what it offers.*

Standards are primarily characterized in the ICT industry as being a specification of the capabilities offered by a given artifact. Less rarely, and different from standards in other domains, does there exist a specification or measure of conformance about how a consumer artifact employs (or even limits) their dependencies to just what is specified in the standard. This leads to later loss of economic value for a standard when a consumer artifact is damaged by a change that should not have had any such impact given that both the changed and pre-change artifact were measured to be "conformant."

In the ICT industry, such a gap has led to the creation of artificial standards, such as the original POSIX standard, in which all suppliers claimed conformance with a standard for which few if any known usages were made. The value of this in actually creating an economic benefit is specious at best, and counterproductive at worst, since the collective effort required to establish and measure conformance to an unused standard consumed resources that could have been more productively used.

Successful ecologies will be able to document an end-to-end linkage between the standards specified to be used and their actual use.

4. *A standard has a community—apply it only to affect that community, and expect it only to affect that community.*

It was noted earlier that the 1980s form of "open systems" did not really deliver the expectations set for it in terms of customer choice. This was because the standards for such systems were based on the specifications used by the programmers of applications, not the end-consumers who were to be the deployers of those applications. The associated UNIX® System marketplace was thus described as fragmented

However, it was not fragmented with respect to the programmer audience for whom the standards were actually written. It was simply fragmented with respect to another audience who were not the intended audiences of the standards that were created—even though they were the intended audience of the marketing message and purported benefits of open systems.

A standards ecology should not be expected to have impact on any entities who are not directly involved with the subject of the standard. Whether it's end-users being appealed to by standards for programmers, or automobile consumers being appealed to by standards for steel suppliers to the auto industry, neither in the end have any direct impact on the economic interest of the mistargeted consumer.

5. *A standard is as strong as its enforcement mechanism, though this varies with time.*

It is necessary that standards exist as specification in order to permit innovation to occur in the non-homogeneous areas of the community enabled by the standard. However, it is not sufficient to provide only this—it must be possible to test for conformance to the standard and

ideally conformance for how the standard is used as well.

It has been the heritage of many standards in the ICT industry to exist without any measures of conformance, or without any means of adjudicating conformance. The economic value associated with the standard is lost to anyone (save an interloper) without a means of testing and ensuring that a specification is being satisfied

Such testing will evolve with time—a mature standard is probably best tested by the field of

---

"An ecology built upon untested standards might as well not employ them at all."

---

deployed uses of the standard, whereas a new standard, without such market penetration, might need buttressing in the form of conformance tests or other means of measuring conformance.

An ecology built upon untested standards might as well not employ them at all—it should always be possible to know how the standards within an ecology are tested.

6. *Consumer investments are never to be undone by a standard.*

It was earlier observed that, if standards are a codification of existing practice, then there must be a deployed practice from which the standard arises. This means that the customers of some supplier have employed the techniques or technologies that are the subject of a proposed innovation to the standard.

It has been a frequent practice of the ICT industry in the "open systems" era to codify such practices in a manner that forces existing deployments to have to change in order to yield a new standard. This effectively denied the purveyor of an innovation any existing benefit from having made the innovation, and created a cost for the consumer who took the risk of helping to establish the practice now being codified as a standard. In the UNIX® System industry, this has effectively meant that on the date of introduction of a standard, there were not (and indeed could not be) any conformance uses of the standard, which effectively undoes any historical economy associated with the codification of the existing practice.

Since we know that innovations have to arrive at the standard through customer deployments, ecologies that support ever growing levels of economic benefit support the customer investments that enabled the codification to take place. It need not be true that the existing deployment actually *be* the standard, but in keeping with the observation that customer deployments are indeed long-lived, it should not be invalidated. Techniques that exist to enable this practice include ecology-specified means of managing the namespaces of the standard and that otherwise enable the ability of a supplier (or consumer) to stake out a claim without fear of later standardization efforts.

Robust ecologies rarely create a requirement to undo an existing practice in order to establish one.

7. *Innovations to the standard must come with "skin in the game."*

A corollary to the previous principle is one that states that not only should a standard codify an existing practice but that it must be true that the innovation arrive with some investment in the outcome that is reflective of the economic benefit of a standard.

The experience of the industry with the POSIX 1003.2 standard, in which a variety of never previously implemented "improvements" to existing practice were foisted upon the industry as a standard, represented a huge economic drain for no effective purpose, since no existing practice was codified. The practice of the relevant standards body, namely the IEEE, was to allow any member to participate who would take the time to comment. Since revised to attach a (small) economic cost to that capability, at the time, the voice of an inspired and sufficiently loud individual could enslave literally millions of dollars of investment on an untried "improvement."

Sound ecologies are protected from poaching.

8. *Innovations must be "within chaotic range" of the standard.*

Since innovation is nominally introduced "on top of" the standard, a healthy ecology exists when the level of innovation that exists in the marketplace is not so large as to cause the consuming entities to view the market as fragmented. A healthy ecology will also permit and indeed encourage a non-fragmenting amount of such innovation to occur, and to sediment out into the standard promptly when sufficient knowledge and experience indicate that such sedimentation is warranted and reflective of the overall economic benefit associated with the standard.

Healthy ecologies do evolve robustly—evidencing neither fragmentation nor stagnation. It is tempting to try to quantify the degree to which innovation is permissible before fragmentation occurs, but in reality the values depend much on the speed of evolution of the overall community as well as its maturity.

9. *The lifetime of a standard is limited to the time it enables innovation in its connected areas.*

As noted in the first principle described here, standards represent homogeneity, which enables a further heterogeneity. The lifetime of a given standard is thus established by the window during which it effectively enables that further heterogeneity—after which, it either encompasses an area absent of any innovation or will require replacement.

Savvy users of a standards ecology will, first, be able to identify the interest of the community in the localized homogeneity provided by the standard. And second, be able to determine what the limits of that interest are so as to understand when they should expect evolution to occur in their standards framework.

Conclusion

Effective standards are living enablers of both innovation and economic benefit. Their effectiveness is directly related to how robust a system of relationships exists among the parties of the community, the properties of the standard involved, and the practice of its deployment and evolution. A number of principles can be derived from the experiences of early and ongoing attempts at building genuine open systems artifacts that help identify the characteristics of ecologies that are robust, and conversely, identify ecologies that are in danger of stagnation or undesired mutation. These standards reflect the set of interlocking tensions that maximize the economic benfit associated with having established the standard, and which also act to guide its healthy and inevitable evolution.

Notes

[1] Gosling, James A., "Phase Relationships in the Standardization Process," http://java.sun.com/people/jag/StandardsPhases/index.html (August 1990), and in Bolin, Sherrie, ed., *The Standards Edge*, (2004).

[2] The Open Group, "The UNIX(R) System Today," Order #G904, UK ISBN 1-85912-296-5 (June 2000).

[3] See http://www.ietf.org.

[4] Joy, Bill, Steele, Guy, Gosling, James A., Bracha, Gilad, *The Java™ Language Specification (2nd Edition), ISGN 0201310082, (Boston, MA: Addison-Wesley Publishing Co., June 5, 2000).*

Standards for Standard Setting: Contesting the Organizational Field

DR. D. LINDA GARCIA

Georgetown University

Abstract: *Over the past several years, IT standardization has witnessed a breakdown in the consensus that hitherto governed the activities of participants in this domain. Not only have new players appeared on the scene; the legitimacy of the old system has also been called into question. In some cases, the Government has been called on to intervene as a third party.*

This state of affairs can best be understood as a crisis within an "organizational field." An organizational field is a recognized domain of human activity in which interdependent actors/organizations interact in accordance with an agreed upon logic or script to achieve some common objective (DiMaggio and Powell 1991). Consensus with respect to objectives does not, however, preclude conflict. To the contrary, organizational fields are highly contested arenas in which actors compete not only for resources but also—and as importantly—for legitimacy (Schwartz 1997). By legitimating their own values and positions within a field, organizations can tilt the "rules of the game," in their favor with long lasting effects (Fligstein 2002).

Viewing a domain of human activities through an organizational field perspective helps to bring the roles of, and the relationships between, public and private realms into greater relief. Generally speaking, organizational fields are relatively self-contained and independent within their own sphere of activity

(Schwartz 1997). However, when fields become the battleground of contesting parties, the autonomy of the field is greatly reduced. Contending parties will seek to reinforce their positions by linking them to the deep-seated values and norms of society as a whole (Bourdieu and Wacquant 1992). It is at this point that the public sector has a unique opportunity—or as some might say a major responsibility—to revisit and reevaluate performance within the field in terms of the broader public interest.

IT standard setting is an organizational field of activities in which the public and private sectors both have tremendous stakes (OTA 1992). Such is especially the case today given a networked economy in

> "...standards serve not only to determine the architecture and topography of the economic infrastructure, but also winners and losers..."

which standards serve not only to determine the architecture and topography of the economic infrastructure, but also winners and losers (OTA 1992; OTA 1994). In a period of rapid technological advance, traditional organizational forms and modes of standard setting are breaking down, while new ones—such as standards consortia, and open source models—are competing intensely for the terrain. There is no reason to believe that the outcome that emerges from this private sector contest will coincide with the public interest (North 1990; Hodgson, Itoh et al. 2001). Thus, as the contenders vie for predominance in the field, the time is ripe for Government, on behalf of the public, to become more engaged in the action by setting some basic standards for standard setters.

Introduction

In the United States, much of the discussion about standard setting has focused on the question of "what is the appropriate division of labor between the public and private sectors in this arena?" With few exceptions, the answer has been to assign the responsibility for setting standards to the private sector.[1] This choice has been based on two basic assumptions. First, it is believed that private sector standards are highly attuned to market forces, so they provide the greatest economic value. Second, the government is understood to have no stake in the outcome of standards processes apart from its role as a "consumer of standards." Thus, by participating in the standards process as a user, the government—it is believed—can fully serve the public's interest.

These assumptions are hardly self-evident. For one, in the case of standards, market forces

---

"...in the case of standards, market forces do not necessarily lead to efficient outcomes."

---

do not necessarily lead to efficient outcomes. Because standards exhibit many characteristics of public goods, standard setting is subject to considerable market failures (Farrell and Saloner 1985; Farrell and Saloner 1988; Berg 1989). Moreover, market failures are especially likely in the case of information technology standards, which give rise to externalities and other network effects.[2] Equally problematic—as the 1992 Office of Technology Assessment report to the

Congress pointed out—even when voluntary standards organizations step in to facilitate standard setting, bureaucratic failures can delay the process, while conflicts of interest—related in part to standards sales—may serve to distort outcomes (OTA 1992).[3]

The second assumption—that government has no "public interest" in standard setting—is equally difficult to justify. Standards constitute an infrastructure or platform that supports and sustains the Nation's economy. As such, standards

---

"Standards constitute an infrastructure or platform that supports and sustains the Nation's economy. "

---

help to determine the efficiency and effectiveness of the economy, the cost, quality, and availability of products and services, and the state of the Nation's health, safety, and quality of life. Not surprisingly, therefore, most other governments play a key role in national and international standard setting processes. In fact, given the increasingly competitive global environment, many now link their standardization efforts to their trade policies, employing national standards as marketing devices to attract and lock in customers worldwide (OTA 1992).[4]

How, then, might we explain the disparity between our basic assumptions about standard setting and the way the process works in practice? To do so, we must look beyond narrow economic explanations that focus primarily on competitive, market strategies. In addition to market variables, we must also examine cultural and political factors. In particular, we must look at how economic actors compete to construct cultural/cognitive maps that serve not only to reduce uncertainty and generate greater stability among interdependent actors, but also to legitimate and perpetuate the prevailing state of affairs (Fligstein 2002).

To capture the entire picture, it is useful to view the standard setting process from an organizational field perspective. In particular, we need to understand how organizational fields serve as economic governance structures. As we shall see, the standards setting process constitutes a unique organizational field that has been governed by a set of legitimating assumptions, many of which are being contested today.

Organizational Fields and Governance Structures

Organizations do not exist in a vacuum. They are open systems, subject in isolation to entropy.[5] Organizations are not only enmeshed in a broad range of societal networks; they are also deeply embedded in a shared and all-encompassing institutional environment (Granovetter 1985). While an organization's networked location helps to determine its resources and power, it is the prevailing set of institutional arrangements—both formal and informal—that provides the incentive structure and the rules of the game by which organizations act (North 1990).

To survive, organizations must be responsive not only to their own internal dynamics, but to external developments and events as well. To maintain themselves, and to fulfill their missions, organizations must have access both to external material resources as well as to institutional legitimacy.[6] For these purposes organizations must not only respond to their environments; they must actively manage them. As Nohria and Gulati have pointed out, much of an organization's structure and behavior can be explained in terms of how it is situated to meet these needs.[7] For example, many organizations seek to become chartered by established collective authorities, so they can better legitimize their own goals and structures. Similarly, powerful organizations may seek to embed their goals and procedures directly into society as institutionalized rules. Likewise, organizations may import external resources and elements not because they yield efficiency, but rather because they reinforce the organization's legitimacy (Meyer and Rowan 1991; Nohria and Gulati 1994).

In negotiating their environments to meet their needs, organizations rarely operate on their own. Rather, they typically act in conjunction with other like-minded organizations, which are engaged in similar or complementary activities, so that the success of each is contingent on all others. In any particular market, for example, firms engage routinely with key suppliers, customers, competitors, and regulators. All have an interest in reducing uncertainty and stabilizing their environments.[8] In their efforts to do so, these organizations develop, over time, a set of structured practices unique to their institutional space. Once these practices become taken for granted, they serve to recreate and reconstruct the existing economic order of things (White 2001; Fligstein 2002).

This set of interdependent actors, as well as the common meaning systems and cognitive maps that govern their interactions, constitute an *"organizational field."* As described by Scott, an organizational field is:

> . . .a population of organizations operating in the same domain, as indicated by the similarity of their services or products. Included also are those others that critically influence their performance, including exchange partners, competitors, funding sources and regulators (Scott 2001).

Four interrelated developments are entailed in the structuring of a field. First, there is a growing interaction among organizations. Next, inter-organizational structures of domination and patterns of coalitions begin to appear. Third, the field becomes increasingly complex, having to deal with more and more information. Finally, organizational participants become cognizant of their interdependencies and aware that they are involved in a common endeavor governed by a shared set of rules (DiMaggio and Powell 1991).[9] Responding to a common environment as well as to each other, organizations within a field eventually become isomorphic (Meyer and Rowan 1991).

Bounded by shared cultural normative frameworks and a common regulatory system, organizational fields are recognizable as discrete areas of institutional life (Scott 2001). They serve to provide stability for interdependent organizations that depend upon, but also must compete with, one another to create markets and access limited resources. Generally recognized as such, organizational fields enjoy a certain degree of jurisdictional autonomy; in the course of their interactions, they develop rules of the game and "conceptions of control" over a given realm of social, economic, and/or political life (Fligstein 2002). In so doing, they help to reconstruct and legitimate existing social arrangements. As described by Mohr:

> Organizational forms provide the containers into which the multiple dimensions of institutional life are poured, and organizations combine kinds of persons, types of problems, and forms of treatment in an ongoing and materially recognizable way. Thus it is through the establishment and institutionalization of organizational forms that one or another set of institutional logics comes to be anchored in place (Mohr forthcoming 2003).

As in all governance systems, organizational fields are characterized by contests for power. Fields are organized hierarchically, so that power is asymmetric. It is the most powerful incumbents in the field who define the meaning of the space as well as the roles and relationships of its occupants and the rules of the game.[10] As described by Fligstein:

> Rules are not created innocently or without taking into account "interests." If the largest firms are able to work under a set of rules that allows them to dominate the main markets of a society and keep workers disorganized, those rules enforce a system of power (Fligstein 2002).

Incumbents can, moreover, strengthen their positions to the extent that they can link their claims to general societal understandings about how things should be done.[11]

Efficient, socially optimal outcomes in power contests over organizational fields are by no means assured, however. To the contrary, achieving a new consensus is not only a costly process; it is subject to problems of collective action (Olson 1971). These problems will be

exacerbated if an organizational field has become so disorganized and unstructured that it has no dominant actor or set of actors to champion a change (Garcia forthcoming 2004). If, under such circumstances, the uncertainties about the distribution of economic rewards becomes too great, and all stand to lose, the actors in an organizational field may look to the state to broker relationships and/or develop a new consensus and a new set of rules, which can be legitimized at a broader, societal level (North and Thomas 1973; Libecap 1989; North 1990).

To appreciate how such a situation might occur, one need only consider the history of railroad regulation. Because of its high fixed costs, fluctuating demand, scale of operations, and need for coordination and specialized engineering skills, the railroad industry was prone to exceptionally high transaction costs. Seeking to achieve greater market stability, the railroad companies alternated between two extreme strategies—cutthroat competition or pooling and price fixing. Neither was successful: cutthroat competition ruined everyone, but cooperative agreements were unenforceable. When private efforts to achieve stability failed, politicians stepped in, establishing the Interstate Commerce Commission in 1887 to regulate this important national industry (Kolko 1970; Kennedy 1991).[12]

Organizational fields are thus embedded in and constitutive of the broader institutional environment in which they operate. At the same time, this institutional context serves not only to constrain organizational options; it also helps to determine and reinforce the criteria by which people develop their preferences and evaluate organizational behavior (Berger and Luckmann 1967; Weick 1969; DiMaggio and Powell 1991).

Given this mutually reinforcing set of interrelationships, one can understand why new organizational forms are relatively rare (North 1990; DiMaggio and Powell 1991; Meyer and Rowan 1991). Challengers to incumbents of an organizational field must not simply compete for resources based on new forms of practices; as importantly, they must reinterpret current practices in the light of an alternative institutional logic. It is on the basis of this new logic that the flow of resources is then redirected towards the new challengers (Mohr forthcoming 2003).

Not surprisingly, changes in organizational fields are generally associated with basic structural changes at the level of society as a whole. Under radically new circumstances, old organizational arrangements, which serve to buttress a prior and no longer viable set of institutional arrangements, become increasingly problematic. Organizational innovations are required not only to redirect attention and behavior towards new ends, but also to reduce uncertainty in a rapidly changing environment (Stinchcomb 1990).

Standard Setting as an Organizational Field

The evolution of standard setting in the United States parallels that of an organizational field. As standards began to assume an increasingly important role in the economy, specialized organizations emerged to develop them. These organizations modeled themselves in keeping not only with American social and political traditions, but also with the forms and practices of one another. Their efforts, moreover, were legitimated by the State, which in effect delegated responsibility for setting standards to these private sector organizational entities. This set of arrangements was relatively stable for more than half a century. It is only in the past several years—and in the wake of major technological and socio-economic changes—that newcomers have been able to effectively contest the field.

The emergence of standard setting as an organizational field is closely linked to the industrial revolution. With the division of labor and specialization, tasks become more interdependent, requiring greater coordination and information exchange (Durkheim 1933). Standards greatly facilitated these processes. One need only consider the role of standards in mass production, which required interchangeable parts. As described by Harold Williamson:

> Chief among the other elements in the pattern of mass production is the principle of standard-

ization. Stemming from the rudimentary division of labor, standardization involved the continuous pursuit, and progressive realization, of uniformity of the materials, operations, and products of industry, which made possible the future subdivision and mechanization of labor (Williamson 1951).

The relationship between standards and mass production was self-reinforcing. Further advances in precision manufacturing required the development of machine tools and precision gauges, which in turn further drove the need for standards and standardized measures.[13]

Standards were also spurred on by the extension of markets across the American continent. As trade became more dispersed, standards were needed to assure that products manufactured in different locals could work together and be easily replicated, assembled, and repaired. Moreover, standards were required to facilitate trading itself. For example, when the railroads extended trade over vast regions, standardized

---

"...standards were required to facilitate trading itself."

---

procedures for billing and exchange—such as bills of lading—were required. Likewise, standardized business practices and procedures, as well as standardized time, were needed to coordinate the increasingly complex railroad operations (Kirkland 1961).

As the role of standards increased, so did the number of people who had a stake in the standards process. Producers, for example, employed standards as trademarks to differentiate their products from their competitors and to price products for different markets. For suppliers, standards specifications meant reduced production costs. Consumers likewise benefited from standards. They not only conveyed product information and provided greater quality control; standardized products were also cheaper. The general public also called for the development of standards to protect against the growing technological mishaps that were associated with industrialization (OTA 1992). Although the Federal Government became involved in standards as early as the mid-1880s through the work of the Office of Weights and Measures, and later with the establishment of the Bureau of Standards, it was not until World War I that the government's stake in standards was really brought home to the Nation. In 1917, product diversity was so great it threatened the war effort. To deal with the problem, the government set up a Commercial Economy Board of the Council of National Defense, whose task was to simplify the use of labor, capital, and equipment for all industries (Cochrane 1966). [14] The government continued its "standards crusade" following the war in and effort to revive the economy. Led by Secretary of Commerce Herbert Hoover, the campaign called for standardization of business practices, materials, machinery, and products; specifications to insure high quality products; and product simplification. To promote standardization, the government organized agencies within the Department of Commerce to provide standards assistance to businesses at their request (OTA 1992).

As more and more stakeholders became involved in standards, it became increasingly necessary to specialize their operations, and differentiate among these groups. Of prime importance was the relationship between the public and private sectors. Although the government actively promoted standardization at the turn of the century, it gradually relinquished this responsibility to the private standards development organizations.

The American preference for private, pluralist solutions is as old as the Constitution itself. From the outset of the new republic, Americans proved to have a penchant for joining factions and establishing associations, a trait that did not escape the observations of Alexis de Tocqueville when he visited America in the mid-1800s. As he described in *Democracy and America,* "Whenever at the head of some new undertaking you see the Government of France, or a man of rank in England, in the United States you will be sure to find an association." (deTocqueville 1963). This

support for voluntary, private associations was reinforced by a general suspicion of the state and preferences for market-based solutions (Wuthnow 1991). Thus, whereas in many other countries government actively sponsored the growth and development of business, in the United States industrial development was managed, directed, and financed primarily by the private sector (Vogel 1987).

The first standards organizations were in keeping with this tradition. Emerging to deal with specific needs as they arose, they took a variety of forms. Often established on an industry-by-industry basis, there was at first little interaction among them. The first American standards organization was the United States Pharmacopial Convention set up in 1829 to establish uniform standards for drugs. The American Iron and Steel Institute, established in 1855, was the first trade association to develop standards. And the American Society of Civil Engineers, which was formed in 1852, was the first scientific and technological society involved in standards development (OTA 1992).

With the proliferation of standards organizations, the need for rationalization and coordination of standards activity soon became apparent. Standards organizations were not only competing with one another to write standards, they were also writing conflicting standards,

---

"Standards organizations were not only competing with one another to write standards, they were also writing conflicting standards, thus defeating the purpose."

---

thus defeating the purpose. Coordination among them proved difficult, however, eventually requiring the prodding and promotion of the Federal Government. The first steps at coordination took place in 1918, during the First World War, when five national engineering societies, together with the US Departments of War, Navy, and Commerce, formed the nucleus of an organization that was to become the

American Standards Association (ASA). The scope of the ASA's activities was broadened further during the Second World War, and its constitution was revised to assure that all of those interested in a particular standard would have a voice in its development. The revised constitution required, moreover, that three members at large be included on the association's board of directors in order to assure a voice for consumer interests (OTA 1992).

The broadening of ASAs mandate had only a marginal effect on its ability to serve as coordinator of private sector standards. Many private sector bodies resisted its mandate, not wanting to sacrifice their own independence. To broaden its support the ASA adopted a new constitution and bylaws, and renamed itself the United States of America Standards Institute (USASI). Characterizing itself as a federation of trade and other organizations, the Institute no longer proposed to develop standards, but only to orchestrate their development through the combined technical talent and expertise of its member bodies. As an umbrella, clearing-house organization, it intended to certify that these standards development bodies adhered to the consensus process. The Government and other members of the standards community resisted the effort of ASA to strengthen its role. The Federal Trade Commission protested the use of the name USASI on the ground that it suggested that ASA was an official organization of the Federal Government. A compromise was eventually reached and ASA became the American National Standards Institute. Having no official charter, ANSI became in effect the "self-designated" national coordinating body for US standards development organizations as well as the internationally accepted member body in the International Organization for Standardization (ISO) and the International Electrotechnical Commission (OTA 1992).

Although nongovernmental standards organizations in the United States continue to operate in a pluralistic fashion, with only 25 percent coordinating their activities through ANSI, together they constitute an easily recogniz-

able and relatively coherent organizational field. Membership in the standards community has been relatively stable over the years, and the players are well known to one another. Moreover, most of the approximately 400 voluntary standards bodies—including trade associations, professional societies, general membership organizations, and third party certifiers—resemble one another in significant ways. In particular, these organizations all arrive at decisions through a process of consensus and provide some level of due process. In addition, they all have mechanisms for participation, comment and appeal. Equally—if not more—important, almost all standards organizations are adamant proponents of the voluntary standards process; whatever the disagreements among themselves, they have consistently joined together to defend against any government encroachment on the autonomy of their field. And, by appealing to the American preference for private sector solutions, US voluntary standards organizations have been highly successful in legitimating their right to govern the field.[15] The Federal Government has rarely intervened in private sector standards activities; instead, it has focused on preventing anti-competitive outcomes as well as on assuring the "fairness"' of the system. The government's preference for voluntary consensus standards was reaffirmed in the 1979 Trade Act, which formally recognizes the private sector's role in standards development, and in the Office of Management and Budget Circular A-119, which directs Federal agencies to use voluntary standards wherever possible in both regulatory and procurement activities (OTA 1992).

Contesting the Field

While staunch in defense of their autonomy, voluntary standards organizations have more often than not been at odds with one another. One major source of their contention has been competition over standard sales. Many of these organizations resemble publishers insofar as they orchestrate standard setting in exchange for the right to sell standards.

Dependent upon standard sales as a means of support, competition among standard organizations has often been rife. In this context, members of the standards community typically disagree about which organizations are the most legitimate, as well as about which produce the "best" standards. For instance, many professional societies claim that their standards are technologically superior, since their members participate not as representatives of any group or interest, but rather as individual engineers. On the other hand, many industry-based groups argue the opposite; contending that standards set by professional societies do not reflect market forces, and are thus not adequately sensitive to industry competitive issues. In a similar vein, the American Society for Testing and Materials (ASTM) insists that true consensus requires the participation of all interested parties, even if this requires subsidizing some groups. In contrast, the American National Standards Institute (ANSI), as well as others, argue that due process requires only that all have an opportunity to participate. Not surprisingly, given the self-contained nature of the standards community, this type of rivalry has been compounded by personality conflicts, some of which date back several years (OTA 1992).

It is important to note, however, that no matter how contentious these conflicts, they have always been self-contained, initiated by incumbents and taking place internally within the standards setting field itself. Moreover, rarely—if ever—did these incumbents question the overall functioning or legitimacy of the system. Thus, it is only recently that the standards setting field itself has become the subject of debate. As one might anticipate, the major challengers are newcomers to the field, having emerged to address the standards issues associated with advances in information technology and the advent of the networked economy.

The present challenge stems from the fact that the formal, voluntary consensus-based standard process is not well equipped to deal with rapidly advancing information-based networking technologies. Relying on the slow and often arduous process of consensus building, standards bodies are hard pressed to keep pace with changing technologies. In an effort to make allowances for technology change, and facilitate interoperability among an increasing number of interdependent parties, networking standards have often been incorporated into elaborate reference models and defined in very broad and generic terms. These types of standards are typically referred to as "anticipatory standards," because the process of setting the standard anticipates the creation of the product. The problem with these standards, however, is that, even after such standards have been formally set, users still have to implement compatible technologies that meet standards specifications; and products need to be certified as to their compatibility with one another (Cargill 1989). This process can be so complex and time-consuming that the window of opportunity sometimes closes and those standards are overtaken by new technologies and events.

In the late 1980s, many vendors, discouraged by this lagging process, started to circumvent the traditional standards-setting process, and to develop standards in more focused interest-based consortia. Included among these, for example, were consortia to develop standards for Switched Multimegabit Data Service (SMDS), Fiber Distributed Data Interface (FDDI) over twisted pair, asynchronous transfer mode (ATM), and frame relay technologies. The major user consortia included the Corporation for Open Systems (COS), Manufacturing Automation Protocol (MAP), and the Technical Office Protocol (TOP) (Weiss and Cargill 1999). Operating in a relatively closed environment, these groups greatly simplified the standards process. Unlike traditional standards organizations, consortia are not bound by rules guaranteeing openness and consensus. Membership is generally restricted to those willing to pay a significant fee. Because of this exclusivity, these consortia often replicate the dynamics of the market; participants invest in the process because of an anticipated "payoff."

One consortium that stands out for its success in achieving both openness and speed is the Internet Engineering Task force (IETF), responsible for developing standards for the Internet. The IETF's open process owes much to the Internet's unique history. Like the network itself, Internet standards evolved in a very informal way as part of the efforts of the Defense Advanced Research Projects Agency (DARPA) to establish computer networks linking researchers across the country. Because the participants were few, and bound together by a common research purpose, they were able to develop standards in a relatively timely fashion. But, even though the Internet has grown by leaps and bounds, the IETF has held to its tradition of openness and inclusivity. By employing the Internet to conduct on-line forums and provide access to standards and standards related activities, the IETF has greatly reduced the financial barriers to participation. Equally important, the IETF process avoids the implementation and conformance-testing problem associated with anticipatory standards because all specifications need to be implemented and demonstrated to be interoperable. Similarly, to become a full standard, a draft standard must be field-tested and proven capable of maintaining a community of interest over time.

Spurred on by the Internet and the growth of the World Wide Web, standards setting proliferated in the 1990s, leading to a major shift in the standard setting field. The World Wide Web Consortium (W3C) was established in 1994 to meet the demand. Designed along the lines of the IETF, but on a more formalized basis, the W3C provided a successful model that others soon emulated. Eager to become part of the action, technology manufacturers and vendors bypassed traditional standards organization and set up consortia to develop standards that were compatible with the Internet and the World Wide Web. Those that did so were highly successful; whereas the standards developed through the more traditional organizations— such as ANSI's X.12—failed to take hold. Today, with more than 260 consortia, it is clear

that consortia have become the organization of choice for IT standards developers (Spring and Weiss 1995; Cargill 2002a). As described by one observer, "a new industry consortium is founded ever week." At the same time, a number of intermediary groups has emerged to support them by registering and cataloging their standards (Libicki 2000).

Based on an entirely new business model, the Open Source movement represents a much more radical shift away from the traditional mode of standard setting. As one might suspect, participants in the movement are all newcomers to the standards field. Like the Internet, the open source movement emerged in the context of a distinct culture of openness and reciprocity dating back to the late 1960s and 1970s when programmers freely shared their source code. In fact, the movement was born in direct response to the renunciation of this norm by computer companies that decided to proprietize their operating system software (Weber 2002). Richard Stallman, a programmer at the MIT Artificial Intelligence Laboratory, led the charge establishing the Free Software Foundation in 1984 with the goal of generating hacker culture by creating a pool of free software, utilities, and programming tools (Moody 2001). To support this effort, Stallman codified these norms in a unique form of property rights—the General Public License (GPL), or copyleft as it is also called. Under this arrangement, software programmers were permitted to modify and enhance open source code, but only if it remained open and was provided to others on the same basis. Although Stallman's project rallied the faithful and provided a vision for the open source movement, it was unable to create a critical mass of supporters, due in part to its strong ideological tone (Moody 2001).

In 1991, Linus Torvalds, a 21-year-old computer science major at the University of Helsinki, had much greater success. Building on a simplified version of Unix, Torvalds created Linux, the kernel of a new operating system. Posting it to the Internet, he invited his peers to modify and enhance it on the condition that functions written by others could also be freely distributed. Torvalds tapped a large, eager audience and within a year 100 people had joined the Linux newsgroup. Ninety renditions and 2 ½ years later, Linux was released to the public (Moody 2001).

Today, the open source movement has a considerable following, and some open source software products are leaders in their application spaces. As of November 2001, for example, the web server Apache was used on approximately 62 percent of active servers across all domains, while Sendmail was used for 75 percent of Internet e-mail. Linux now has 21 million users worldwide. Impressed by this growth, many major corporations, including Hewlett-Packard, IBM, and Dell, are developing and using open source software. Even more telling, Microsoft has identified Linux as its chief competitor both in its international communications as well as in antitrust proceedings. The big question is whether or not the open source movement can maintain this momentum without generating private claims on residual resources. For the present, at least, private claims are not a problem. The movement's institutional structure, together with its culture of reciprocity and sharing has served to maintain the common pool problems typically associated with open access (Frank and Jungwirth 2002).[16]

Faced with such competition, traditional standards development organizations have not remained on the sidelines. Recognizing that information technology standards represent a new and unique challenge with respect to both time and the need for interoperability, these organizations sought to streamline their procedures and speed up their processes. ANSI, for example, set up a fast track program for IT standards, whereby ANSI provides accreditation for standards that had been developed in other, consortia-like forums. Relatively few groups took advantage of it, however. Reforms were also undertaken at the international level in organizations such as ISO, which adopted a Publicly Available Specification Process, allowing standards adopted in other forums to move quickly through the ISO acceptance process.

Again, notwithstanding these changes, most companies continued to place their bets—as well as their financial resources—on consortia.

To maintain their privileged positions, traditional standards bodies continually seek to define the standards field in their image. In particular, in promoting their cause, they have emphasized the open, voluntary consensus aspect of their organizations, linking it to the American political tradition of openness and voluntarism. To this end, for example, these organizations have contended that the US law mandating the government's use of voluntary consensus standards excludes—by definition— standards developed within consortia. As described, for example, in ANSI's strategic plan:

> the U.S. government should encourage more use of the principles embodied in accreditation by recognizing the ANSI process as providing sufficient evidence that American National Standards (ANS) meet federal criteria for voluntary consensus standards. [In addition] Non-traditional standards organizations should review their objectives to determine whether closer interaction with the formal system will help add value to their efforts (as cited in Cargill (2002).

Faced with this opposition, the consortia have been no less adamant in touting their claims. As described by Cargill, ". . .both groups believed they were in a "do or die" situation, in which their specific survival depended upon their ability to diminish (but not destroy) the other side whilst retaining hegemony for their set of beliefs (Cargill 2002b: 33). In legitimating their approach, the consortia have focused on economic issues, while downplaying those related to process. Accordingly, they characterize their policy of restricting access to those who "pay to play," as the key to their success. What matters, they contend, is not that the process is open to all, but rather that standards are developed, which are widely used. As proof, they point to the willingness of so many businesses to invest their funds in consortia.

This emphasis in their rhetoric on economic outcomes is not surprising, given that the rational and legal basis for setting up consortia is the National Cooperative Research and Production Act of 1993, the purpose of which was to support the creation of business alliances as a means of promoting US competitiveness.

Joining together in what might be characterized as a cause-based social movement, advocates of open source software have likewise sought to redefine the field of standards setting. And much like the proponents of competing approaches, they use rhetoric that links their way of doing things to fundamental social values. Thus, for example, to overcome any negative connotations associated with the original name "free software," the movement's leaders substituted the name of "open source software." Similarly, open source advocates characterize their movement as the Magna Carta for software users on the grounds that it provides users the freedom to choose. Their argument has resonated with many who, when faced with an economic downturn and suspicious of dominant companies such as Microsoft, have welcomed such lower cost non-proprietary solutions.

Opponents of open source software have responded in kind, questioning the fundamental legitimacy of the open source process as well as the quality of the product. Among the movement's most vociferous opponents is, of course, Microsoft. After originally downplaying the importance of open source software, Microsoft began a major public relations and lobbying campaign to undermine its credibility. To this end, it has created a counter-narrative, accusing the open source movement of being both anti-capitalist and un-American (Shankland and Wilcox 2001; Kertstetter, Hamm et al. 2003). Microsoft has also challenged the viability of the process, arguing that the GPL is unenforceable in court. At the same time, it has actively lobbied the government against the use of Linux on security grounds.

Paradoxically, as the role of IT standards has loomed larger, the field of standards setting has experienced greater disarray. Given much higher stakes, companies are competing more intensely than ever to define standards, forum shopping whenever the need arises. The "pay to play" basis of many of today's consortia facilitates this process; denied the prize in one standard's arena, companies have little compunction to seek out or establish another where they may have more to gain. Under the circumstances, organizational turnover is relatively high, so the institutionalization of the process is low and there is no general, or transparent set, of principles that govern these standard activities. At the same time, the traditionally more open and well established IETF is becoming bogged down not only by the demand for standards but

---

"Given the lack of cohesion within the standards field, it will be difficult to generate the number of standards and the level of interoperability required for today's networked society."

---

also by the its commitment to achieve a rough consensus among participants. As a result, there has been a multiplication of working groups and a splintering off of discontents (Libicki 2000). Traditional standard setting organizations are similarly in a state of flux. All in all, the situation is not a promising one. Given the lack of cohesion within the standards field, it will be difficult to generate the number of standards and the level of interoperability required for today's networked society.

Standards for Standard Setters

Actors in an organizational field enjoy a certain measure of autonomy by virtue of the fact that their activities are generally consistent, or at least congruent with, the needs and traditions of the larger environment of which it is a part. When there is considerable dissension within the field, and the gap between private and public goals becomes very great, those field participants who are most discontented will likely bring their issues to the policy realm.

And, if the stakes are high enough, the government may decide to intervene (Garcia forthcoming 2004). Such is the case in the standards field today.

Paradoxically, it appears that, precisely because the stakes are so high, the ability of standards organizations to set standards is inversely proportional to the need for them. As evidenced by the growth of competing standards consortia, businesses are more inclined than ever before to employ standards

---

"Setting standards for standard setters is precisely what is needed today."

---

processes strategically, so as to gain competitive advantage. An open, interoperable architecture is not likely to be the result. Yet, as the advent of the Internet and the World Wide Web made clear, to reap the full economic benefits of ICT, networks and network components must be interoperable and open for interconnection. Open standards reduce transactions costs, as well as the costs of barriers to entry, thereby encouraging competition. Moreover, interoperable systems reduce networking costs, thus encouraging technology diffusion. In addition, open standards encourage innovation by providing a platform on which businesses can add value and develop new products and services.

What might be the Government's response? Historically, as we have seen, the government has intervened in the field of standards setting at those points in time when the nation's security and economic welfare were at stake. However, the role that the government played was for the most part indirect; instead of setting standards, the government helped to facilitate and promote the standards setting process by playing an informational and brokerage role. In addition, the Government established the normative and legal framework within which standards organizations operate. Setting standards for standard setters is precisely what is needed today. The standards perspective that served well for an industrial age, in which the primary need was for product standards, is no longer appropriate in a networked society, in which the overriding requirement is for interoperable standards that can provide an open platform to support all economic, political, and cultural activities. Unfortunately, in today's hyper "deregulatory" environment, there is no voice, such as that of former Secretary of Commerce Hoover, to articulate a coherent vision of the role of standards and standards organizations and how—in a networked society—they relate to our fundamental values such as first amendment rights, national security, intellectual property, antitrust, etc.

Notes

[1] This preference for the private sector was reaffirmed in the 1979 Trade Act, which formally recognizes the private sector's role in standards development, and in the Office of Management and Budget (OMB Circular A-119, which directs Federal agencies to use voluntary standards wherever possible in both regulatory and procurement activities.

[2] For example, network technologies often have large installed bases, making it particularly costly for users to shift to a new, more technologically advanced standard. Thus users may fail to adopt a superior standard due to what economists call "excess inertia." At the same time, these technologies also

exhibit "increasing returns to adoption," a situation that occurs when the benefits to the user of a technology increases with the number of users. Under these circumstances, the wrong standard might be chose due to "excess momentum." Not wanting to be left off the network when a major user moves to a new standard, other users may rush too quickly to jump on the bandwagon.

[3] As the OTA report pointed out, for example, "The interests of some standards organizations are beginning to diverge from those of manufacturers. In a highly competitive global economy, for example, it is important for manufacturers to have their standards adopted on an international basis. They

may even want to "give" their standards away in an effort to develop new markets. However, such a policy is not in the interest of those standard setting organizations, whose livelihoods generally depend on standard sales" (OTA 1992).

[4] More and more industries are not only dependent upon trade but also affected by standards. It was estimated, for example, that for the year 1977, $69 billion of US exports were affected by standards activity. No comparable figure is available today. However, in 1992, it was estimated that of $85 billion in exports of manufactured goods, some $45 billion was subject to European Community product safety standards alone.

[5] As described by Katz and Kahn, "To survive, open systems must move to arrest the entropic process; they must acquire negative entropy. The entropic process is a universal law of nature in which all forms of organization move toward disintegration or death. Complex physical and biological organisms also run down and perish. The open system, however, by importing more energy from its environment than it expends, can store energy and can acquire negative entropy. There is then a general trend in an open system to maximize its ration of imported to expanded energy, to survive even during periods of crisis to live on borrowed time (Katz and Kahn).

[6] Legitimacy can be defined as "a generalized perception or assumption that the actors of an entity are desirable, proper, appropriate within some socially constructed system of norms, values, beliefs and definitions" (Suchman 1995: 574).

[7] As described by Nohria and Gulati, " . . .a firm's structure is influenced on the one hand by the institutionally legitimate solutions for a broadly defined task environment and on the other by the pragmatic concerns of addressing local contingencies. This tension is mediated by the rhetoric that managers employ and the actions that they take to create, present, and account for the organization's structure" (Nohria and Gulati 1994: 530).

[8] As described by Fligstein: "There are four threats to a firm's survival. First, suppliers can control inputs, raise prices, and make firms who require their inputs unprofitable. Second, competitors can engage in price competition, take over market share, and eventually drive the firm out of business. Third, gaining cooperation from managers and workers in the firm present problems of interpersonal conflict

and politics that can jeopardize the ability to produce goods and services as well. Finally, products may become obsolete. These problems are most acute under conditions of economic turbulence that occur most frequently at the beginning of a market, but that also can reflect a sudden downturn in the market (Fligstein 2001: 17).

[9] DiMaggio and Powell identify three forces leading to isomorphism: formal and informal pressures exerted by other organizations, a common legal environment, and organizational benchmarking, especially during periods of uncertainty (DiMaggio and Powell,1991).

[10] As Fligstein points out: "Markets (and this includes almost all modern production markets) are mainly structured by sellers looking for buyers. A given market becomes a "stable market" (i.e., a field) when the product being exchanged has legitimacy with customers, and the suppliers of the good or service are able to produce a status hierarchy in which the largest suppliers dominate the market and are able to reproduce organizations to make the good and create social relations between competitors to govern competition (Fligstein 2001:31).

[11] Characterizing Bordieu's perspective on this subject, Swartz notes: Both the dominant establishment and the subordinate challengers, both orthodox and heterodox views, share a tacit acceptance that the field of struggle is worth pursuing in the first place. . . .Challengers and incumbents share a common interest in preserving the field itself, even if they are sharply divided on how it is to be controlled—referred to as the *doxa. Entry into the field requires the tacit acceptance of the rules of the game, meaning that specific forms of struggle are legitimated whereas others are excluded (Schwartz, 125).*

[12] The rail owners were not alone in questioning whether the market, functioning on its own, could solve the problem of too much competition. Because the railroads were at the center of national activity, the bankers were among the first to intervene. To force a solution, J.P. Morgan—acting as a neutral third party—sequestered many of the key railroad owners on his yacht. Acting under duress, they were able to come to terms. However, they were quick to renege on their agreement when there was no longer a means of enforcing it (Neuman, et al, 1997).

[13] Of particular importance, for example, was the vernier caliper, which was first made in the United

States in 1851. Inexpensive and capable of reading to thousandths of an inch, the new caliper permitted ordinary machinists—whether they were gun smiths, watchmakers, or sewing machine manufacturers—to develop precision, interoperable parts (Green 1951).

[14] According to Cochrane, "Labor savings in the manufacture of products from clothing to coffins reportedly reached as high as 35 percent. Savings over prewar consumption of materials in some instances rose to 50 percent as simplicity ruled and plentiful wood, paper, zinc, and cotton replaced the steel, tinplate, copper, brass, bronze, pig tin, nickel, and raw wool consumed by the war. The country had experienced nothing like it before." (Cochrane 1966: 167)

[15] The division of labor between the public and private sectors has strong support in the US standards setting community. At hearings held in 1990 by the National Institute of Standards and Technology to determine whether the government should be more active in standards setting, especially in the international arena, the response of those testifying was an emphatic "No." See proceedings, National Institute for Standards and Technology Public Hearings, "Improving U.S. Participation in International Standards Activities," April 3, 1990.

[16] Free riding, for example, does not have a negative impact in the context of open source. Contributing their time and expertise in part to secure their reputations, open source programmers benefit from an extended audience. Because leadership positions are allocated in accordance with a peer reviewed assessment, rewards adequately reflect a programmer's contribution. Equally important is the General Public License, which generates trust by preventing defection. Other things being equal, programmers will continue to contribute to the movement so long as they believe no one can privatize their contributions (Franck and Jungwirth 2002).

References

Berg, S. (1989). "Technical Standards as Public Goods: Demand Incentives for Cooperative Behavior." *Public Finance Quarterly* **17**: 35-53.

Berger, P. and T. Luckmann (1967). *The Social Construction of Reality.* New York, Doubleday.

Bourdieu, P. and L. J. D. Wacquant (1992). *An Invitation to Reflexive Sociology.* Chicago, IL, The University of Chicago Press.

Cargill, C. (1989). *Information Technology Standardization: Theory, Process and Organization.* Boston, MA, Digital Press.

Cargill, C. (2002a). Uncommonly Commonality. *The Standards Edge.* S. Bolin. Ann Arbor, MI, Bolin Communications.

Cargill, C. (2002b). The Role of Consortia Standards in Federal Procurement. The *The Standards Edge.* S. Bolin. Ann Arbor, MI, Bolin Communications.

Cochrane, R. C. (1966). Measures for Progress: A History of the National Bureau of Standards. Washington D.C., National Bureau of Standards.

deTocqueville, A. (1963). *Democracy in America.*

DiMaggio, P. J. and W. W. Powell (1991). The Iron Cage Revisited: Institutional Isomorphism and Collective Rationality in Organizational Fields. *The New Institutionalism in Organizational Analysis.* P. J. DiMaggio and W. W. Powell. Chicago, IL, Chicago University Press.

Durkheim, E. (1933). *The Division of Labor in Society.* New York, NY, Free Press.

Farrell, J. and G. Saloner (1985). "Standardization, Compatibility, and Innovation." *Rand Journal of Economics* **16** (spring): 70-83.

Farrell, J. and G. Saloner (1988). "Coordination Through Committees and Markets." *Rand Journal of Economics* **18** (summer): 235-252.

Fligstein, N. (2002). *The Architecture of Markets.* Princeton, NJ, Princeton University Press.

Frank, E. and C. Jungwirth (2002). "Reconciling Investors & Donators: The Governance Structure of Open Source,". Zurich, University of Zurich.

Garcia, D. L. (2004). The Evolution of Property Rights in a Networked Economy. *The Emerging Global Information Policy Regime.* S. Braman. Basingstoke UK, Palgrave.

Granovetter, M. (1985). "Economic Action and Social Ctructure: The Problem of Embeddedness." *American Journal of Sociology* **91**(3): 481-510.

Hodgson, G. M., Itoh, et al. (2001). Introduction. *Capitalism in Evolution: Global Contentions--East and West*. M. I. Geoffrey M. Hodgson, and Yomokawa Nobuharu. Cheltenham, UK, Edward Elgar.

Kennedy, R. D. J. (1991). The Statist Evolution of Rail Governance in the United States, 1830-1986. *Governance and the American Economy*. L. Cambell, Hollingsworth, JR, and Lindberg, L. N. New York, Cambridge University Press.

Kertstetter, J., S. Hamm, et al. (2003). "The Linux Uprising." *Business Week*: 78-84.

Kirkland, E. (1961). *Industry Comes of Age: Business, Labor, and Public Policy*. New York, New York, Holt, Rheinhard, and Winston.

Kolko (1970). *Railroads and Regulation. 1877-1916*, W.W. Norton & Norton Company.

Libecap, G. D. (1989). *Contracting for Property Rights*. Cambridge UK, Cambridge University Press.

Libicki, M. C. (2000). *Scaffolding the New Web:Standards and Standards Policy for the Digital Economy*. Santa Monica, CA, Rand Corporation.

Meyer, J. and B. Rowan (1991). "Institutionalized Organizations: Formal STructure as Myth and Ceremony,". *The New Institutionalism in Organizational Analysis*. W. W. P. a. P. J. DiMaggio. Chicago, Illinois, Chicago University Press.

Mohr, J. (forthcoming 2003). "The Differentiation of Institutional Space: Organizational Forms in the New York Social Welfare Sector, 1888-1917. *Bending the Bars of the Iron Cage: Institutional Dynamics and Processes*. W. Powell and D. Jones, University of Chicago Press.

Moody, G. (2001). *Rebel Code: Inside Linux and the Open Source Revolution*. Cambridge, Massachusetts, Perseus Publishing.

Nohria, N. and R. Gulati (1994). Firms and Their Environments. *The Handbook of Economic Sociology*. N. J. Smelser, Swedberg, Richard. Princeton, New Jersey, Princeton University Press.

North, D. (1990). *Institutions, Institutional Change and Economic Performance*. New York, NY, Cambridge University Press.

North, D. C. and R. P. Thomas (1973). *The Rise of the Western World: A New Economic History*. Cambridge, UK, Cambridge Unviersity Press.

Olson, M. (1971). *The Logic of Collective Action: Public Goods and the Theory of Groups*. Cambridge, Massachusetts, Harvard University Press.

OTA (1992). Global Standards: Building Blocks for the Future. Washington DC, US Congress, Office of Technology Assessment.

OTA (1994). The Electronic Enterprise: Looking to the Future. Washington DC, US Congress, Office of Technology Assessment.

Schwartz, D. (1997). *Culture and Power: The Sociology of Pierre Bourdieu*. Chicago, Il, University of Illinois Press.

Scott, W. R. (2001). *Institutions and Organizations*. Thousand Oaks, CA, Sage Publications, Inc.

Shankland, S. and J. Wilcox (2001). Why Microsoft is Wary of Open Source. CNETNEWS.com.

Spring, M. and M. Weiss (1995). Financing the Standards Development Process. *Standards Policy for Information Infrastructure*. Cambridge, MA, MIT Press.

Stinchcomb, A. L. (1990). Social Structure and Organizations. *Handbook of Organizations*. J. G. March. Chicago, Illinois, Rand McNally.

Vogel, D. (1987). Government-Industry Relations in the United States: An Overview. *Comparative Government Industry Relations*. S. Wilks and M. Wright. Ox ford, UK, Clarendon Press.

Weber (2002). "The Political Economy of Open Source,". *BRIE Working Paper 140, E-conomy Project*.

Weick, K. E. (1969). *The Social Psychology of Organizing*. New York, NY, Random House.

Weiss, M. and C. Cargill (1999). "Consortia In the Standards Development Process." *Journal of the American Society for Information Science* **43**(8): 559-565.

White, H. (2001). *Markets from Networks: Socioeconomic Models of Production*. Princeton, NJ, Princeton University Press.

Williamson, H., ed. (1951). *The Growth of the American Economy*. New York, NY, Prentice Hall.

Wuthnow, R., ed. (1991). *The Voluntary Sector in Comparative Perspective*. Princeton, NJ, Princeton University Press.

3

The Sisyphus Agenda: Standardization as a Guardian of Innovation

CARL F. CARGILL
Sun Microsystems, Inc.

Abstract: *This paper treats standardization primarily as a managerial tool for business. As such, standardization can be said to consist of a process that creates a standardized specification, the implementation of that specification in a product, and the use of that product in a commercial setting. At any time during standardization, innovation may be present. Through use of standardization, a manager can control the introduction, rate, and acceptance of standardization within the technical area being considered for standardization. This chapter begins with an examination of standardization in the Information and Communications Technology (ICT) industry (based on the current practices), reviews the impact of that methodology on the market, and then discusses the challenges that the market presents for standardization and standardization presents for the market. This chapter concludes with a gloomy assessment of the future of standardization as a guardian of innovation, given the lack of significant academic and government involvement in the formulation and creation of this nascent discipline. It is written reflecting my bias, which is as an empowered, embedded, and impartial (mostly) participant who participates in the standardization processes as a representative of the commercial sector.*

The Environment

"Standardization is one of the hallmarks of an industrial society. As a society becomes increasingly complex and its industrial base begins to emerge, it becomes necessary for the products, processes, and procedures of the society to fit together and interoperate. This interoperation provides the basis for greater integration of the elements of the society, which in turn causes increased social interdependency and complexity." [1] I believe that, within the Information and Communications Technology (ICT) industry (and increasingly within other information intensive arenas), this statement is no longer adequate; standardization is both the initiator of technical innovation as well as the guardian of this innovation. With this increased scope, the nature of standardization changes— and it is this change with which the industry is now attempting to cope.

For the commercial sector (the vendor, provider, or seller side), standardization is (or can be) a potent management tool, which is used to manage the "market." It impacts all industries that depend upon the ICT industry—from automobiles to retail to chemicals to airplanes. Because ICT can gather such vast amounts of data, and because this data can now be analyzed and used, a smooth flow of information is not only desired, it is absolutely necessary. This smooth flow can only occur because the systems that gather, process, and report the information

---

"...standardization allows the participants to look for—and reward—some type of innovation, rather than having to worry about infrastructure technologies."

---

interconnect and interoperate. In the main, this interoperation is the result of standardization, rather than serendipity.[2] From the user (or the buyer side), standardization promises either second sourcing or choice of implementations. For both sides, standardization allows the participants to look for—and reward—some type of innovation, rather than having to worry about infrastructure technologies.[3]

However, standardization is one of the more complex managerial tools, requiring a knowledge of technology, psychology, marketing, and strategy if it is to be used successfully over a long term. Practicing standardization as a provider within the ICT industry today is similar to the task of Sisyphus[4]—we are condemned to push large rocks up increasingly steep slopes. Unlike Sisyphus, however, the reason that the

---

"...standardization is one of the more complex managerial tools, requiring a knowledge of technology, psychology, marketing, and strategy if it is to be used successfully over a long term."

---

industry undertakes this task is not because we are condemned. Rather, we do it because we know that we must, and because the alternatives are too painful to consider. To make the task more daunting, the environment in which we practice the art of standardization changes constantly and at an accelerating rate, requiring the activity of standardization to change to mirror new and increasingly complex requirements.[5]

The evolution of the environments is no surprise, as it is obvious that the ICT industry must constantly establish ways to either add to value-networks or to create new value networks entirely,[6] and hence, generate new opportunities for innovation. As it establishes these new ways and opportunities to add value, it is also establishing new business practices and new requirements for interoperation. And with these new requirements for interoperation come the need for establishing new ways of ensuring that systems interoperate when they are introduced. With the introduction of new processes, the need for new ways to "do standardization" becomes critical.

The Process

Standardization, as the term will be used in this paper, refers to the deliberate and consensual creation of an "open specification" (also known as an "open standard") by a group of players (usually joined together in some form of standards setting organization) who usually compete in the marketplace.[7] An acceptable definition for a standardized specification is one where the creation process has been marked by at least rough consensus, which produces a specification that can actually be implemented, and for which there are competing and independent implementations. This last point—one of competing implementations—is the acid test for an open specification. The competing implementations requirement ensures that the user has multiple sourcing of provision and that the vendors have room to innovate in their products.

The organizations and the concepts under which they are organized vary widely. Over the past several years, the Standards Department at Sun Microsystems has been engaged in reviewing the basic nature of standardization groups, and we believe that we can make the following overarching statements:

All standardization models share several basic beliefs.

1. "There are rules to participate in a standards organization and you agree to accept these rules." The most common feature of any

standardization movement is a set of rules that attempt to set/simplify/clarify relationships between the participants. The existence of rules allows some order to be brought into a chaotic situation.

2. "There is a set of common interests that bind the standards organizations participants." This belief is absolutely necessary; absent it, there is mutual distrust by the participants and an inability to progress work.

3. "The result of the organization's work will result in change to the current situation from which all participants (and the market generally) will benefit." The non-parenthetical statement is axiomatic for any organized activity; however, standards succeed only if the market changes and accepts/uses the output of the standards group.

4. "An organization will help to set direction and guide the market by publishing standards, which will be accepted by the market." The whole reason for standardization organizations lies in the assumption that they guide/lead/structure the market through the creation and promulgation of common procedures and methods called standards. The belief that the market will accept and use these standards is predicated upon the industry leaders being part of the standards organization.

5. "Participation by multiple independent groups legitimizes the activities of the organization, when compared to a standard offered by a single entity." The belief behind this statement lies in the folk saying "one person can keep a secret, while three can't." By expanding the base of participants, a wider trust (on the part of the market) can be built and more influence to behave "openly" can be brought to bear.

All of these beliefs feed a theme that is key to standardization – that is, a group of well-intentioned people in an organization can achieve more (and in a more trusted manner) than any individual acting alone, no matter how well-intentioned or competent the individual. The group also believes—usually very sincerely—that their activities serve a larger good by making the market more open, or safer, or bigger, or more equitable. This belief in a quasi-idealistic mission that succeeds through group synergy is absolutely necessary to inspire people to strive against long odds and what, at times, appears to be common sense and reality. (Again, the Sisyphus complex coming into play.)

If these principles are valid, and experience tends to prove that they are, the next step is to examine how the practice of these activities has changed as the ICT industry has changed. The collapse of the product life cycle in the ICT industry (from more than six years to less than 18 months) has had a significant impact on how the processes have been forced to change. This change has gone largely unstudied except by professionals in various companies who have had to lead their companies through the changes in standardization.

The Evolution

Please note that the first half of this section (the evolution of the formal standardization arena) is heavily biased towards the creation and development of primarily Information Technology (and not Communications) specifications from the time period of 1975 onward. There are two primary reasons for this bias. The first is that, by 1975, the majority of companies involved in the creation of IT products were based in the US and tended to use the US processes as the basis for their standardization efforts. Second, the telecommunications market was still largely regulated and the standardization processes, because of this regulatory overlayment, were much less subject to evolutionary pressures than those practiced within the IT community.[8]

The initial standardization organizations were those that operated under the rules and organizational constricts of the American National Standards Institute (ANSI), following in the footsteps of all the other industrial standardization activities in the United States. It was during the period that much of the fundamental hardware standardization activities were occurring, ranging from common interconnections for the keyboard and mouse to printers and storage systems. The negotiations that created these standards—which were complex and confined to a relative handful of providers—were usually under the aegis of one or two standardization committees in the United States.[9] They usually dealt with things that would stay standardized for a long time. The formal national bodies under the aegis of ANSI in the US and the international bodies under the International Organization for Standardization and the International Electrotechnical Commission (ISO and IEC) were referred to as Standards Developing Organizations (SDOs) and were the source of standardization for the IT industry.

However, in the later 1980s, a different form of standardization activity appeared, beginning with an organization called "X/Open."[10] Providers began to move technology standardization away from the formal ANSI and ISO recognized SDOs to those of consortia, which did not have the intricate processes of the SDOs. The formal processes, which were both time consuming and often Byzantine, were necessary because "[m]ost delegates represent[ed] personal, professional, national, disciplinary, and industry goals…,"[11] and managing this vast and sometimes contradictory set of expectations forced these groups to create intricate rules to make sure that all voices were heard. On the other hand, because consortia usually consisted of groups of like minded participants (either for technical or market reasons), they did not need to have lengthy discussions over the mission and intent of the proposed standardization activity—an organization's presence was, in many cases, proof of a general agreement.[12] The archetypal consortium was the Internet Engineering Task Force (IETF), the group that is recognized as the creator and steward for Internet infrastructure specifications. The success of this group in both keeping the Internet a leading-edge technical architecture leader as well as clear of most greed, parochialism, and lethargy is a significant accomplishment.[13]

This shift was amplified by the introduction and ensuing popularity of the World Wide Web in the early 1990s. The establishment of the World Wide Web Consortium (W3C)[14] in October 1994 was a turning point within the IT industry; after this date, consortia were the logical place to develop joint specifications, whereas before they had been the "alternative place." The generation of IT practitioners who are now leading much of IT development, which is largely focused on Internet technologies, do not have an awareness of ANSI and ISO as sources for standards. Their world is largely bound by consortia such as W3C and the IETF. They see no need for ANSI or ISO standardization—a message that they carry to their companies.[15] With the maturity of the Web, an increasing number of consortia are being created to standardize Web based technology. (Nearly all e-Commerce organizations develop their specifications in arenas that are either consortia or consortia-like.)

The reason for the use of consortia lies not so much in the speed of technical development, but rather in the willingness of the consortia to use expedited processes. The IETF has been using the Internet to communicate among interested parties, post specifications, achieve rough consensus on technical features and functions, and then move forward on standardization. The specifications that the IETF adopts are usually based upon extant practice, with at least two implementations required for specifications on the standards track, and are available for widespread public review and comment. This practice of using its own technology to permit faster standardization of follow-on technology is another step that sets the IETF apart from its contemporary organizations of the 1980s. The use of its technologies as a basis for its standardization practices ensures workable and implementable specifications, but more importantly allows the IETF to develop into a truly international organization. When the specification is complete, it is posted on the IETF web site with free access for all.[16]

The W3C operates in a similar, though somewhat more formal, manner. W3C is a good model for the operation of many other consortia. These consortia realize that the key elements are speed and accessibility—accessibility to those who are concerned about their work. As *The Economist* has pointed out, "…the Internet has turned out to be a formidable promoter of open standards that actually work, for two reasons. First, the web is the ideal medium for creating standards; it allows groups to collaborate at almost no cost, and makes the decision-making more transparent. Second, the ubiquitous network ensures that standards spread much faster."[17] These features have made the IT community turn to consortia and similar structures for their standardization needs, in both hardware and software. The creation of highly open, highly visible specifications—widespread in their adoption and use—is essential to the continuing evolution of the IT sector and IT industry.

Another aspect of consortia that separates them from traditional SDOs is their dependence upon the market, rather than institutions, for relevance. A consortium succeeds or fails by its ability to attract members to accomplish its technical agenda. It receives little or no funding other than what its membership is willing to pay; money received from the government is rare and is usually in return for some exact service that the consortium renders to a specific government agency in the role of a contractor.[18] While this dependence upon its members for financing can be seen as a limitation on the consortium's freedom of action, it reflects the state of the market in formal SDOs as well, except that formal SDOs do not shut down if all of the commercially important members (those who would implement the specification) walk away. There is a delicate balance between an independence that leads to an unused standard and a financial dependency that produces a constrained specification.

The final stage of the evolution to date is the Open Source movement. Open Source mythology ascribes the beginning of open source to sometime in the past. Phrases such as "In the 1960s, when computers were cumbersome and esoteric, all software was essentially 'open source'… In the close-knit community of computer scientists, programs and ideas were shared freely. Beginning in the 1970s…software became proprietary in the interest of profit."[19] Richard Stallman and the Free Software Foundation (FSF) are usually cited as well. While all of these are possible antecedents in the way that the carriage was the antecedent of the car (it did have tires and did go from place to place), I would suggest that there was a prototype activity that foreshadowed the re-activation of Open Source in the Linux world—the X Consortium.

The Project X at MIT originally started as a research program focusing on user interface software where it pioneered the use of a multiplicity of independent programmers contributing their time and effort to a complex program, published source code and documentation for that code freely, and ensured that the code was of sufficient quality to actually work. Bug fixes were published within the community, and the code formed the basis of a rationalized GUI.

The X Consortium, the successor to the MIT X Project, continued in the same vein for several years. Although roundly condemned by Richard Stallman for its refusal to embrace "copyleft" (and hence his philosophy), they did achieve a significant following among developers. By embracing the concept of "an open source specification," the X Consortium put in place the basic underpinnings of the system mechanics—and showed that it could work in a corporate (for profit) arena. They anticipated the "Open Source" use of the Internet as the virtual team, they had Bob Scheiffler and his staff as the "gurus," they published both books and specifications, and they proselytized the technology through the companies upon whose technologists they depended. The role played by Robert Scheiffler cannot be overstated; he once described himself as a "benevolent dictator" for the project. He was the prototype for the role played by Linus Torvalds, but without the adoration ladled on him as Eric Raymond did for Linus in *The Cathedral and the Bazaar*.

If the X Consortium served as the archetype for what has followed, then the history of open source is easier to track. Following the proof of concept demonstrated by X, it is reasonably easy to watch the Linux phenomena launch. Raymond, in *The Cathedral and the Bazaar*, describes how he had been doing open source for years, but it wasn't until Linux hit that he realized what it was that he'd been working on. Following Torvalds' lead, he set out to describe the underpinnings of open source. Needless to say, the creation and the ferment engendered by the World Wide Web did not hurt the cause of Torvalds and Raymond; both used the Web as a significant communications medium. Jamie Zawinski of Netscape probably provided the largest boost to the open source movement when he convinced Netscape's management to make the source for Netscape's browser into open source—a move partially born of desperation, since Netscape realized that it could not compete with Microsoft in engineering resources. This distrust of Microsoft and other large companies contributed a second (minor) strain to the open source movement.

Since its inception, Open Source has grown into a significant activity in the corporate environment. The key to the success of Open

---

"The key to the success of Open Source lies not so much in the availability of Open Source programs for sale (which raises the question of how a developer makes money), but rather in the use of Open Source within the corporate environment to write application programs that will never leave the creating organization."

Source lies not so much in the availability of Open Source programs for sale (which raises the question of how a developer makes money), but rather in the use of Open Source within the corporate environment to write application programs that will never leave the creating organization.[20] Open Source is merely another form of standardization—if you examine the five principles in the section labeled "The Process,"

you will see that they apply to the Open Source movement as well.

The Challenge for Standardization

The challenge now facing standardization is the fact that the environment—described in the first section—has become so interconnected so rapidly. Because standards are created within and by organizations (from ISO to the W3C), there is a natural tendency to attempt to maintain a relative degree of independence by all of the various Standards Setting Organizations (SSOs), a term encompassing all organizations that produce open and consensual specifications. Additionally, because there is no "central standardization authority," it is relatively easy to create a new organization. At the time that I wrote this, I believe that there were over 500 extant consortia, and new consortia appear on a weekly basis. When this is coupled with the over 270 ANSI accredited organizations in the US alone, the complexity of the management issue becomes apparent.

There are two problems that spring from this: complex standardization portfolio management and technical specification incompatibility. The first is obvious—it is difficult to manage an environment that is in a constant state of flux, resists centralization, and has no duty or obligation to help achieve a state of coherence. There are no governance methodologies to keep track of the organizations, let alone what the organizations are doing. The best attempt at cataloguing the

---

"From a pragmatic, managerial, and commercial point of view, the situation in standardization portfolio management is grim."

---

consortia has been by John Ketchell at CEN/ISSS;[21] when I last visited the site, he was listing slightly over 200 consortia and similar fora whose function was open specification creation.

From a pragmatic, managerial, and commercial point of view, the situation in standardization portfolio management is grim. Even large corporations are beginning to have trouble managing their standardization portfolios; the exasperation is apparent among all of the participants. There appears to be no way to limit it, however, which is probably a response by the market to a complex and confusing environment. The initial gleams of hope have appeared with the movement towards consortia consolidation; the best known example so far is the creation of the Open Mobile Alliance (OMA),

> *"SSOs are producing technical specifications that are not interoperable with specifications produced by other SSOs."*

which has integrated five "microfora" into a single larger entity, both for expense and management reasons.

The technical managerial difficulties are founded in a problem that is becoming more common (and is also a problem of our own making). SSOs are producing technical specifications that are not interoperable with specifications produced by other SSOs. This lack of interoperation can range from something as small as a bit setting in a line of code to a completely different architectural approach. However, the solution to this problem lies within the power of the creating organizations to fix. The solution to the technical incompatibility issue is an agreement among the providers and users NOT TO USE A SPECIFICATION that does not play well with others.[22]

The reason the problem of technical specification incompatibility is so absurd lies in the fact that the organizations and specifications are being created by the "usual crowd of suspects" —mainly the same companies that have funded competing and contradictory SSOs. When one speaks of the "wireless market," one is probably referring to less than 10 major participants who have created, driven, and productized the initial base level standards that defined the market. Within the IT industry, the situation is the same —there are not more than a handful of major

companies. Yet, far from being monolithic, these companies often present a completely fragmented face to the industry, funding increasing numbers of SSOs while complaining about the proliferation of the very organizations they create.

This problem does admit of a solution—but a solution that is neither quick, easy, or inexpensive.[23] It is, however, an action necessary to make heterogeneous standardization useful in a complex networked environment. The solution is one that has had currency in the past, and which several SSOs have, on their own, initiated for the specifications they produce. The solution is conformance testing to validate that the vendor product implementations of the specifications agree with the specifications themselves.[24] This, in itself, is not new, but it is an activity more honored in the breach than in the practice. It is also an immensely unpopular activity politically, since there are specific legal implications associated with conformance testing. The solution for individual SSOs does exist; the will to use the solution does not. This leads to a series of problems that confront standardization, and its role with respect to innovation.

The Role of Innovation in Standardization

The role of innovation in standardization is problematic. The classic argument from engineers is that standardization squelches innovation because it forces engineers to use the same old designs and concepts, and does not permit them to try or experiment with new and unusual ideas. The argument has merit—if all engineers were paid to design new and unusual things in their work. Unfortunately, over 80 percent of the day to day work in a corporate environment is about sustaining or production engineering, especially in the software arena. Therefore, the argument that standardization hampers innovation seems to be specious in the corporate, or production, environment. I will grant that there are cases where a poor standard and poor management have combined to create a culture where innovation is discouraged.[25]

On the other hand, how many engineers can

design a really good Local Area Network? It would seem to be much easier to assume that the LAN you need to use meets the standardized specification and that the engineer (or other implementers) can assume that it is "just there." Similarly, one assumes that the Internet is "just there" and that HTML is ubiquitous. It is true that, at times, one is constrained by the capabilities of the extant standardized services. This constraint is usually known well in advance, however, and innovation occurs when someone designs around a weakness or shortcoming.[26]

Additionally, standards are not immutable. They do change over time as the market needs new and different features added to the capability stack of the specification. One needs only to look at the evolution of the Internet Protocol

---

"In many cases, standardization serves as a change agent to the ICT industry."

(now up to Version 6) or of HTML (now at Version 4) to understand how change occurs in standardization. In many cases, standardization serves as a change agent to the ICT industry; it is an economic phenomenon written about by many economists. Most of these writings are theoretical, describing a reasonably sterile and predictive economic model of standardization. What is less understood is exactly how and why standards committees function the way that they do.[27]

"There are three distinct categories into which … standards creation activities can fall: (1) Standards that plan to change the industry; (2) Standards that reinforce existing patterns; (3) Standards that cause change that is unplanned."[28] The second of these options—the standards that are "culturally congruent"—that is, they modify existing practice to help it evolve in the market place, is the most common standardization activity. The first of these options—the standards for planned change—are usually massive undertakings, involving the movement of an entire market to a new arena. The Open

Systems Interconnect (OSI) activity was one such attempt, and it failed as a standard that was not widely implemented. While it involved all of the major IT vendors at the time and consumed thousands of man-years of effort over a ten year period, it was a market failure because it was overtaken by a simpler and less complex solution to the problem called the Internet.[29] On the successful side, one only needs to look at the work of ETSI (and its Scandinavian predecessors) in the creation of the GSM mobile telephony standardization suite. While GSM may not have been the most innovative technical solution, the problems that it resolved to allow mobile roaming telephony were staggering. And the innovations in the application of the technology have helped to create a multi-billion dollar industry. (One might note that the innovation necessary in the creation of this phenomenon ranged from new battery technology to satellite placement.)

The third category—unplanned change—also provides a home for an incredible amount of innovation. I do not believe that the creation of HTTP and HTML was a deliberate attempt to change the market—rather, existing technologies were used in a clever way to achieve a point solution to a problem.[14] The larger impact of the Web on technology and society has been significant. It can be seen in the creation of new businesses, the development of new business methods, the internationalization of trade and culture, and even in things as mundane as tax laws and import and export controls. Within the ICT environment, an entirely different way of computing was created—it was network based computing, which bids fair to be a more substantial market than that created by the emergence of the PC. None of this was planned as a result of the standardization of HTTP and HTML; it was unplanned change. Once the technology of the Web began to become widespread, innovation became the watchword of the ICT industry.

This innovation brought with it a set of problems however. The success of the Web created a large new market. The technology threatened established methodologies and the installed base of products. There were attempts by all parties to co-opt the technology and shut down the unplanned change that was occurring. The creation of the World Wide Web Consortium (W3C) in October of 1994 was a significant shift in the attitude for the ICT industry; it was one of the first times that an implemented technology with a large market pull had a consortium created to protect it from being captured by a clique of vendors. The resulting standardization has led to more sustained innovation in the ICT industry than has been seen before.

It is in the case of the World Wide Web (based upon the work of the W3C and the IETF) that we see the clearest and most significant role of standards as guardians of innovation. Absent these organizations, the technology would probably have been stunted or moved to a slower growth plane. As it is, the activities of these SSOs permitted innovation to occur in a relatively neutral and protected arena, and then allowed exposure of the innovative technology to the market to test its appeal.

This is the essential and new role for standardization with respect to technological innovation—it provides a safe haven for initial

---

"This is the essential and new role for standardization with respect to technological innovation—it provides a safe haven for initial development and possible deployment."

---

development and possible deployment. It is a role with which the SSOs are just now coming to terms. It also provides a counter argument to the idea of "micro-fora proliferation." If the micro-fora are incubation centers for substantial innovation, then their existence is uncomfortable but necessary. On the other hand, if the creation of these micro-fora is merely an opportunity to create a specification to end-run an existing SSO, then their existence is bad. The problem is telling the "good" groups from the "bad" groups. The problem becomes one of "Whose ox gets gored."

There is, however, another and larger problem with the proliferation of SSOs. The problem derives from the administrative activities of the groups—as I noted earlier, each group has a set of rules by which it plays. One set of these rules deals with Intellectual Property Rights (IPR). It is this problem that may ultimately cause the failure of network based standardization activities and possibly the entire standardization arena.

The Problems and Possible Ways to Proceed

The issues facing ICT standardization and its role as both incubator and guardian of innovation are twofold. Both have their origin in the success of the Internet and the Web, themselves based upon standardization. Both issues are derived from the systemic nature of ICT computing today. And both have their solutions in a better education on the subject of standardization, which creates a greater awareness and participation by the academic and public sector.

Technical issues

The first issue is technical in nature and consists of two parts. First, there is the problem of non-conformance with a standardized specification. This problem has been around for quite some time, and is the bane of some SSOs, legitimate providers, and users. Basically, product conformance is claimed with an existing specification when, in fact, conformance either does not exist or the the product implements the specification in such a way that it does not interoperate. For specifications that deal with only one feature or aspect of a system, this failure can quickly be called out and the provider made to correct it. However, there are circumstances where the market power of the provider is such that the users have no choice but to accept the crippled implementation of the specification, leaving the market with, in effect, a proprietary standard.

This is a problematic situation. If, as has been postulated, standards are a market activity, the acceptance of such a "proprietary standard" can be justified by saying it is what the "market wanted." On the other hand, activity such as this can be seen as violation of antitrust and anti-competitive rules, since it violates the spirit and intention of what a standards policy should do. **There is a body of literature that suggests that there may be a remedy to this situation, however.**

In a major Congressional Office of Technology Assessment (OTA) study completed in the early 1990s, the following comment commands attention:

> Other goods, like education and standards, are impure public goods. These combine aspects of both public and private goods. Although they serve a private function, there are also public benefits associated with them. Impure public goods may be produced and distributed in the market or collectively through government. How they are produced is a societal choice of significant consequence. **If decisions about impure public goods are made in the market, on the basis of personal preferences alone, then the public benefits associated with them may not be efficiently produced or equitably distributed.**
> [Emphasis added] [30]

The right (or possibly the duty) of the government to intervene in such a situation is significant. The failure of the private side in the 1960s and 1970s to manage standardization fairly and legitimately led to Congressional hearings and an antitrust case, as well as the creation and empowerment of the current hierarchy. Since that time, there has not been a significant change in the U.S. government policy towards standards, which, considering the economic, social, and political changes that have occurred, is only a little short of remarkable. It is a situation that, I believe, bears investigation, but one that is fraught with political danger in the US.

The European Community has looked at standardization differently and has tried to use the discipline to effect some attitudinal and social change, especially in the encouragement of Small and Medium Enterprises (SMEs). However, they have also taken significant steps to recognize the power of standardization to cause change and innovation.

The second part of the technical issue lies in the lack of cross-SSO conformity and interconnection testing. It is not a problem that can successfully be addressed by governmental activity; it is a reasonably pure market play. However, government, as a major user of ICT equipment, can have an impact on this area through its procurement policies. Additionally, there is a substantial lack of education on the entire area of

---

"It is interesting that most graduate engineers know less about standardization and the utility of standards than any working electrician, plumber, or builder, since these last three depend upon standards as part of their livelihood."

---

technical standardization worldwide. Typically, students are taught to compete, not cooperate, in innovation. The ability to optimize a point solution and sub-optimize a system is, I believe, much easier to teach than the reverse. It is interesting that most graduate engineers know less about standardization and the utility of standards than any working electrician, plumber, or builder, since these last three depend upon standards as part of their livelihood.[31]

Social and legal issues

The second issue—a social/legal issue—is also a two-part problem and only now beginning to be recognized as a possible poison pill for standardization.

As SSOs have evolved, they have, of necessity, created their own rules for operation. These rules are part of its marketing package to attract members. Organizational structures, elections of officers, processes for creating specifications, openness procedures, and rules for technology submission are all variable. One other important rule is also variable from SSO to SSO—the methods by which the SSO handles the intellectual property rights of the members. The most generally accepted formula through the mid-1990s was the concept of guaranteeing Reasonable And Non-Discriminatory (RAND) licensing of essential technology by the owning organization if the patent was used in a standard, and a commitment to disclose the patent sometime during the standardization process.

RAND originated with the three large formal standardization organizations: the International Organization for Standardization (ISO); the International Electrotechnical Commission (IEC); and the International Consultative Committee on Telephony and Telegraphy (CCITT) of the International Telecommunication Union (ITU), now simply known as the ITU-T (for telecommunications), based in Switzerland. These three organizations have similar patent policies—that is, RAND of essential patents. These policies worked very well in the 1980s and halfway through the 1990s, although there were signs that IPR (especially patent rights) was becoming problematic. Probably the bravest attempt to change the nature of the IPR issue came from the European Telecommunications Standards Institute (ETSI). Most large SSOs were unwilling or unable to act. Negotiation of a new and comprehensive set of patent rules was difficult; alone among the organizations engaged in standardization, ETSI attempted something different. "At its inception in 1988/89, ETSI in-

---

"The terms and conditions of RAND are a major stumbling block in the creation of innovation."

---

sisted that it was born into a 'new environment of European standardization' [Tuckett, 1993] in which emerging standards would be 'littered with IPRs'. Although the fledgling institute later estimated that the IPR-problem would only involve about 2% of its standards work [ETSI document, 1994], the perception that the danger had ceased to be an academic problem encouraged it to seek new measures to tackle the eventuality. Alas, it was not alone in this prognosis in

the late 1980s and early 1990s. International voluntary SDOs like the former CCITT [now ITU-T] also recognized but 'avoided the temptation' of defining procedures to address the potentially damaging IPR problem."[32]

The terms and conditions of RAND are a major stumbling block in the creation of innovation. Until the mid-1990s, the majority of players in standardization were large companies who would cross-license IPR, settling the differences in the value of portfolios with cash payments. The licensing of technology to smaller companies was something that occurred, but was not a major issue. The phrase "Reasonable" was bland and non-controversial and usually not argued over extensively.

This changed with the advent of the Web and the growth of mobile computing. In the GSM telephone, there are 137 essential patents. The ability of a small company to enter this market is limited if they don't have a large patent portfolio from which to deal. At the same time, Tim Berners-Lee of the W3C has estimated that every time someone clicks a mouse in a web application, thirty patents are invoked. Again, if a small company does not have a significant patent portfolio with which to deal, they are at the mercy of the patent holders who own essential patents in the standards.

This situation is becoming intolerable to some SSOs. In late 2002, the W3C circulated for comment a proposed patent policy requiring that all essential technology submitted for a specification be offered on a limited license Royalty Free (RF) basis. This is similar to that of the Open GIS Consortium, which has also established a RF IPR policy. At the same time, the Open Source community, the antithesis of captive intellectual property in software, has served notice on companies that use IPR to stop or limit innovation that this practice is considered unethical. While the efficacy and impact of these policies are unknown, they represent a brave first step towards addressing a severe problem confronting the SSOs —that of IPR and strangulation of innovation.

There is a second problem related to the issue of IPR in standardization —and this one speaks to the lack of commonality among SSOs. As noted earlier, every organization has a slightly different approach to IPR. Additionally, most organizations have somewhat sketchy rules even when they do have a policy. They have never needed to have a more complete policy, because there were very few violations of the organization's IPR policies. Since the companies were usually equally large and all held substantial patents, little legal trouble was expected. The Web changed all that, however. While the new participants were not litigious, they were also not part of the "old boys network" or gentlemen's club that had been running things before. There were two startling facts that jumped out at them.

First, where the SSO failed to adequately define its processes, the law of the land in which the SSO was domiciled became the overriding law. Hence, where ISO failed to provide a complete process, the laws of the canton of Geneva became the laws for the resolution of disputes that were not clearly covered by ISO rules. One such question would be "What does reasonable mean?" Depending upon the national bias and where the trial was held, the answer could vary tremendously.

Second, and most importantly for a systemic approach to standards, the organizations did not line up when their standards were to be used in a system. Using a wireless scenario as an example, if a specification called for a WAP Forum (now part of OMA and a UK based SSO) specification to tie into a W3C (not an SSO, but a multilateral agreement based in the MIT, ERCIM, Keio) specification, and then include an ETSI (based in France) specification, we would have three different, incomplete IPR policies from three different countries. Each of these countries has slightly different laws, which all must be contended with in defending an implementation. Basically, this means that there can never be unencumbered systemic specifications unless all organizations accept similar IPR policies.

Again, the solution to these problems lies in whether or not governments believe that standardization is worth the extra amount that they would have to invest to help a segment of the

industry (the RF and Open Source community) succeed by using legislative right to help establish a criteria for what is an acceptable IPR policy for SSOs as part of a procurement process.

If this statement is accepted, then the efficient functioning of standardization is a matter of public and private interest and government intervention is acceptable (and possibly necessary) when the private sector fails. As of this writing, there is little to indicate that the SSOs are making an effort to confront this problem in a manner that is acceptable to the market—the users, providers, and other concerned parties.

The solution would be to create acceptable criteria for an ideal SSO IPR regime, which would provide incentives for SSOs to use the model as a basis for their own efforts. The IPR policy would first have to be crafted to meet the needs of using nations, since no SSO can afford to be single-nation focused. Once this policy is agreed upon, it should be submitted to the WTO for consideration as part of its definition of what constitutes a legitimate standardization organization. Simultaneously, accreditation of organizations to permit preferential status for

---

"Unless some method can be found to create a single and generally unified IPR regime for all SSOs, there can and will be little progress made in attempting to create a singular open network."

---

governmental procurements would also serve to provide incentives for SSOs and their members to accept the new IPR rules.

The variegated IPR regime that is the legacy of a flawed evolutionary process represents a real and true barrier to standardization. Unless some method can be found to create a single and generally unified IPR regime for all SSOs, there can and will be little progress made in attempting to create a singular open network. The lack of a standard—whether it be for IPR or technology—serves only those who would keep information, and the ability to manage one's own information, under proprietary control. And this becomes the overarching fear.

It would also be interesting to see more academic legal review of the status of standards, especially the intellectual property provisions— including the impact that software copyright will have on the US and European differences in this area.

Gloomy Assessment

The discipline of standardization is the basis for a multi-billion dollar industry. *The Economist* made the statement over ten years ago that "[t]he noisiest of those competitive battles (between suppliers) will be about standards. The eyes of most sane people tend to glaze over at the very mention of technical standards. But in the computer industry, new standards can be the source of enormous wealth, or the death of corporate empires. With so much at stake, standards arouse violent passions."[33] Ten years later, *The Economist* reports "… the Internet has spawned institutions, such as the Internet Engineering Task Force (IETF) and the World Wide Web Consortium (W3C), which have shown that it is possible to develop robust common technical rules."[34]

Yet, what studies have been done to show how standards actually work? The best studies that I've found in the last five years on standards (actually talking to participants to find out what happened) have come out of Europe and have been largely funded by the EU. Industry doesn't (usually) fund studies; there are exceptions to this (I've sponsored several IPR sessions in standardization groups), but generally vendors are loath to invest in research on standards because they don't think it that important.

The reason that they don't think it important lies in the lack of education on this subject. MBAs get loads of courses on marketing, but none on standards. Engineers get many courses on chip and GUI design—but none on standards. The same holds true for lawyers (I believe), accountants, and all other business and technical students in the US and most of Europe. Look at business books on the subject of strategic planning from Porter forward. Standards are suspiciously absent. Academia has (or maybe only is) failing business. If you read about innovation, most writing is silent on standards.

Basically, the ICT industry participates in standards on faith. We fund what research we need, and when we must, we take the time to create a standard. It is not a well reasoned way to move forward, but it works. In the meantime, the academic and government ability to influence standardization is rapidly fading as more consortia and SSOs are brought up on line and less time can be taken by providers to understand how these things work together. If the situation is not reversed, the utility of standards will decline over time. As the decline occurs, something will take standardization's place, whether it is a form of marketing or commercial joint ventures or other activity.

The fear of this replacement process—the fear that drives those who would reform standards—is that the replacement may not be nearly so kind to innovation as is standardization. As innovation declines, so will that change, the dynamism, and the excitement that has been the hallmark of ICT. Most importantly, I fear that the social benefits of the ICT industry may be lessened or slowed at precisely the wrong time for society. And this would be the ultimate tragedy of the failure of standardization.

Notes

[1] Cargill, Carl F. *Standards,* in Ralston, Anthony et. al. editors, *Encyclopedia of Computer Science, Fourth Edition*, Nature Publishing Group, 2000, London, pp. 1677-1683

[2] There has been much discussion of the nature and growth of ICT standardization. The industry believes that the use and the need for standardization is growing (it seems to be glaringly obvious), but we have no firm empirical data to support this belief.

[3] As an example, users do not now have to worry about whether the LAN card for their PC will work within the environment. Because of standardiza-

tion, they know that an 802.11 card allows them to connect to wireless networks. They are now able to buy differentiating features on top of the standard offering. These can include performance, robustness, price, or whatever other feature that the provider believes will appeal to the consumer.

4 According to Greek legend, Sisyphus was a king condemned by the gods to roll a huge boulder to the top of a steep hill, only to have it roll back down each time he neared the top (*Odyssey*, xi. 593).

5 I would imagine that, from the user side, the task is no less, and possibly even more, daunting. The user is faced with a myriad of choices on the technology and the implementation of that technology within their business environment. They worry about the standards that impact the entire range of their business, from safety and environmental standards, to new manufacturing standards, to social responsibility standards. While providers also have those concerns (as a part of their business), the standardization of the ICT product attributes within the IT development process has become the focus of what is called "ICT standardization."

6 Apocryphal stories exist about Thomas Watson seeing a need for only five computers in 1943; Ken Olsen of Digital Equipment Corporation once asserted that no one needed a home computer. Even Bill Gates has fallen into the trap of resisting change to the value chain with his assertion several years ago that the PC would always be necessary. All have been proven incorrect—or at least misguided. All were happy with the status quo, until they were rudely shocked out of it. In some cases, it leads to bigger and better markets; in other cases, companies fold. In either case, change occurs.

7 My casual disregard for the International Organization for Standardization (ISO) approved definition of a standard (basically, a document produced by a Standards Developing Organization [SDO] whose process has in some way been vetted or accredited by an ISO endorsed body) comes from a recognition that, within the ICT arena, a declining percentage of specifications are produced by ISO committees. The specification creation work of the Internet Engineering Task Force (IETF), the World Wide Web Consortium (W3C), and scores of other groups concerned with the Web and Internet are not ISO recognized but are still deliberate, open, and consensually created.

8 It is also worth noting that the two technology cultures did (and still do) operate under different underlying assumptions. The IT culture rewards innovation at the expense of system interoperation, while the Telecommunications culture rewards interoperation at the expense of disruptive innovation. As a proof point, I submit that people often boast about innovative IT devices that provide unique capabilities but rarely boast about a unique feature on their phone that cannot be shared with other subscribers.

9 These were the ANSI accredited standards committees called Accredited Standards Committee (ASC) X3 and Accredited Organization (AO) IEEE (Computer Systems). Approximately 85% of the key standards were created in X3, including storage interconnect, languages, and so on. The IEEE dealt with physical interconnects (such as local area networks) and eventually moved into software interfaces.

10 In 1996, X/Open merged with the Open Software Foundation to create The Open Group. X/Open was originally created in Europe to embrace and extend UNIX ® to limit the spread of US companies into the European IT arena. After 10 years of existence, and before its merger, it was largely dominated by major US IT providers, with Siemens as its sole surviving European member.

11 Cargill, Carl F. *Information Technology Standardization: Theory, Process, and Organizations*, Digital Press, Bedford, MA, 1989, p. 117.

12 The reason that consortia are often more visible within a company than formal organizations is that consortia are more directly tied to the product success of a company. A company will join a consortium to promote the creation of a specification that it needs for market reasons—there is an imperative behind the consortia's creation. The same imperative is not necessarily found in formal organizations.

13 The IETF describes itself in the following way: "The Internet Engineering Task Force (IETF) is a large open international community of network designers, operators, vendors, and researchers concerned with the evolution of the Internet architecture and the smooth operation of the Internet. It is open to any interested individual. The actual technical work of the IETF is done in its working groups, which are organized by topic into several areas (e.g., routing, transport, security, etc.). Much of the work is handled via mailing lists. The IETF holds meetings three times per year. The IETF working groups are grouped into areas, and managed by Area Directors, or ADs. The ADs are members of the Internet Engineering Steering Group (IESG). Providing architectural oversight is the Internet Architecture Board,

(IAB). The IAB also adjudicates appeals when someone complains that the IESG has failed. The IAB and IESG are chartered by the Internet Society (ISOC) for these purposes. The General Area Director also serves as the chair of the IESG and of the IETF, and is an ex-officio member of the IAB." See http://www.ietf.org

[14] See http://www.w3.org/Consortium/ for a detailed description of both the creation of the underlying vision of the Web by Tim Berners-Lee and the initiation of the W3C by MIT, INRIA, and Keio University.

[15] In the case of HTML 3.2 (a specification developed and promulgated by W3C), ISO/IEC JTC1 SC18 (the committee charged with standardization of this technology) tried to standardize HTML 3.2 with "JTC1 improvements," but only after W3C had standardized HTML 3.2 and users had implemented it in millions of Web sites. After serious negotiations by W3C and major users and providers, SC 18 agreed not to make their standard different from the W3C standard, which was in widespread use.

[16] The IETF uses an Internet based method of specification creation, unlike many of the JTC 1 (ISO based) committees. All specifications are posted to the Internet, and anyone may comment on the specification. Contrast this method with the JTC1 Committees, which allow only specific delegates from participating countries to review the specifications.

[17] The Economist Newspaper, "The Age Of The Cloud, Survey Of Software," Special Supplement, April 14-20th, 2001, 111 West 57th Street, New York, NY 10019-2211

[18] Spring and Weiss discuss the problems of private sector funding of the formal standards organization in their article in *Financing the Standards Development Process* pp. 289-320, in *Standards Policy for Information Infrastructure*, edited by Kahin, Brian and Abate, Janet, MIT Press, 1995.

[19] (The Case for Government Promotion of Open Source Software. A NetAction White Paper, Mitch Stoltz [http://www.netaction.org/opensrc/oss-history.html])

[20] Bruce Perens has estimated that nearly 80 percent of Open Source software is being created inside of major corporations. It is the "home grown applications"—those that run a majority of corporate functions—that appear to be the primary hotbed of Open Source activity at this time.

[21] Ketchell, John, Consortia survey, 7th edition, October 2002, at The CEN/ISSS web site, http://www.cenorm.be/

[22] This approach, of course, would probably be socially (and possibly legally) unacceptable and would look like an attempt to control the market using a standardization process. Also, there is the problem of exactly which specification is out of consonance with the other specification. As H.L. Mencken said so clearly, "For every complex problem, there is always a simple solution. And it is wrong."

[23] And therefore, if we are to believe Mencken, has the possibility of being correct.

[24] The concept of the "Connectathon," in which multiple companies gather to demonstrate the interoperability of products, tests only for a single specification or family of specifications from a single SSO. However, the theory could be expanded with little trouble.

[25] If this were not occasionally true, comic strips like Dilbert wold have no raw material from which to work, and the character of Dilbert's "pointy hair boss" would not resonate so widely and so well.

[26] However, standardization is the bane of engineers who believe in gratuitous innovation. A general rule that I have heard cited is that, if one is going to change an existing piece of code, one should be prepared to offer somewhere between a 25 and 50 percent improvement in efficiency or other major capability. Tweaking because one can is usually a waste of an engineer's time and should be devoted to more challenging and useful tasks.

[27] Martin Weiss, Michael Spring, and Joel West are among the very small group of academics who have actually participated in standardization committee activities, and whose writings on the subject are unusually relevant contributions to those of us who actually practice standardization within the industrial settings.

[28] Cargill, Carl F. *Open Systems Standardization: A Business Approach*, Prentice Hall PTR, Upper Saddle River, NJ, 1997, p. 57.

[29] It might be argued that another reason for the success of the TCP/IP protocol was the fact that it cost nothing for the specifications or most of the technology, which was usually delivered as Royalty Free for use in the Internet environment. TCP/IP was a lightweight protocol compared to OSI, and was easy enough to implement so that small and medium size companies could master and implement it quickly.

[30] U.S. Congress, Office of Technology Assessment, *Global Standards: Building Blocks for the Future*, TCT-512 (Washington, D.C.: U.S. Government Printing Office, March 1992) p. 14, footnote 23.

[31] I recognize that the last three also labor under the requirement to use standards because of regulatory requirements, but I believe that the fact that these disciplines use standards to encourage innovation (be creative, but use the standard) is telling.

[32] Iversen, Eric J. Standardization And Intellectual Property Rights: ETSI's Controversial Search For New IPR-Procedures, proceeding of the 1999 SIIT conference, Aachen, Germany, available at http://www-i4.informatik.rwth-aachen.de/~jakobs/siit99/proceedings/

[33] The Economist Newspaper, 23 February, 1993

[34] The Economist Newspaper, "The Age Of The Cloud, Survey Of Software," Special Supplement, Apri14-20th, 2001, 111 West 57th Street, New York, NY 10019-2211

ICT Standardization: Changing the World for a Better Tomorrow

JOHN HILL
Sun Microsystems, Inc.

Abstract: *Undeniably, ICT (information and communications technology) standardization is at a critical crossroads. The needs of the marketplace in terms of timeliness, functionality, and interoperability, once so well served by traditional standardization processes, are not being met. Something must be done or the industry's progress of the past four decades will be lost, risking a return to market dominance by the very few wealthiest and most powerful providers. The single best hope is that the ICT standardization industry becomes so healthy and responsive that standards-based products become preferred over proprietary products.*

The question is not whether to fix the situation—it obviously has to be fixed. The question is how to fix it. And the answer to that question encompasses a wide variety of opinion. One company, Sun Microsystems, together with numerous partners, has begun identifying the specific problems, collecting and analyzing relevant data, and taking constructive action. This paper discusses their progress in this initiative.

Two Days in December 2002

Against the vocal opposition of many entrenched powers in the ICT standardization industry, the Information Technology Industry Council (ITIC), the US Department of Commerce (DoC) and Massachusetts Institute of Technology (MIT) held a conference. They invited CEOs and CIOs, together with other movers and shakers, to spend a day and a half addressing known problems of ICT standardization. The attendees came from industry, government, and academia. The true experts of standardization in the ICT industry addressed these influential people. The speakers' expertise spanned the subjects of organization and structure, the role of government in standardization, the economics of standardization, and intellectual property rights (IPR). To be sure, there were no universal agreements about how improvements in these subjects could be attained. There was unanimity, however, that improvements are needed, and fast.

This was no boring, typical conference. The audience felt so strongly about the issues that 'Happy Hour' refreshments had to be delayed— a rare occurrence in the realm of standardization conferences.

This conference used two innovative features. They are worth mention here because they show the depth of concern the sponsors have for the health and well-being of the ICT standardization industry. First, the hosts conducted a survey of the conference attendees. It was a simple, 20-question survey aimed at determining the collective opinions about the severity of the four subject/problem areas. An independent statistician analyzed the results and prepared a 150 page report. The results are important. They showed that all four problem areas are serious and deserve additional analysis. It is necessary to understand the roots of these problems in order to effectively address them. But what was really innovative is that now reliable data exists on which to build real solutions. We can now go forward, not as we usually do, armed only with anecdotes, but with data. Sure, the results represent the collective opinion of only the attendees. That is certain. But it is a start.

The second innovative feature is a book entitled *The Standards Edge™.* Each attendee received this book containing academic articles and case studies concerning ICT standardization. This, too, is a beginning. It is the beginning of gathering together the collective wisdom of ICT standardization experts. The beginning of a body of coherent knowledge that is necessary to maturing and healing the ICT standardization industry.

Somewhere in the not too distant past a folk philosopher said, "Anyone can start things. Few complete them." That is precisely what Sun is doing. They are building on the results of that conference, applying a staff that has more than 90 years ICT standardization experience, and helping evolve the changes so desperately needed. They are all realists. Some just dream more vividly than others.

Changing the World as We Know It

Sun is applying two tools to each of five problem areas, and they're doing it all over the world. Those problem areas, with a brief description, follow.

1. **Organization and Structure:** Organizations dominate the processes of ICT standardization and they all face similar problems. They all need revenue to pay their bills. They all need to produce results the industry values. The downturn in the worldwide ICT markets has adversely affected all the organizations. Their collective well-being is a necessary prerequisite to a healthy ICT standardization industry. The key question is "What should

be done to improve these organizations?"

2. **The Role of Government:** Many governments seem to address standardization inconsistently. Different agencies within the same government participate in ICT standardization in different ways and conflicts due to overlap are often the result. Additionally, meaningful gaps (i.e., areas of nonparticipation by governments) also exist. Every government should conduct a strategic assessment of their role in ICT standardization.

3. **Economics:** It is a fact of standardization that members of organizations send real people to work for them in standardization activities. It costs those members real money, and often the people they send are scarce resources, valuable in other roles. It is important that these member organizations make sensible decisions about the manner and extent of their participation in ICT standardization. The relevant questions are "What is a good strategy to follow in determining how best to participate in standardization"' and "What should the business case for ICT standards look like?"

4. **Intellectual Property Rights:** Today, all ICT standardization organizations are working IPR issues. Patents, copyrights, trademarks, and trade secrets are all subject to different laws in virtually every country of the world. Compounding the problem is that each organization involved in standardization seems to have different IPR policies. The main question is "Since a great many standardization organizations have members from multiple

---

"Worldwide, there are only pockets of training programs and very few academic courses that address standardization."

---

countries, what should an individual organization's IPR policies be?"

5. **Education:** ICT standardization is more than 40 years old while standardization in general

is vastly older. The thing is, standardization, for all its age and importance, does not have the respect it deserves. Worldwide, there are only pockets of training programs and very few academic courses that address standardization. It seems that standardization is a career endpoint and not a waypoint. The key questions here are "Is standardization a profession?" and "If so, what kind of training is needed?"

Sun is using two tools to catalyze the addressing of these problems: conferences and workshops. Many conferences, based on the successful model of the December 2002 conference, are either occurring or are in the planning stages at the time of this publication. Most of these

---

"Sun is using two tools to catalyze the addressing of these problems: conferences and workshops."

---

conferences will focus on individual problems although a few will address multiple challenges. While the timing, audiences, problems, and location all differ, these conferences have several common elements. Surveys will be conducted and analyzed in order to better understand the causes of the problems and build a body of standardization data. And, books will be written to further consolidate the standardization knowledge. These books can then become course texts for training and education.

The workshops are the second tool being used. They will address focal issues such as the following:

1. What are the best practices of standardization organizations for obtaining revenue?

2. What are the roles of governments in ICT standardization?

3. Is the use of standards increasing?

A View of the Future

It is impossible to predict with complete precision and accuracy what future ICT standardization processes will consist of. There are, however, certain things that are known. The processes will:

- be more responsive to the marketplace than today's processes

- exhibit measurable improvements in:
  – organization and structure
  – role of governments
  – economics
  – intellectual property rights
  – education

- have been developed using the collective wisdom of persons and organizations that are uninvolved today, including managers and leaders in business, government, and academia.

The world of ICT standardization has needed these improvements for a long time. Only now has the thought leadership come forward with the resources to make them happen. But it will take the participation of government, business,

---

"It will take the participation of government, business, and industry to strengthen the current standardization system into one that is healthy, economically viable, and responsive to market needs."

---

and industry to strengthen the current standardization system into one that is healthy, economically viable, and responsive to market needs.

5

Innovation and Standardization Policies in the Information Age

KEN KRECHMER

International Center for
Standards Research,
University of Colorado

Abstract: *In the information age, governmental policies in support of innovation are having a growing impact on trade and free market coordination. A balance between innovation and coordination is often achieved by market-sensitive standardization. Governmental policies that interfere with the balance that market-sensitive standardization can achieve are not usually successful. But governmental policies that recognize the changes that are occurring in the information age and support corresponding changes in innovation and standardization policies are needed.*

Introduction

In the information age, available electronic communications such as TV, telephone, and the Internet are "freedom of the press." This ability to communicate electronically is the basis of the information age. As communications technology becomes more widely utilized, standards that define the compatibility between different devices used to transfer information (TV, modems, cellular telephones, fax machines, PC software applications, etc.) become important to almost everyone.

Previously, communications standardization was supported by public communications utilities such as AT&T, Deutsche Bundespost, or NTT. With the conversion of public communi-cations utilities into commercial companies, conflicts between the rights of different stakeholders (equipment developers, government, carriers, and users) have emerged and such conflicts have split communications standards development into the de jure process (formal communications standards development organizations, FCSDOs)[1] and de facto consortia.[2] The previous success of FCSDOs is being undercut by commercial consortia driven by short term economic interests. This change is occurring because the FCSDOs no longer balance the legitimate interests of all their stakeholders, so the stakeholders look elsewhere. If the FCSDO standardization system is to continue, and there are good reasons that it should, rebalancing the process to support the legitimate interests of all stakeholders will require government policy support.

An example of the impact of governmental standardization policy on trade is the dramatic difference in economic growth between some European and US cellular communications equipment manufacturers. Standardization for cellular telephony, the new technology for wireless communications, was approached quite differently in North America and Europe. North America pursued a laissez faire policy, letting the commercial organizations do as they wished. This policy resulted in three competing cellular standards.[3] The European Union pursued a single unified standard, GSM, for all EU countries. In Europe two equipment developers, Nokia and Ericsson, pulled far ahead of their largest competitor, Motorola, headquartered in North America. This occurred even though Motorola was initially a much larger wireless communications equipment manufacturer.

Certainly the success of Nokia and Ericsson is not wholly due to standardization policy. The "home court" advantage of Nokia and Ericsson in the European markets was significant but Motorola held major patents on cellular technologies.[4] Even with US intervention to protest (and change) the GSM cellular patent policy, Motorola was not as successful in the GSM cellular market as its European competitors. Conversely, during the same period an emerging US cellular communications equipment company, Qualcomm, grew dramatically by taking advantage of the US laissez faire standardization regime and promoting a different technology (CDMA) for cellular service. In the case of Qualcomm, the laissez faire US standardization policy was very desirable.

These examples of the impact that different standardization regimes had in the same industry and time period suggest that complex mechanisms link standardization and innovation policy. It also suggests that the policies that impact the formal standardization process have significant economic import. The purpose of this paper is to identify and explain these mechanisms and propose new approaches to modify the innovation and standardization policies to improve the innovation and growth of free market economic systems.

All Standards Do Not Cause the Same Effect

As the complexity of technology increases, the complexity of standards that define the technology also increases. When the complexity of the technology increases sufficiently, a paradigm shift occurs that is often described as a new age. The transition from the industrial age to the information age is one such paradigm shift. The author uses the term similarity standards to describe the standards most closely related to the industrial age and compatibility standards to describe the standards most closely related to the information age. Similarity standards define the things produced as a result of repetitive processes (manufacturing). Compatibility standards define the interfaces between communicating devices (e.g., the relationship between a transmitter and a compatible receiver). Compatibility standards are necessary for any and all public communications.

The economic impact of similarity and compatibility standards is different.[5] The economic gain associated with similarity standards for devices accrues to the manufacturer and related distribution channels; such gains are relatively easy to quantify. The economic value associated with compatibility standards (e.g., the wireless air interface in cellular systems) accrues to the end user. However, end user economic value is notoriously difficult to quantify. In fact, creating a "walled garden" of users (incompatible with the users of similar communications equipment from other manufacturers) is often thought to be more advantageous to the manufacturer as it minimizes competition and maximizes profit. Walled gardens are examples of undesirable free market practices.

Intellectual property regimes also impact devices built to similarity standards and interfaces built to compatibility standards very differently. The use of patents has been very successful to motivate innovation when the patents apply to similar goods. Such patents reward the inventors and bring their inventions to the market more rapidly. More recently, patents have been applied to interfaces. This practice has created problems. In most cases interfaces are created by agreement rather than invention, so patents that favor one party of the agreement over another only provide an incentive to disagree. Such disagreements are now common and burdensome in formal communications standards development organizations (FCSDOs). Sometimes these disagreements have been resolved by patent cross-licensing, which tend to favor the older and larger organizations (with more patents to cross-license) rather than the newer, smaller, and possibly more innovative firms. Such favoritism does not appear useful when a free and innovative market is desired. Patents as a concept are not the problem here. Rather the problem stems from patents being applied to interfaces that are created by agreement. Patents that serve to con-

---

"Patents that are applied to interfaces (patents on compatibility) appear to sow disagreement, slow innovation, and tax users without representation."

---

trol similarity for the inventor's advantage have proven to be a valuable incentive to economic progress. Patents that are applied to interfaces (patents on compatibility) appear to sow disagreement, slow innovation, and tax users without representation.

The concepts of similarity and compatibility are closely intertwined. Consider a standard clay brick (e.g., M114, American Association of State Highway and Transportation Officials). The manufacturer may control or patent some unique way of mixing the clay or coloring the brick—this is exactly what the patent system is designed to protect. If the patent system allowed a manufacturer to patent the standard brick size (which meets the compatibility needed for the brick layer [user] to quickly build a wall), then all other brick manufacturers would be forced to pay a royalty even though the size of a standard brick was only based on mutual agreement among the brick makers and users. Users of a brick patented to have a unique color or texture may choose to pay extra for the unique features the patent protects. Users of bricks when the size is patented are forced to pay a royalty to have multiple sources for the same size brick.

Examining the communications interface or a cell phone air-interface is more difficult, but the same issues of similarity and compatibility are present. If the manufacturer of a cell phone has

a clever physical design pleasing to the user or a better circuit design that offers longer battery life, patents function to motivate the manufacturer to continue to create such improved products. But patents that cover the transfer of electronic signals between the cell phone and the cellular network (i.e., compatibility patents), provide economic advantage to a single manufacturer but no incentive to any manufacturer for further product or system improvement. In fact the controlling manufacturer has considerable incentive to prevent competing systems from emerging. Microsoft is an example of a controlling manufacturer working to maintain control of the Microsoft application programming interfaces (APIs).[6] Microsoft does all it can to prevent competing products from using their APIs. Supporting patents—or other forms of control—on compatibility is not the best means to promote and stimulate free markets.

The initial European GSM patent policy, which wanted no royalty-bearing patents on GSM, and the US policy, which accepted any royalty-bearing patents on GSM, were both poor ways to encourage a free market system to maximize innovation. Creating an economic

---

"Creating an economic system that motivates innovation yet supports standardization is a more complex problem than changing the patent office procedures or demanding open standards. Changes are also necessary in the standardization process itself."

---

system that motivates innovation yet supports standardization is a more complex problem than changing the patent office procedures or demanding open standards. Changes are also necessary in the standardization process itself.

The standardization processes for similarity standards have been developed over 150 years. During this period, many changes have occurred to mold the similarity standardization process to new requirements. However, the change from similarity to compatibility standardization is a paradigm shift. Accommodating this shift requires changes in the government's innovation policy as well as basic changes in the FCSDOs.

To develop new policies and standardization processes that address the unique aspects of compatibility standardization, it is first necessary to understand the changes that are being forced from other directions on the communications standards development process. For compatibility standardization to be addressed successfully, the changes caused by the shift away from public communications carriers must also be accommodated.

The Changing World of Communications Standardization

Beginning in 1984 with the divesture of AT&T, the economics of and participation in the formal standardization process have changed dramatically. This transition from a worldwide public telecommunications network to a private telecommunications network instigated three external effects that have significantly impacted the FCSDOs process:

- *Public utility changes.* Prior to 1984, the public carriers worldwide were the dominant organizations active in communications standardization. Their research, development, and deployment capabilities were beyond anything independent developers and users could achieve. After the privatization of public carriers, research and development migrated from the carriers to the private companies (developers), while users (consumers) have become the major means for deployment of new communications services in North America via commercial distribution systems. The economic trends away from public carrier dominance of development and distribution that have impacted the North American communications markets have also changed the rest of the world's public communications carriers.[7]

- *Market changes.* The personal computer revolution and the Internet explosion empow-

ered the consumer. The personal computer revolution brought computer power to the individual, creating new distribution and support systems (e.g., help desks, computer stores, value added resellers, walk-in computer repair facilities, Internet sites) to serve the personal computer user's needs. No longer was the computer user dependent (whether they liked it or not) on a public utility for acquisition, installation, and technical support of communications equipment.

- *Process changes.* The Internet supports communications between computer users (email) and provides access to the largest library imaginable—the World Wide Web. These facilities have the ability to dramatically improve any standardization process, making it more efficient, more inclusive, and more effective. Now any group looking to develop communications standards can form, attract members, and begin a standardization process that appears to match the FCSDOs in offering a broad and open process.

In sum, these three sets of changes have redrawn communications standardization. With the public carriers no longer the leaders of communications technology, the developers of communications technology are emerging as the driving force in the development of new communications systems and equipment. Since the mid 1980s and the beginning of privatization of the national carriers, the organizations that provide the leadership of the FCSDOs' standardization committees have shifted from public carriers to developers. AT&T was once the largest US carrier and the organization that provided the leadership of almost all US-related FCSDO committees. Today AT&T plus all the other US carriers provide less than one-third of the leadership of ATIS TI committees and far less of the TIA committees. This change in influence can also be seen in the parallel drop in ITU standardization committee leadership by the European public carriers.[8]

Prior to these changes, standardization of

communications systems was the purview of the public carriers who internally developed specifications for their national requirements and coordinated their specifications (with national government approval) in the ITU (International Telecommunication Union) to develop worldwide recommendations (the ITU term for standards). The public carriers, as representative of the national government, had implicit governmental approval and, as public carriers, they were expected to represent the user/consumers' interest as well. Thus this standardization system brought together the developers, government, and consumers in a single organization, the public carrier. In hindsight this was an efficient way to develop public standards but a cumbersome way to introduce new communications technology.

The shift away from public communications carriers has unbalanced the formal standardization process by reducing the little user representation that existed. In a society that strives to maintain democratic processes, this is a serious change that warrants resolution. Interestingly, it appears possible to address the issue of balanced shareholder involvement as well as the paradigm shift of compatibility standardization with similar policy and standardization changes.

The Basic Requirements of All Stakeholders

The fundamental purpose of communications standardization is to define communications interfaces. All other communications standardization activities are in support of this purpose. Those affected by this standardization process are developers, users/consumers, service providers, and governments. All of these stakeholders each have legitimate requirements.

Developer requirements:
1. A single stage to create worldwide communications standards
2. A means to negotiate required intellectual property associated with a communications standard

User/consumer and service provider requirements:
3. Compatibility (forward and backward)
4. Maintained standards
5. Public (low or no royalty) communications interfaces

Government requirements:
6. A means to address the standardization aspect of political issues (e.g., pornography, rights of those with a disability, privacy, security, taxation, sovereignty)

Requirements of all:
7. A fair, fast, and efficient standardization system

The seven basic requirements presented above are not prioritized. Serving one of these requirements in a specific situation might not serve others. But it has always been the task of each standardization committee to determine how to strike technical and operational balances.

This list is one attempt to create a set of basic communications standardization requirements for each stakeholder group. Certainly far broader consideration should be given to defining these basic requirements. Perhaps the ITU, as a United Nations (UN) charter organization, would be an appropriate venue to initiate such consideration of the basic requirements of all communications standardization stakeholders.[9]

The desire for the three user/consumer requirements noted (3-5) has been described in different terms. "Open standards" is the current user rallying cry for the basic requirements of users to be supported in the standardization process. These requirements are the three most direct user oriented requirements of ten total requirements developed in a separate paper that evaluated the principles underlying the concept of open standards.[10]

Table 1 examines how different standardization organizations address these seven requirements. The x indicates which of these requirements the standardization organization generally meets (in the author's opinion).

Table 1. How different standardization organizations meet seven stakeholder requirements

Reqmts.	ITU	ETSI	IEEE	ATIS T1	TIA	IETF	Consortia
1			X			X	X
2							X
3	X (note 1)	X	X	X	X	X	
4 (note 1)	?	X	?	?	?	?	
5	(note 2)	X					X
6	X	X					
7	X	X	X	X	X	X	X

Note 1: see requirements 3 and 4, below.
Note 2: see requirement 5, below.

Requirement 1: A single standardization process to create worldwide standards. In the case of the IEEE and IETF, past successes (Ethernet and Internet, respectively) cause developers to believe these organizations offer the ability to create worldwide standards. In the ITU's case, the creation of worldwide standards is their remit. However, the ITU is fundamentally an organization of governments (or agencies accredited by governments), so technical positions must be taken first at a national or regional level and then submitted to the ITU. This creates a lengthy two stage standardization process that does not serve developers' needs for fast standardization for worldwide markets.[11]

Requirement 2: Negotiated intellectual property rights. No formal communications standardization organization allows the negotiation of intellectual property rights as part of their standardization process. In many cases, consortia require developers to agree to licensing terms as a condition of joining the consortium. Most consortia developing communications standards also serve developers by operating on a worldwide basis (requirement 1). The fact that consortia support requirements 1 and 2 is corroboration of these developers' requirements, as developers dominate almost all consortia.

Requirements 3 and 4: Ongoing compatibility and maintained standards.[12] The FCSDOs,

when they were dominated by public carriers, demonstrably supported these requirements. Certainly FCSDOs continue to maintain their standards (requirement 4), but with less input from users and carriers this is a requirement that bears watching. Currently no FCSDO (to the author's knowledge) uses the Internet (or other active means) to notify users prior to each transition among the four stages of standards maintenance (fixes, updating, availability, and recision). Yet these transitions are of considerable economic import to users. Consortia often avoid addressing the requirements for future compatibility and standards maintenance for reasons discussed further below.

The ETSI web site states: "ETSI is a not for profit organization whose mission is to produce the telecommunications standards that will be used for decades to come throughout Europe and beyond." "Used for decades" suggests active support of requirements 3 and 4 of the users' and providers' interests.

Requirement 5: Public interfaces. Now that public carriers no longer do the bulk of the development and provide the fruits of their development (intellectual property rights) as part of their public service, the use of formal communications standards no longer means that associated intellectual property is available at little or no cost. This was not a formal standardization policy decision but a fact created by the transition in the formal communications standardization technical committees from public carriers to service providers and developers. Interestingly, consortia often recognize that competitive pricing is necessary for market development and demand licensing arrangements that allow economical communications interfaces.

During the GSM standardization process, ETSI attempted to force the GSM developers to provide free worldwide licenses for GSM technology. Although exceptional, this action does demonstrate ETSI's desire to promote the users' interest in terms of very low cost intellectual property rights. Political pressure from the US government and Motorola's unwillingness to license its essential GSM patents on nondiscriminatory terms prevented ETSI from requiring GSM developers to offer such licenses. However, a number of the European public carriers required their suppliers to agree to cross-licensing. This effectively enforced ETSI's interest in low cost intellectual property rights for GSM.[13]

Requirement 6: Address political issues. ETSI provides a direct means to address the European Union governments' requirements. The ITU provides a direct means for national governments to address national standardization issues. The other organizations do not.

Requirement 7: Fast fair and efficient standardization. Every honorable standardization committee attempts to be fair, fast, and efficient, although often fairness is only taken to apply to the participants of that standardization committee. For example, ANSI Essential Requirements on due process support this requirement. As a result, this requirement no longer offers any observable differentiation between the major standardization organizations whether they are formal or consortia.[14]

Creating Solutions

Considering the paradigm shift that compatibility standardization causes and the changes that are occurring to the FCSDOs, changes in government policy and standardization processes are necessary. The seven require-

ments identified point to the changes needed if the FCSDO process is to continue to be utilized to create communications standards.

Requirement 1, a single process. The two stage standardization currently employed by formal communications standardization organizations is an anachronism in the fast paced communications technology world. Under

---

"Each country should support worldwide standardization of communications interfaces as a policy."

---

this standardization system, standards are first developed in a single country or region and then they are taken as drafts to an international organization (e.g., ITU, ISO, IEC) for international standardization. When electronic communications markets are worldwide, national standardization is not effective. Each country should support worldwide standardization of communications interfaces as a policy. Without such support the existing formal communications standardization system will be bypassed, which is occurring more and more. Such bypass leaves the government out of the standardization process. This is undesirable when governments have a legitimate need to address such public issues as pornography, privacy, security, health, and safety.

Requirements 3, 4, and 5 (ongoing compatibility, maintained standards, and low cost IPR) are where there is a legitimate conflict between the rights of users/service providers and developers. Backward compatibility (requirement 3) may not be desirable to developers proposing a new technology direction as it is often costly to create and maintain that technology. Yet backward compatibility may be critical for users and carriers to allow the effective use of their capital investment and an efficient transition to new communications technology.

As was noted earlier, compatibility standards have quite a different impact than similarity standards. In order to support the rights of users, compatibility standardization committees may want to develop different procedures to deal with compatibility standardization. Some of these are noted below under requirement 5. Where no other solution is acceptable, the standardization committee can support the inclusion of an independent negotiation layer (etiquette) to negotiate among multiple compatibility approaches, standard, or proprietary. Such an approach might be desirable to negotiate among the multiple technologies of the ITU 3G cellular standard IMT-2000.

Requirement 4: The maintenance of standards by developer organizations represents an economic burden that does not increase their sales. Conversely, maintained standards allow users and carriers to optimize the value of their capital investment. Consortia do not often devote significant efforts to the maintenance of standards as developers have an economic disincentive to maintain them. Developers would much prefer if users purchased the latest version and did not use a well-maintained previous version. Currently most communications standardization organizations also make little attempt to involve users in standards maintenance decisions, likely for the same reason. Yet users have the largest stake in well maintained standards.

The rapid expansion of new technology has obsoleted and replaced older communications technology, dramatically reducing the need to maintain older communications standards. Now that the worldwide telecommunications markets are in a period of economic consolidation, poorly maintained communications standards may become a greater burden on users and service providers. Currently the effects of limited standards maintenance are most noticeable in

---

"If private industry is not able to address these public requirements, eventually the government must."

---

third tier markets (third world countries and charitable organizations) where older communications equipment is often used. The maintenance of standards that describe information

is intrinsic to the information age. Libraries are already struggling with the difficulty of maintaining their electronic resources in an available electronic form. If private industry is not able to address these public requirements, eventually the government must.

Requirements 5 and 2, balancing and negotiating intellectual property rights issues among the stakeholders, presents a difficult conflict that often relates to compatibility. It is possible that where the users' interests in compatibility are maintained, the markets are more likely to grow and more value may be created for all the stakeholders. Further study is needed in this area. The current FCSDO approach to intellectual property rights supports only identification of intellectual property holders, not negotiation of intellectual property to identify and control costs. This is not sufficient to support the developer's basic right to control the costs of the goods they plan to sell. Two examples of other approaches to compatibility standards that would require governmental support are:

- Closer liaison between formal communications standardization committees and patent examiners to make available the resources of the standardization committee in the evaluation of any proposed patent covering compatibility

- A separate and parallel legal process to the standardization process (possibly under the WTO) to negotiate the value and royalty requirements of patents related to compatibility[15]

Both of these examples require significant changes in both standardization as well as governmental innovation policies that can only occur in the longer term. Compatibility standards accentuate the basic conflicts between the manufacturer and the consumer need.[16] By addressing the basic rights of all stakeholders, the standardization process can reduce inherent conflicts and represent all the stakeholders more equally. Consortia have taken over much of the communications standards development work from the FCSDOs. This has broad impact in the industrial age. The US government has recognized this impact and reviewed standardization issues before. This paper attempts to provide a more structured view of the communications standardization processes and their impact on the public, who, in the information age, are the standardization stakeholders.

Focusing on Stakeholders' Basic Requirements Will Better Serve the Information Age

The standardization processes developed and refined for the industrial age are not sufficient for the information age. Compatibility standardization introduces new strains in the relationship between manufacturers and consumers. The basic communications standardization requirements must be identified for each standardization committee's constituency and made an overt part of that organization's procedures

> *"The standardization processes developed and refined for the industrial age are not sufficient for the information age."*

to ensure that active efforts will be made during the standardization process and standards usage period to address these requirements. This is a new and different way for FCSDOs to operate and will likely require broad interest and support before any FCSDO makes such a fundamental change in their operation. Changes of this magnitude in the communications standardization procedures and patent processes will not occur without government policy support.

The author would like to thank Stephen Oksala for his detailed review and dialog, and Elaine Baskin for editing.

Copyright © Ken Krechmer

Notes

[1] Examples include: TIA—Telecommunications Industry Association; ATIS—The Alliance for Telecommunications Industry Solutions (Committee T1); TTC—Telecommunications Technology Committee; TTA—Telecommunications Technology Association; ACIF—Australian Communications Industry Forum; ETSI—European Telecommunications Standard Institute

[2] Examples include: Internet Engineering Task Force (IETF), W3C, Bluetooth Special Interest Group, CableLabs

[3] Time division multiple access (TDMA), code division multiple access (CDMA), and global system for mobile communications (GSM)

[4] Ari T. Manninen, Elaboration of NMT and GSM Standards, PhD thesis published by the University of Jyvaskyla, 2002

[5] Ken Krechmer, Fundamental Nature of Standards: Economic Perspective, paper presented at the International J.A. Schumpeter Society Economics Conference, June 28 - July 1, 2000, Manchester, England

[6] Ken Krechmer, The Microsoft Anti-Trust Litigation:

a Case for Standards, *Standards Engineering*, Vol. 52 No. 5, September/October, 2000

[7] This point is made in several submissions to the ITU - TSB Informal Consultation Group, Martigny, February 28-29, 2000, including Document No. 8, AT&T, C. Dvorak / M. Armstrong (http://www.itu.int/ITU-T/tsb-director/martigny/martigny1/index.html).

[8] 13 out of 14 ITU Study Group Chairmen (including TSAG) are from Sector Members [commercial organizations], slide 21, Houlin Zhao, Director ITU-T, ITU Standardization and its new Environment, Stanford University, July 23, 2003

[9] This suggestion was first developed in: Ken Krechmer, Recommendations for the Global Information Highway: A Matter of Standards, *ACM StandardView*, March 1996 Vol. 4, No. 1.

[10] Ken Krechmer, The Principles Of Open Standards, *Standards Engineering*, November/December 1998, Vol. 50, No. 6, p. 1-6

[11] "When the marketplace is global, so must be the standards." Richard B. Gibson, The Global Standards Process: A Balance of the Old and the

New, *Standards Policy for Information Infrastructure*, MIT Press, 1995

[12] "First, standardization should help avoid technological dead ends, where incompatible options trap users in a doomed technology." George Ferne, Information Technology Standardization and Users: International Challenges - Move the Process Forward, *Standards Policy for Information Infrastructure*, MIT Press, 1995

[13] Eric J. Iversen, Standardization and Intellectual Property Rights: ETSI's Controversial Search for New IPR-Procedures, *The Standards Edge*, edited by Sherrie Bolin, 2002

[14] "The findings show that, according to paper procedures, formal standards bodies and standards consortia roughly work in the same way." Tineke M. Egyedi, Consortium Problem Redefined: Negotiating 'Democracy' in the Actor Network on Standardization, *International Journal of IT Standards and Standardization Research*, Vol. 1 No. 2, July-Dec 2003

[15] Ken Krechmer, Communications Standards and Patent Rights: Conflict or Coordination? Telecommunications Industry Association, *Standards and Technology Annual Report (STAR)*, 1997

[16] This issue is also discussed in Joseph Farrell, Arguments for Weaker Intellectual Property Protection in Network Industries, *Standards Policy for Information Infrastructure*, The MIT Press, 1995, page 368-375

6

Cooperation in the Age of Chance

HOULIN ZHAO

Telecommunication Standardization
Bureau, International
Telecommunication Union (ITU)

Abstract: *International standardization will play an important role in helping the telecommunications industry to come out of its recent hiatus. Standards bodies need to work together to challenge the emergence of ad hoc standards that threaten the development of the whole industry. Much has already been done to coordinate the work of the various standards bodies, and this will stand us in good stead as we enter the information society of the 21st Century.*

The financial downturn has hit the telecommunications sector particularly hard, one result being the scaling back of "nonurgent" telecommunications activity by private sector companies. This situation has had a widespread impact on standardization activity over the last few years. While international standardization activity has undoubtedly declined, technological development hasn't. In fact, technological complexity is increasing significantly, and now more than ever, telecommunications users need open, international standards-based platforms that can interoperate in a heterogeneous environment. New technologies need to work with legacy systems, without themselves becoming obsolete proprietary millstones.

In July 2003, senior figures from the world's premier Information and Communication Technology (ICT) standards groups joined together to foster a new age of cooperation. Organized by the International Telecommunication Union (ITU) and held in San Francisco, the Informal Forum Summit marked a new stage in standards development—one in which cooperation, rather than competition and duplication, would dominate standards activities in the coming years.

The ITU 2003 Informal Forum Summit was attended by 69 chiefs from 34 standards development organizations (SDO) active in the fields of Internet, mobile, software tools, broadband, and optical networking. Half of the summit attendees were from carriers—an encouraging indication of how crucial open standards are to customers. As well as drafting a mission statement to improve interoperability across the multiple communication technologies and industries they represent, the participating SDOs will collaborate in an effort to leverage economies of scale. These actions address the duplication of time and effort in standardization that is delaying the time to market and causing the implementation of conflicting standards, creating a situation that is proving costly not only to the SDOs, but also to industry and, ultimately, to consumers.

A number of particular technology developments were highlighted including passive optical networking, metro Ethernet, and wireless. Action plans for sharing information between special interest groups were initiated for approximately 25 current and future core technologies.

There are a number of commercial and regulatory incentives for carriers to take a significant role in the standards process. Telecommunications is an industry where service providers need to work with each other as a matter of course either through interconnecting, peering, or regulatory issues such as local loop unbundling. It is imperative, for instance, that management and operational support systems from all service providers interoperate to further develop the competitive telecommunications landscape. The same can be said for broadband networking, mobile networks, signaling systems, and Internet architectures.

Equally important, the supply side and service providers must have access to global, open technologies and protocols. Finally, it is crucial for all SDOs involved in telecommunications to ensure their standards are harmonized wherever possible.

Importance of Cooperation

It is critical to the fragile telecommunications industry that both larger and smaller, specialized SDOs can work together more productively on developing particular standards. While each has its own remit, user base, or geographical

---

"It is critical to the fragile telecommunications industry that both larger and smaller, specialized SDOs can work together more productively on developing particular standards."

---

coverage, global interoperability of key technologies is the shared goal for both supplier and user alike.

One of the greatest challenges the industry and its users face, however, is not from competing standards from internationally recognized forums and groups, although this is a concern, but from ad hoc "standards" that have developed around monopolistic technologies. While there is a temptation for some suppliers to congregate around a widely deployed platform because it can often be developed more quickly than reaching industry consensus, it is a shortsighted, disingenuous strategy.

This situation can only be avoided with the widespread adoption of international standards. This is not only important for integrating with existing network services and support systems, but also for brand new technologies such as passive optical networking, PKI security, and seamless global roaming over multiple wireless and wired networks. With international standards, third party content developers are more encouraged to develop value added applications when they only have to write once to use anywhere.

hieve greater economies of scale, which has a positive trickle down effect on customers and their customers. This has been the case with ADSL, dialup modems, PKI (Public Key Infrastructure) (X.509), SS7 signaling, and many other important technologies. The larger the market, the more likelihood there are adequate numbers of skilled staff to develop, deploy, and support products. This has particular importance for countries where telecommunications is still undergoing modernization, liberalization, and deregulation.

Many more suppliers and carriers from developing countries need to be more involved in the international standards process than there are at present. They have more to gain from international standards than most developed markets. Carriers from developing countries find it particularly difficult to soak up the mistakes of implementing legacy or non-standardized equipment, so they should be involved more in helping to define standards that encompass their needs, rather than suffer the consequences of standards developed by and for more modernized markets.

Critical for Economic Growth

We are now entering an important stage in the development of Information Communication Technologies. While the mass media has concentrated on the short-term drama of dotcoms, accounting discrepancies, and 3G license fees, the telecommunications industry has weathered the storm, continually developing new services and improving customer relations. Better economic conditions will return and the industry will be unshackled to once again flourish.

The telecoms industry must be in an orderly state to capitalize on these expected fertile economic conditions. Standards will play a massive role in this, creating a level playing field for young and old, small or large companies.

"Many engineers would agree that a standard is an extremely valuable thing, but some decision makers within companies view standardization more often as a cost on the basis of time consumption, rather than as an investment."

Even during these tough times, the ITU-T (ITU's telecommunication standardization sector) has managed to attract new members.

Too often the value of standards is not sufficiently understood at the management level. And getting this message across is an important challenge that we, the standards setters, face. Many companies have a tough time putting a dollar-value on their standardization activities. How much a company's standardization activities contribute to revenue is very difficult to measure. Many engineers would agree that a standard is an extremely valuable thing, but some decision makers within companies view standardization more often as a cost on the basis of time consumption, rather than as an investment.

Research proves the opposite, however. The German Institute for Standardization, DIN,

carried out a study estimating the benefits of standardization for the German economy. [1] Although the study did not focus specifically on ICT companies and consumers, its findings are illuminating. DIN's research shows that standardization is worth approximately one percent of Germany's gross national product, it is responsible for one-third of its economic growth, and contributes more to the success of enterprises than patents and licenses.

Innovation is not enough to remain competitive in the world economy; innovation has to be shared, and standards are an excellent way to spread innovation and spur economic growth. Diminishing standardization activity is an unavoidable result of the state of the global economy, but it does not mean that the development of standards is any less important.

Participation in standards setting is beneficial for all levels of business. Participants can influence the outcome of work and gain advance knowledge of standards—benefits that translate into faster Return on Investment (ROI), reduced Total Cost of Ownership (TCO), and increased sales. Clearly, standards should be an important part of any business strategy. In many ways, getting that message across is the biggest challenge that SDOs face today.

The modern world is undergoing a fundamental transformation as the 20th century's industrial society becomes the information society

---

"ICTs have become too important to the world's future development to leave their evolution purely to market forces."

---

of the 21st century. Politics, democracy, health, education, entertainment, literacy, financial markets, and poverty are all being changed irrevocably by the ICT revolution. ICTs have become too important to the world's future development to leave their evolution purely to market forces. Standards, competition, and innovation need nurturing and fostering. The work of the ITU and other SDOs at the Informal Forum Summit should go a long way to facilitate a smoother, more economical introduction of new standards, topologies, protocols, and interfaces. *This is the age of cooperation.*

Copyright © Houlin Zhao

Notes

[1] DIN German Institute for Standardization e. V.: 2000, Economic Benefits of Standardization

7

The Need for Singularity: A Look at the Need for True International Standards

JACK SHELDON
International Electrotechnical
Commission (IEC)

AHARON AMIT
International Electrotechnical
Commission (IEC)

Abstract: *This paper briefly explains the role of International Standards, then goes on to discuss the limits of the system, before proposing an alternative solution.*

The Role of Standards

Why have standards?

What purpose does a standard have and what value does it offer? The simple answer is that a standard is a document, established by consensus and approved by a recognized body that provides, for common and repeated use, rules, guidelines, or characteristics for activities or their results.[1] A standard provides a basic description or measure that allows for comparison. It is this idea of comparison that is essential. A manufacturer might say to a potential customer: my product is safe to use and performs as expected. A standard will allow the customer to examine the truth of that statement by comparing that product with specific parameters. Once this examination is finished, the customer then possesses knowledge to make more effective choices about future actions such as buying a product from competing alternatives. By serving as a benchmark that both manufacturer and customer recognize, a standard provides specific parameters for the manufacturer to meet and gives the customer the opportunity to test and compare when buying.

Why have International Standards?

While an International Standard performs the same functions as a national standard, but obviously on an international scale, developing these standards poses new challenges. For example, agreeing upon the meaning of a definition within a single language can be difficult. Agreeing upon a meaning across differing languages could potentially try Job's patience and give Solomon a headache. How

> "By serving as a benchmark that both manufacturer and customer recognize, a standard provides specific parameters for the manufacturer to meet and gives the customer the opportunity to test and compare when buying."

can a buyer in one country, speaking one language, be sure he or she is getting exactly what is expected from a supplier in another country, who speaks a different language? An International Standard, adopted in different countries, helps to eliminate that problem. Once both parties know they are speaking the same *technical* language, they can feel confident that understanding will be enhanced. Ultimately, understanding and agreement about the technical parameters leads to trust, which is the basis of a business relationship.

Why have IEC standards?

The IEC encourages its members to engage their governments in discussions to support globalization, the WTO (World Trade Organization), and the drive to eliminate technical barriers to trade. Technical regulations often make reference to standards. When they do so, International Standards are the best solution for both industrialized and developing countries, as they are the result of a consensus process that allows contributions from all interested parties.

Industry repeatedly says that it cannot do without IEC standards and that being involved in helping to develop them is an essential activity for many. So it is clear that industry draws great benefits from *using* IEC standards. This includes accessing new export markets, reducing manufacturing costs by rationalizing the production processes, and speeding up time to market. Those companies that become involved in developing IEC standards experience additional benefits that include influencing the direction and ultimate outcome of the standard.

Industry focus

The IEC was created by industry for industry and is maintained by industry as evidenced by its technical committees (TC), which prepare IEC standards. Fully 90 percent of all IEC TC chairmen and secretaries come from industry, not from national standards bodies. The IEC is very much an industry-driven organization and takes its responsibility to respond to industry needs in a timely fashion seriously. Masterplan 2000, which is IEC's principle strategic document, places focus squarely on market needs and industry requirements.

Result

Governments adopt IEC standards to make them national standards. The IEC prepares standards. By adopting these standards and incorporating them into legislation, the government facilitates import and export for industry.

However, classical international standardization as described above has its limits. The section below tells the story of a well-known failure of the traditional standards development process.

The Limits of Standardization— Electrical Plugs and Sockets for Domestic Use

Background

When the IEC was founded in the first decade of the 20th century, its first endeavours concerned standards for electrical machinery, including the associated nomenclature and symbology. It was only after the first World War (1914-1918) that IEC's attention turned to the newer applications of electricity and its widening use in the home and office.

Early days

In the early 1930s the international representation in IEC was made aware of standardization work going on in Europe in the field of electrical power distribution by an organization called the IFK (*Internationale Fragens Kommission* or *International Questions Commission*). It comprised delegates from electricity suppliers and electrical test houses in 12 countries, some of whom were also representatives on IEC National Committees.

At its meeting in Paris in January 1933, the IEC's Committee of Action (CA) agreed that the IFK be contacted with a view to collaboration on matters of mutual interest. At the CA meeting at Prague in October 1934 it was recorded that a complete IEC/IFK agreement on cooperation had been reached and a new technical committee No. 23 was created to deal specifically with the standardization of electrical fittings.

The work of this committee took a long time

to take off and at its meeting in Torquay, UK in June 1938, the CA urged the new TC (now with the title Electrical Accessories) to hold its first meeting "*next year, in order to consider the question of plugs and sockets.*" However, at the next CA meeting, in June 1939, nothing had yet happened within TC 23 and the CA, clearly annoyed, gave instructions to initiate work as soon as possible and to consider meeting some time in 1940. The world then fell apart with the outbreak of World War II.

The start of work

After the war, and its subsequent economic recession, work on domestic plugs and sockets got under way at the first meeting of TC 23 in Luzern in October 1947. By this time, the European work had moved to the CEE (International Commission on Rules for the Approval of Electrical Equipment) and TC 23 discussed co-operation with the CEE in the field of "*Unification of the International Standards relating to sockets, plugs and connectors.*"

The CEE work led to the first edition, in 1951 of its Publication 7, which was a selection of the most widely used plugs and sockets in Europe, excluding the UK and Ireland.

The early work in TC 23 led to the eventual issue in 1957 of the first edition of IEC Publication 83, *Standard for plugs and socket-outlets for domestic and similar general use*. This publication was essentially a collection of the European plug and socket designs of CEE 7 together with those of the USA and of Great Britain, which were used in many other countries. Rather than an International Standard, this publication was a catalogue of national standards, and this was recognized by giving its second edition in 1975 the status of a Technical Report.

The universal plug and socket system

However, it was always recognized by the IEC as a long-term objective that a truly universal system of domestic plugs and sockets should be aimed for. It was realized very early on in IEC that, even were agreement to be reached on such a standard, implementation would take decades in view of the massive investment in existing installations and the associated manufacturing plants.

Serious work on this matter started in IEC in 1970 with the creation of subcommittee 23C (*Worldwide plug and socket outlet system*). Earlier, TC 64 (*Electrical installations*) had been formed and it was inevitable that, in its considerations of domestic wiring installations, it would face the problem of the plethora of plugs and sockets in use and this provided the IEC with further impetus to find a global solution or, at least, attempt to reduce the varieties.

The essence of the work concerned safety and, in particular, trying to prevent dangerous situations from arising during the periods when the new system and the multitude of existing ones had to exist side by side.

The first drafts of a universal system considered by subcommittee 23C proposed all flat pins and were pursued for many years. However, at the voting stage, objections grew and many National Committees expressed themselves more in favour of a round pin solution. The other serious problem encountered was in trying to find a unique solution for 125 V and 250 V distribution systems. After long, and often acrimonious, discussion, the committee came to an agreed solution that was finally published in 1986 as IEC 906-1[2] (now IEC 60906-1) for 250 V installations using round pins and in 1992 as IEC 906-2[3] (now IEC 60906-2) for 125 V installations using the familiar US flat pin design.

In the 1990s, the European Committee for Electrotechnical Standardization (CENELEC) was pressured by the European Commission to devise a harmonized plug and socket system for Europe. Incredible as it may seem, there does not seem ever to have taken place, in Europe or elsewhere, an assessment, even at a superficial level, of the economic consequences of the implementation of a universal system. The view of the Commission appears to have been based entirely on political considerations!

CENELEC took as its starting point the IEC standard of 1986 and spent thousands of man-hours undertaking the almost impossible task of modifying the design with the aim of ensuring 100% risk-free operation of the system when used in conjunction with all the existing types in Europe. Naturally, apart from the technical difficulties, there was the clash of the many vested commercial and political interests and it was not surprising that, after much work and many meetings, CENELEC had to admit defeat and abandon its efforts, much to the chagrin of the Commission.

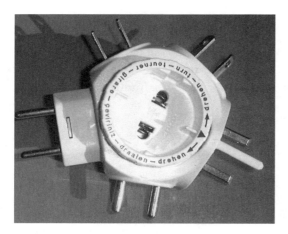

Figure 1: The winner of the contest

However, as the IEC continues to point out, internationally agreed standards for domestic plugs and sockets for the 250 V and 125 V ranges do exist and are, even today, available to any country that cares to implement them.

Other than the political and commercial interests that hampered this work, the failure to take a long term view and to understand the technical developments and future portability of electrical appliances also contributed to this disaster. If the experts working in the committees had been correctly briefed and had understood the implications of globalization and device portability, there might have been increased incentives to reach agreement.

The story of the worldwide plug and socket raises smiles today. However there are lessons to be learned and the IEC has recently come up with a number of alternatives, the most interesting of which is the ITA.

ITAs – A Solution?

What are ITAs?

The most recent of the new products from the IEC are Industry Technical Agreements (ITAs). In essence, they are aimed at fast-moving technology sectors where products have short life-cycles. ITAs are not the same as International Standards because they do not pass through the same consensus procedure. Indeed, they are not produced in the committee structure that is used for developing standards.

Any group of interested parties may create an ITA, whether this means a single large company or consortium. The IEC recognizes the need to limit participation to key market interests, but prefers a process that is as open as practicable. The IEC will not determine who may or may not participate. It is up to the industry players to agree amongst themselves.

The process begins when a proposal, which includes a list of other relevant market players, is submitted from an interested party to the IEC. Together, they form a "consortium." Before the actual work can begin, the IEC and the consortium agree upon the subject and participants. It should be stressed that while a consensus International Standard usually take a number of years to produce, ITAs are generally completed

> "...while a consensus International Standard usually takes a number of years to produce, ITAs are generally completed in a matter of months. There is a clear statement on the cover of each ITA stating that it is not a consensus standard."

in a matter of months. There is a clear statement on the cover of each ITA stating that it is not a consensus standard.

How are ITAs produced?

ITAs are developed in workshops, in fora or in project teams. The key to its success is simplicity. Instead of requiring global consensus, the participants themselves decide what is and is not to be addressed in the ITA as subject matter. Thus the participants are the sole arbiters of technical content. They decide what goes into the document, when sufficient agreement has been reached and when it is ready to be issued.

The IEC acts as mediator, administrator and publisher of the project. IEC Central Office is both convenor and project manager, supplying a staff member as project officer to coordinate the effort. The IEC also supplies IT support, along with editing and publishing services.

However, there is an important issue: intellectual property rights (IPR). In this case the parties producing the ITA announce proprietary interests and agree on terms amongst themselves and for other parties. In short, the parties own the IPR content unless they agree to release it. However, participants do cede publishing rights to the IEC. Each ITA becomes available as a multi-logo publication from the IEC, which will negotiate revenue sharing from sales with the parties that developed the document.

Since an ITA is expected to have a short life, it will be withdrawn when the parties agree that it is no longer market relevant, and a new ITA may be initiated as a result. On the other hand, if there is a clear market need, the ITA may be submitted for adoption as an international consensus standard or an IEC technical report. In this case, adoption will then be subject to the IEC's rapid consensus process.

Who benefits?

ITAs are targeted at the global market. Since they can be developed and published rapidly, they can help industry to launch new products or start production once the ITA specifications have been established. Their low cost brings the added benefit of low risk. Since the IEC is recognized by the WTO as the authoritative body for international standardization in electrotechnology, they also carry a kind of intrinsic "seal of approval."

In the short term, industry benefits by having a new tool available to help it bring products to market with the support of the IEC. In the long term, customers benefit by enjoying high-quality goods and services, which are based upon essential parameters as defined by principle industry players.

Copyright © 2003 IEC

Bibliography

[1] ISO/IEC Guide 2:1996, *Standardization and related activities. General vocabulary*, ISO/IEC.

[2] IEC 60906-1:1986, *IEC system of plugs and socket-outlets for household and similar purposes – Part 1: Plugs and socket-outlets 16 A 250 V a.c.*, IEC

[3] IEC 60906-2:1997, *IEC system of plugs and socket-outlets for household and similar purposes – Part 2: Plugs and socket-outlets 15 A 125 V a.c.*, IEC

8

Getting to "Yes" with the IETF: A Guide for the Perplexed

JAMES KEMPF
NTT DoCoMo
DoCoMo Labs USA

Abstract: The increasing integration between tele-communications and information systems has led to a need for more interaction between standards bodies that formerly operated autonomously. Standardization bodies serve different constituents and have evolved customs and operating procedures that reflect their constituent's needs and the historical circumstances under which the standardization bodies originated and evolved. Dealing with another standardization body that doesn't share the same customs and proce-dures can be as frustrating as trying to find directions in a foreign country. In this chapter, we discuss how the Internet Engineering Task Force (the IETF) operates as a guide for helping outside bodies achieve more effective interaction with the IETF.

Introduction

The value provided by network products and services increases as more systems are interconnected, allowing more cus-tomers to access a growing service offering. This phenomenon, sometimes called "the network effect," powered the integration of telecom-munications and information systems through the 1990s and is still active today. Increasingly, formerly independent systems and networks are being connected and the interconnection me-dium, by and large, is the TCP/IP protocol suite (IP). Standardization of protocols built around IP is the responsibility of the Internet Engineering Task Force (the IETF). The IETF evolved from the coordinating body for the U.S. government DARPA Internet research project, which was commercialized in the early 1990s. Today, the

> *"As the integration between telecommu-nications and information systems proceeds, the TCP/IP protocol suite as an underlying integration medium has become more important for new services."*

IETF oversees the engineering of new protocols based on IP as well as the ongoing maintenance and development of existing protocols.

As the integration between telecommunica-tions and information systems proceeds, the TCP/IP protocol suite as an underlying integra-tion medium has become more important for new services. Recent examples of new services offered on IP are real time voice telephony and wireless networks. The existing interoperable application protocols and associated system designs for these services have historically been standardized on network protocols that have been the concern of other standardization bodies. As the services move to an IP base, these groups often have specific requirements for IP-based protocols or need assistance in understanding how the protocols and services they standardize could best be put on top of IP. As a result, these standardization bodies must often interact in some way with the IETF.

People who have been active in other standardization bodies often feel frustrated when dealing with the IETF. Unlike other standardization bodies, the IETF has no fixed membership. People become active in the IETF by participating in discussions on mailing lists, contributing drafts on technology, or simply showing up at meetings. All contributions are by individuals, not organizations as in many other standardization groups. At first exposure, the workings of IETF may seem mysterious. How decisions are made and who makes them is often unclear to those unfamiliar with how IETF works. Even less clear is how an outside standards body with particular requirements or needs for IP protocol standardization should approach the IETF. This chapter presents some basic information about how the IETF works and provides some guidance about how outside standardization bodies can approach the IETF in a way that is more likely to facilitate effective communication.

IETF: The Basics

The bulk of the technical work in the IETF is done in Working Groups. A Working Group is formed around a community of interest, involving a group of individuals who volunteer to do the work. A proposal for new work requires the community of interest to first organize an email list where preliminary discussion takes place and to write one or more documents describing the technical issues involved. These documents may include a problem statement, description of requirements and architecture, or even preliminary designs for a protocol, depending on how advanced the technical work is at the time the community of interest wants to form the Working Group. At an IETF meeting, a Birds Of a Feather (BOF) meeting is typically

held to discuss the new work with the intent of determining whether there is general consensus to move forward with forming a Working Group. As a rule, a maximum of two BOFs are allowed. To hold a BOF requires a BOF description, a suggestion for co-chairs, a mailing list, and the approval of at least one Area Director (see below for a more detailed description of the role of Area Directors).

If there is consensus to start a Working Group, a Working Group charter may come out of the BOF or out of discussion on the mail-

---

"The Working Group charter states the problem the Working Group is trying to solve, the approach to be taken, and milestones for completion of the work."

---

ing list. The Working Group charter states the problem the Working Group is trying to solve, the approach to be taken, and milestones for completion of the work. A Working Group charter should be viewed as a contract between the Working Group and the IETF; charters commonly limit the scope of activities in which a Working Group will get involved to keep the Working Group focused. Working Group tasks consist of writing documents on various aspects of the networking technology under development, participating in design teams to work out the design of such technology, and discussing drafts on the IETF email lists. The charter typically only lists document milestones, however. It is then reviewed by the IETF leadership (see below for more information) and, if approved, the Working Group is formed. Working Groups occasionally are created directly by Area Directors, without a BOF or mailing list discussion, if they see a need for a technology but this is fairly rare.

The majority of IETF discussion occurs on email lists. Actual face to face meetings of Working Group members take place typically only three times a year, though some Working Groups may have interim meetings. Meetings for individual Working Groups at the triennial

IETF meetings only last a few hours, unlike other standardization bodies whose working groups often meet for a full week. Working Group technical results are distributed via documents called Internet Drafts. When finished and approved by the Internet Engineering Steering Group (IESG), Internet Drafts become IETF specifications (called, for historical reasons, RFCs, which stands for "Request for Comments"). Both Internet Drafts and RFCs are freely available via the IETF Web site (http://www.ietf.org). Each IETF Working Group also has a home page at the IETF Web site, containing the Working Group's charter and links to the current set of Working Group documents.

Each Working Group is led by at least one, and usually two, chairs. The chairs split the duties of organizing the face to face meetings, guiding discussion on the mailing lists, and interacting with the Working Group members on the mailing list to further completion of the goals in the Working Group's charter. The chairs are responsible for ensuring that Working Group meetings proceed smoothly and that discussion is on topic. When the time arrives for a technical decision, the chairs are responsible for judging whether Working Group consensus has been reached around a particular decision and, therefore, whether the decision should be included in the documentation of the Working Group's technical work.

There are two leadership groups in the IETF: the Internet Engineering Steering Group (IESG) and the Internet Architecture Board (IAB). The IESG is responsible for managing the technical work in the IETF and for approving the publication of completed work as a numbered RFC. Each Working Group in the IETF is assigned to a particular Area. Currently there are eight Areas: Applications, General, Internet, Operations and Management, Routing, Security, Sub-IP, and Transport. However, the number fluctuates depending on the needs for Internet standardization at any particular time. Two members of the IESG manage work in each area, so the IESG members are therefore also known as Area Directors. Each Area Director has particular Working Groups that they direct, and the Area Director for a Working Group is sometimes called the shepherding AD.

The IAB is responsible for the longer term vision of the Internet architecture and for hearing appeals about decisions made by the WG chairs and the IESG. It periodically publishes drafts on issues of architectural or procedural concern to the IETF and occasionally holds workshops to discuss longer term issues in the evolution of the Internet architecture. Of particular importance to participants in other standardization bodies, the IAB is responsible for approving and managing liaison relationships between the IETF and other groups. A list of current IAB-appointed liaisons can be found at http://www.ietf.org/ietf/1ietf-liaisons.txt. Together with the IESG, the IAB reviews and approves charters for new Working Groups. It also has oversight responsibility for the RFC Editor function, which publishes Internet Standards and other documents of interest on Internet technology, and the Internet Research Task Force (IRTF), which undertakes

---

"All IETF decisions, both in Working Groups and among the leadership, occur through rough consensus, where "rough" implies that unanimity is not strictly necessary."

---

research (as opposed to standardization and engineering) work on Internet technology.

All IETF decisions, both in Working Groups and among the leadership, occur through rough consensus, where "rough" implies that unanimity is not strictly necessary. Working Group chairs and the chairs of the IAB and IESG are responsible for declaring when rough consensus has been reached for the groups they chair, and the IETF leadership at all levels takes this responsibility very seriously. However, unlike voting or other types of decision-making procedures that are followed by other standardization groups, developing rough consensus may take somewhat longer. The advantage is that people typically (but not of course always) fall in line fairly quickly behind a decision when rough consensus has been reached, rather than having a minority that is unhappy and agitating for changing the decision. Consequently, standard-

> *"The advantage is that people typically (but not of course always) fall in line fairly quickly behind a decision when rough consensus has been reached, rather than having a minority that is unhappy and agitating for changing the decision."*

ization groups that need to interact with the IETF should keep this in mind if they have aggressive schedules requiring particular technology from the IETF.

For more detailed information about how the Internet standards process operates, see RFC 2026 and RFC 2418.

Interacting with the IETF

Outside standardization bodies wanting to interact with the IETF have a variety of options about how to do so. This section explores those options.

Through participation in an existing working group

If the issues are fairly complex or technical in nature—for example, involving requirements for changes in protocols—or there are many issues, then direct participation in an IETF Working Group is usually the option most likely to achieve a successful result. In that case, having a few engineers or researchers from the standardization group actively involved in the IETF Working Groups of interest allows technical discussions to more easily proceed with the IETF community. The participants from the other standardization body will then be in a position to present the requirements and suggested solutions needed by the other standardization group directly to the IETF community.

When a standardization group has a new issue of broad scope that they would like to develop with the IETF, the first step is identify-

ing which Working Group or Working Groups are responsible for the work. The responsible parties in the standardization group should check the Working Group charters and ask the Working Group chairs if the appropriate Working Groups are not self-evident. Should that step fail to locate the appropriate Working Groups, the standardization body can contact the responsible Area Directors for the areas in which the work might fall. The Area Directors can provide guidance about which Working Groups are the appropriate ones. Working Group chairs and Area Directors can be contacted by email or by attending an IETF meeting.

Through an official liaison

If the number of issues that need addressing are few or are not primarily of a technical nature, then communication through an official IETF liaison is another option. Liaisons appointed by the IAB are responsible for periodically reporting to the IAB on matters involving the group they liaise with and often also report to the IESG. A standardization group wanting to interact formally with the IETF can request a liaison from the IAB chair (email address available from the IETF web page). However, the IAB tends to have fairly strict standards for what constitutes a candidate for an official liaison. Standardization bodies with international scope are typically the only acceptable candidates. National standardization bodies and industry fora with narrow scope are not candidates.

Some standardization bodies themselves often appoint liaisons to the IETF. One mistake sometimes made by other standardization bodies is to assume that if they appoint a liaison to the IETF then that person also constitutes an official liaison from the IETF as well. This is not always the case. IETF liaisons are appointed by the IAB, as described above. Liaisons from other standardization bodies participate in the IETF as would any other participant. That is, when they speak in meetings or on mailing lists, they are accorded no special status because they " represent" the other standardization body and its viewpoint. At the present time, the IETF Secretariat is developing a Web page for communication of official liaison statements to the IETF from other standardization bodies. The exact location of the web page will appear on the IETF web site when the page is complete.

If a standardization body has an officially appointed liaison from the IETF, official communications with the IETF can be run through that liaison. The communication can take the form of email, business letters, and forwarded documents from the other standardization group, or face to face meetings at IETF or other meetings. Communication to the IETF liaison about an issue should provide some guidance about how to direct the communication inside the IETF, especially if a timely response is expected. The communication should explicitly address to which IETF Working Groups, Area Directors, or the IAB the communication is intended, whether a response is expected, and by when.

Through starting a new working group

Sometimes (but typically very rarely), the work required by the other standardization body might not be covered by any existing IETF working group. In this case, holding a BOF and forming a new Working Group might be appropriate. The procedure outlined above and described in detail in RFC 2026 should be followed to determine whether community consensus exists to form a Working Group. However, before undertaking this step, the representatives of the other standardization body interested in obtaining IETF help should exhaustively explore whether the work is appropriate for an existing Working Group, since the criteria for forming a new working group are very strict.

Conclusion

The information provided in this chapter is really just an overview and the relevant RFCs should be consulted for details left out here. While this information is intended to eliminate the mystery surrounding how the IETF works and to smooth the process of interaction, it is by no means a foregone conclusion that all sources of disagreement will thereby be eliminated. Outside standardization bodies often have underlying assumptions about how their systems are architected, and these assumptions are sometimes at variance with the basic principles of the Internet architecture as viewed by the IETF. While utilizing IP protocols does not, in principle, require that an outside standardization body accept the principles of the Internet architecture, these principles are the time-tested basis of the global Internet. Standardization bodies that take the time to understand the concerns of the IETF community are more likely to achieve a design that reflects the proven positive properties of the Internet. Clear understanding of the principles of the Internet architecture (as articulated in, for example, RFC 1958) is crucial before rejecting them. Consultation with appropriate architects and others in IETF about issues of large scale system design using Internet protocols is the best bet for ensuring a well-designed system.

Bibliography

S. Bradner, "The Internet Standards Process - Revision 3," RFC 2026, October, 1996.

S. Bradner, "IETF Working Group Guidelines and Procedures," RFC 2418, September, 1998.

Internet Architecture Board, "Architectural Principles of the Internet", B. Carpenter, editor, RFC 1958, June, 1996.

Section 2

Government Influence

If you think that government doesn't have much influence over standardization—even with the "hands off" approach in the US—think again. Standards impact 80% of the world's commodity trade—and that fact alone is enough to grab government attention. Considering their effect on trade barriers, nascent industries, public safety, quality, anticompetitive practices, intellectual property rights, and innovation, coupled with government's position at the top of the ICT consumer list, it is obvious that government is and must be involved at some level in standardization.

Where and how much respective governments are involved depends on the country, the industry, and the situation at the time. However, with global markets becoming the norm, governments must increasingly work together, creating a dynamic tension between domestic and international needs, local and national government agencies, public and private interests, and the countries themselves. These governments are often turning to standardization as an effective tool for managing this tension and creating solutions that ultimately benefit the global economy.

This section examines the current involvement of governments in standardization and proposes areas for further activities. The European Union (EU) has demonstrated strong support of ICT standardization, especially in its creation of a single market.

In "Standardisation and European Policy," Erkki Liikanen, European Commissioner for Enterprise and Information Society, describes how standards are helping to make the eEurope Action Plan a success. The US government is also placing greater emphasis on standardization, and Secretary Don Evans has directed the US Department of Commerce to assist in building a fair and equitable standards playing field. See the article by Phil Bond, Under Secretary for Technology for the US Department of Commerce, to understand what Evans' Standards Initiative will entail and how it will impact your organization.

High level policies are built on detailed experiences and processes. Evangelos Vardakas discusses the evolution of the EU standardization system and the new level of SSO accountability. Once conditioned only to respond to the needs of its members, EU SSOs must now be accountable to all public authorities and society stakeholders, whether they are directly involved in the standardization process or not. Roger Marks of the National Institute of Standards and Technology (NIST) and Robert Hebner of the University of Texas at Austin argue that outcome rather than process should be the ultimate gauge of standardization and describe how the US and EU governments are involved in modifying the standardization system.

Industry and consumers should have a say in how governments impact standardization and to do so they must actually communicate to them. In every meeting that I have attended in Washington, D.C., I received the same request: Tell industry to come talk to us about where they want government involved in standardization. The need for this communication is no more evident than in the article by US Representatives Mark Udall and Zoe Lofgren, who state that many of their colleagues believe that the US Government *is* the US standards setting body and are unaware of the numerous voluntary standards bodies that currently exist. Regardless of what country you reside in, governments need to understand the value of standards, the needs of industry, and where industry desires government help. Once solutions have been implemented, industry must take the responsibility of providing feedback to these government agencies.

The areas for potential government involvement are numerous and this book covers just a few. In its article, the Center for Democracy and Technology looks at standards setting organizations as venues for public policy, arguing that standards bodies and government must work together to protect public interests. Dale Hatfield, former FCC Chief Technologist and Chief of the Office of Engineering and Technology, now Adjunct Professor at the University of Colorado at Boulder, discusses

government involvement in creating public network architectures and the increasing importance of these networks in public policy.

Of course, ICT standards become worthless if their promised ability to ensure interoperability is not kept. When this occurs, they undermine public trust and the standardization system as a whole. Dr. Susan Zevin, Acting Director of the Information Technology Laboratory at NIST, discusses the role of NIST and the need for new testing paradigms and technologies that measure the interoperability of components in integrated systems.

Throughout the world, governments are increasingly involved in standardization as an effective management tool on a global and domestic scale. And the actions of those governments—even those governments that are not your own—will directly impact your industry, your trading abilities, and your business. Industry, as the subject matter experts in both standardization and ICT products, must take a more active role in educating government on all aspects of standardization, especially in the areas where they desire government assistance. After all, if a sleeping giant suddenly awoke in your town and asked for directions, would you give them to him, directing him down the safest path for the town, or let him find his own way?

9

Standardisation and European Policy

ERKKI LIIKANEN

European Commission,
Enterprise and
Information Society

Abstract: *Erkki Liikanen, European Commissioner for Enterprise and Information Society, explains why standards are so important to Europe, the role they play in key areas of the European economy, and how ICT standards, in particular, are helping to achieve the objectives of the eEurope Action Plan.*

The European Commission is involved in some of the most strategic, innovative, and forward-looking EU policy areas. Innovation and information and communication technologies (ICT) are vital to the European Union's aim of becoming the world's most competitive and dynamic, knowledge-based economy.

The Commission is striving to foster entrepreneurial activity and recognizes that the EU single market is of major importance for European competitiveness. To enable industry to keep pace with change, and deliver world-class goods and services, a sound regulatory environment is essential.

In Europe we believe that policies and legislation that are standards-receptive can help to build this sound regulatory environment, and this is why we are strongly committed to standardisation in general. As standards play an ever greater role in meeting public policy aims, so it becomes ever more important to involve all stakeholders in shaping them. Business leaders and other societal groups need to recognise this and get involved in the process.

A number of studies have illustrated the economic and strategic significance of standards. The sheer amount of human and financial resources that companies dedicate to standardisation proves the point. However, more needs to be done to raise the awareness of business leaders. Much can be said about the impact of standards, the efficiency gains they can bring and how new types of standardisation products are responding to market needs. However, all

> *"In Europe we believe that policies and legislation that are standards-receptive can help to build this sound regulatory environment, and this is why we are strongly committed to standardisation in general."*

these benefits also need to be brought to the attention of decision-makers.

Equally, the importance of participation by groups representing consumer, environmental, or worker interests, has to be recognized. Consumers are affected by standards and should, therefore, have the opportunity to represent their views in the development process. Each time they contribute to the development of a standard, they help to ensure its quality and strengthen their partnership with other stakeholders.

If we want a practical demonstration of European standardisation supporting a specific policy, we can look in more detail at the fast-moving ICT sector.

Given the rapidly changing standardisation environment and the ever-shorter product and technology life cycles, the European Commission has welcomed initiatives of the European Standards Organizations [1] to provide more flexible procedures for their new types of specifications, called "new deliverables." These are now being offered to respond to the needs of those who would normally do their standardisation work in private consortia. These new deliverables can better address fields with extremely short product and technology cycles, such as ICT.

In some areas, the Commission has requested these new deliverables to support specific legislation. For example, in the case of the European Electronic Signatures Standardisation Initiative (EESSI), the Commission issued mandates (requests) for standardisation work to the European Standards Organizations. The main objective was that the use of electronic signatures in commerce, administration or by the general public, should be based on EU-wide, commonly agreed technical specifications. The response to the Commission's request has been very encouraging; we now have the first set of new deliverables for EESSI and there have been positive signals regarding their use.

The Commission sees the development of these new deliverables as complementary to formal standardisation. We should not forget the benefits of the traditional system, where the drafting and decision procedures are stringent and mature. These guarantee the highest degree of consensus with respect to public interest, openness, competition rules, and accountability. On the other hand, the process for new deliverables is more flexible and allows for very fast elaboration times. However the EU cannot consider them as automatically responding to policy

needs. Instead, they have to be evaluated on a case-by-case basis.

Such measures help to ensure the continued reliability and the transparency of the European standardisation system with regard to e-business issues. We can avoid the situation where some stakeholders or interest groups take a dominant position. We have to remember that the accep-

---

"We have to remember that the acceptance of technical solutions also depends on how societal stakeholders and SMEs, not only multinational companies, are consulted in the process."

---

tance of technical solutions also depends on how societal stakeholders and SMEs, not only multinational companies, are consulted in the process.

This principle of developing solutions and policies in a manner that includes all interests is very important to Europe. In order to make eEurope happen and bring people and businesses closer to the information society, the EU has launched the eEurope Action Plan (ESAP).[2] Most Member States of Europe have national action plans for information society policy, many of which inspired, and helped to shape, ESAP.

For the implementation of ESAP, widely accepted technical solutions are necessary and these will be provided by standards. The first common technical solutions are now starting to emerge; in the B2B arena, the specifications now offer generic platforms and sector-specific applications (such as for the furniture industry) for e-business. Results can also be seen in areas with strong public interest such as health IT and learning technologies. These examples show that within the scope of ESAP, technical specifications are being produced for a wide spectrum of daily and business life.

As you can see from the above ICT example, the European model for using standards in policy presents challenges but it is, nevertheless, a successful one.

Europe has a strong collaborative tradition and collaboration is fundamental to standardisation. At the same time we are convinced that good standards must not stifle competition nor restrict choices. From a free trade perspective we have worked to build a single market, and the role standards play in this is pre-eminent. The search for common standards, rather than competing standards, has prevented us from investing in losing technology whilst keeping up with the strict EC regime governing competition.

We are the only region in the world with such

"The search for common standards, rather than competing standards, has prevented us from investing in losing technology whilst keeping up with the strict EC regime governing competition."

---

a track record, which is why it is only natural for Europeans to commit to multilateral trade rules and international standards bodies that allow for the equal partnership of all trading nations. Our example is of interest to any other region heading for integration, for example Mercosur in Latin America and the South African Development Co-operation. In an increasingly global economy, our model is ever more appealing. We are committed to working with the international standards bodies as these bodies reconcile national positions. Global and free trade is in everyone's interest and the challenge is to demonstrate to free trade opponents that globalization can only be mastered in a framework of common, preferably multilateral, rules.

In Europe, we have also succeeded in deregulating our markets by replacing very detailed technical regulations with voluntary standards designated by the regulator as one option to fulfill the law. If we want regulators to leave their hands off of technicalities, we need an international standards system giving all trading nations an equal opportunity to participate in the process. Europeans do not impose their standards on other sovereign nations, and in particular not for regulatory purposes. An example of our commitment to this can been seen in the electrotechnical sector where over 75

percent of European standards are identical to, or based on, the international standards from the International Electrotechnical Commission (IEC). Nor do we want our Member States' national standards bodies to claim international status. We recognise the primacy of international work for the mutual benefits it offers.

European enterprises do not need to spend time lobbying governments to pick "their standard," as the standardisation system is the catalyst for bringing out a Europe-wide solution that is acceptable to regulators. Likewise, international standards bodies representing national delegations have the credentials to offer acceptable solutions to the international trading community. It is up to companies and other standardisation stakeholders to decide whether they prefer to work in a trustworthy international system or whether they want to rely on lobbying.

Spreading the gospel from a European point of view will certainly help to better master the challenges of free trade and globalization. We

---

"In Europe, we have also succeeded in deregulating our markets by replacing very detailed technical regulations with voluntary standards designated by the regulator as one option to fulfill the law."

---

are encouraging the European standards organizations and their members to become more active in promoting our standardisation system and its close links to the international bodies. We are good at cooperating in Europe, and we can also do it on an international scale.

Notes

[1] European Committee for Standardisation (CEN), European Committee for Electrotechnical Standardisation (CENELEC), European, Telecommunications Standards Institute (ETSI)

[2] http://europa.eu.int/information_society/eeurope/2005/all_about/action_plan/index_en.htm

10

Technical Regulations and Standards in Europe: Achievements and Problems

EVANGELOS VARDAKAS

European Commission

Abstract: *The history of the interaction between European legislation and standardization, especially in the framework of the legislative technique of the "New Approach," is briefly explained. The repercussions of this organized co-existence of laws and standards on the European Standardization system are highlighted. Some problem areas are noted and some forecasts for the future are given.*

The Search for the Abolition of Technical Barriers to Trade in Europe

The European Union (EU) is the largest group of independent countries in the world, which has continually made efforts to abolish technical barriers to trade (TBTs). These efforts are based on the very Treaty establishing the EU and they are supported by a legal dispute settlement system (the European Court of Justice), which can be used as a last resort. The dispute settlement system is accessible, in most cases, to individuals as well as to countries and the resulting decisions are directly enforceable.

This dispute system was necessary since, from the very beginning, the basis of forming the EU was to create a genuine internal market. Efforts for developing technical regulations applicable to the markets of all Member states also started very early. However, it quickly became evident that a new method was needed to advance these development efforts after examining the procedures, the decision making process in relation to laws of similar character, the qualifications of the persons involved in this process, and the large volume of TBTs that needed to be tackled.

On closer examination, it also became apparent that the range of areas covered by each country's technical regulations system did not coincide. Something that was regulated in one Member state was not necessarily regulated in another. Theoretically the (European) technical regulations should cover the totality of areas covered in every single Member state. The volume of questions to be tackled reinforced the need for another solution.

The first breakthrough: the Low Voltage Directive

In 1973, the Council of Ministers adopted the Directive 73/23/EEC better known as the "Low Voltage Directive." It covered the free movement of goods operating between 50 and 1000 Volts AC or between 75 and 1500 Volts DC. Obviously, governments could not imagine subjecting every single electrotechnical product to a special law in such a large trade area. The situation was even more difficult since, at that time, the agreement of nine governments was needed on the technical requirements for these products.

Thanks to the advancement of International standardization through the International Electrotechnical Commission (IEC), a large number of safety related international standards on electrotechnical products were already available and implemented (in some cases, with minor modifications) in the individual European countries. This made it possible, after numerous meetings with experts, to adopt the directive, which made open reference to these standards, once the standards bodies of the countries of the European Communities had commonly adopted them.

In Article 5, the Directive stipulated that: [1]

"The Member States shall take all appropriate measures to ensure that, in particular, electrical equipment which complies with the safety provisions of harmonized standards shall be regarded by their competent administrative authorities as complying with the provisions of [the present Directive]

Standards shall be regarded as harmonized once they are drawn up by common agreement between the bodies notified by the Member States in accordance with the procedure laid down in Article [...], and published under national procedures. The standards shall be kept up to date in the light of technological progress and the developments in good engineering practice in safety matters.

For purposes of information the list of harmonized standards and their references shall be published in the Official Journal of the European Communities."

This text introduced several important innovations:

- The notion of "harmonized standards," which was defined as identical standards for all Member states that conformed to the "safety objectives" of the legislator.

- The elegant solution of "presumption of conformity," which considered that products designed and produced in accordance with

these (harmonized) standards also met the legal requirements. This gave an advantage to these standards without making them mandatory.

- The text also pre-empted and politically supported the establishment of CENELEC [2] as the place to produce "by common agreement" the harmonized standards.

The second breakthrough: the "Cassis De Dijon" ruling

The Treaty establishing the European Union has amongst its principles, at least regarding the free movement of goods, that of "mutual recognition." This principle remained vague until the Court of Justice of the European Communities (ECJ), in one of the most important of its judgements, [3] concluded in 1979 that:

"Obstacles to movement within the Community resulting from disparities between the national laws relating to the marketing of the products in question must be accepted in so far as those provisions may be recognized as being necessary in order to satisfy mandatory requirements relating in particular to the effectiveness of fiscal supervision, the protection of public health, the fairness of commercial transactions and the defence of the consumer."

This case was brought before the ECJ because of the legal difficulties encountered when one company attempted to export a French liqueur called "Cassis de Dijon" to Germany.

The repercussions of this ruling were tremendous:

- It would not give any advantage to a certain Member state by allowing it to introduce technical regulations—and therefore, to create technical barriers to trade—if the (national) regulation could not fulfill the conditions imposed by the ruling (i.e., "*...being necessary in order to satisfy mandatory requirements relating in particular to the effectiveness of fiscal supervision, the protection of public health, the fairness of commercial transactions and the defence of the consumer*").

- All previously adopted national technical regulations imposing requirements on products outside of these areas could not be used to block the marketing of nonconforming products.

- The Community does not need to legislate on the free movement of goods, except when addressing the previously mentioned subjects.

- Any product that does not fall within these areas and is legally circulating in one of the Member states can automatically circulate freely in all of the Member states.

The "transparency" Directive

The 98/34/EC Directive [4] (initially adopted in 1983 as 83/189/EEC) sets up a procedure that imposes an obligation upon the Member states to notify the Commission and each other of all draft technical regulations concerning products and, with its 1998 extension, Information society services before they are adopted into national law. This procedure aims at providing transparency (thus its name in the European Community's jargon is "the transparency Directive") and control with regard to those regulations. This transparency procedure is also voluntarily extended to the EFTA (European Free Trade Association) countries and (even before their entrance to the European Union) to a large number of acceding countries. As of today, some 26 countries participate in this exchange.

In reality, this Directive imposes limitations on the freedom of national legislators (including Parliaments) to introduce national technical regulations before the other participating countries and the Commission verifies their compatibility with the Treaty principles and the Community legislation. Since they could create unjustified barriers to trade between countries, notification in the draft form and subsequent evaluation of their content during the procedure help to diminish this risk. It should be noted that the national draft laws notification system in the framework of the WTO/TBT agreement is largely based on the principles and mechanisms of this Directive.

Apart from the technical regulations, this Directive deals with national (voluntary) standards. It creates the basis of the relationship between the European Union and European

Standards bodies by listing the "recognized" national and European standards bodies and obliging the national standards bodies to publish not only their draft standards but also their annual standardization programs in advance. For the time being, it is the basic (yet minimal) legal document covering the activities of the European standards bodies and their relations with the Union.

Its adoption served as a first impetus for strengthening the cooperation between the national standards bodies in the framework of CEN[5] (CENELEC was earlier reinforced through the Low Voltage Directive –"LVD"). ETSI[6] was created much later (in 1988) and included in the list of recognized European bodies.

The "Single Market" project

In June 1985 the Commission President Delors and the Commissioner Lord Cockfield drafted a white paper on the completion of the internal market.[7] It set out a comprehensive list, largely based on the "Cassis de Dijon" ruling, of what needed to be done to abolish borders in Europe and introduced the ambitious deadline for Internal Market completion by the end of 1992.

This project created a major change in the mentality of all actors and put important pressure on the European legislation. The list of measures considered necessary in this white paper was rather long. New methods had to be followed in order to be able to produce the vast legislative body. The Community no longer had the luxury of discussing and negotiating legislative proposals for an infinite number of years.

For the free movement of goods, the "method" had already been invented approximately one month earlier, in May 1985, when the Council of Ministers agreed to the "New Approach to technical harmonization and standards."

The "New Approach"

The new regulatory technique, the "New Approach to technical harmonization and standards" was laid down in a Council Resolution of 7 May 1985. It established that legislative harmonization should be limited to essential requirements that products have to meet in order to freely circulate within the Community. In other words, the legislator should establish in a concise but precise enough form the objectives (regarding, for example, safety) to be satisfied by the products. The laws shall not describe design specifications but specify the performances of the products in a way that they can be uniformly enforced in the Community. They shall also require the manufacturer to perform a risk analysis and elaborate the design specifications to satisfy the corresponding

---

"The New Approach intends to reduce regulatory intervention to the minimum necessary to protect the public interest whilst maintaining the high standards of safety and legislative quality."

---

essential (performance based) requirements. Furthermore, the laws define one or more conformity assessment procedures, which manufacturers have to apply to demonstrate compliance.

The affixing of the CE marking, being obligatory for the free movement of products falling in the field of application of every law (Directive), means the manufacturer declares that the product conforms to the essential requirements and other stipulations of the Directive (including conformity assessment requirements).

The New Approach intends to reduce regulatory intervention to the minimum necessary to protect the public interest whilst maintaining the high standards of safety and legislative quality. However this legislative technique is not easy to develop.

Standardizers within the European Standards bodies were asked to interpret these requirements in a more concrete form. But again, the application of the "harmonized standards" produced in this way remained voluntary.

The essential requirements — the legislator's objectives

Elaborating on the "essential requirements" presents the most difficult part of the New Approach legislation. As seen in the 20 or so

Directives that have followed the pattern of the New Approach so far, the "essential requirements" are not always perfect in their conception and expression. This is because creating concise and concrete descriptions of the legislator's objectives requires a deep knowledge of the sector and a distance from the traditional practice for drafting technical specifications in laws. The additional feature requested from well-written essential requirements (i.e., to be uniformly and directly enforceable) presents the most difficulties as they must enable direct assessment of the product conformity.

The Council Resolution introducing the New Approach took care to give the enterprises a valid, more detailed interpretation of these requirements. This was especially helpful to small and medium-sized enterprises, which do not usually possess the technical capacity for designing their

---

"The Council gave a privileged position to European standardization by assigning the non-exclusive task of interpreting these essential requirements in their standards to the European standards bodies."

---

products "ex ovo." The Council gave a privileged position to European standardization by assigning the non-exclusive task of interpreting these essential requirements in their standards to the European standards bodies.

The interpretative function of mandated European standards

As stated before, New Approach directives do not contain the definitive technical detail needed to make a product; they contain broad safety requirements. Manufacturers therefore need to translate these essential requirements into technical solutions. One of the best ways to achieve this translation or "interpretation" is through European standards. To this end, mandates (i.e., official requests) are issued by the European Commission to the relevant European Standards bodies for the development of necessary standards including, where necessary, guidance from public authorities on specific aspects of these standards.

European standards allow technical solutions to be developed by all those with an interest in the product sector—they are open, transparent, and lead to the sharing of innovation and best practices. Most importantly, European standards ensure that different manufacturers have a uniform interpretation of the essential requirements in the Directives and, therefore, a level playing field.

Something that is very often forgotten by those who do not know the legal situation well and therefore, is necessary to repeat here, is the fact that they are not obligatory. If a manufacturer wishes, it may use its own solution. The only burden it then faces is the obligation to prove that his solution conforms to the essential requirements of the law. In other words, the introduction of the standards in the New Approach only inverses the burden of the proof. If a manufacturer has produced according to the relevant standards, the public authority controlling the market has to prove that the product is not in conformity.

The success

The New Approach has been praised often for its success at the European level. It has already been used as a basis for creating an international model for WTO/TBT's conforming technical regulations in the framework of the United Nations Economic Commission for Europe (UNECE).[8] It has provided a common basis for nearly 30 countries that enables the free trade of sensitive products with a volume of some thousands of billions of Euros, providing a fair place for those directly involved to influence the system under a transparent, cost-efficient, politically credible, and democratic route such as the standardization process.

In a recent reflection document, which the Enterprise Directorate General of the European Commission presented at a Seminar in 2003, important possibilities for expanding the New Approach (including areas outside of the free movement of goods) were identified:

"The implicit conclusion of the Council Resolution of 1985 is that any industrial or entrepreneurial activity operating within the Internal market could adopt the New Approach as it is currently applied, as long as the public interest is adequately protected. Such activities could range throughout the product cycle, from research and innovation to market." [9]

The European Standardization System

The "New Approach" brought a tremendous tension to the standardization system in Europe. No legislator would naturally agree to give a blank check to the standardizers without a minimum degree of confidence in them and their system. The case was relatively easy in Europe—in practically every country one (and only one) national standardization system was recognized. In some countries (like Germany) this recognition was based on a contractual relation, called Normenvertrag, between the government and the standards body. In other countries, the recognition was more direct since it was included in or based on a law (this was, for example, the case in Greece, Portugal, France, and, in a similar way, a royal charter in the UK).

At the European level, recognition was made without significant problems through the "transparency Directive."

Learning to work together

The national standards bodies in Europe, among them some of the strongest in the world such as AFNOR, BSI, and DIN,[10] had a tradition of working independently and competing in the world market. Over the years, different philosophies were developed on several aspects including the way standards are written and presented. For example, the German philosophy emphasizes "thin" content for each standard to allow for easy revisions while the British prefer self-standing documents that provide the maximum amount of possible information to their users.

The Franco-German standards disputes at the end of the 1970s and efforts to diminish them, supported by top-level politicians of both countries at the time, led to the experiment of recognizing equivalence between them. The fruits of these efforts were mediocre. It became evident that the only solution was to work together and jointly develop standards. This belief arrived at the same moment that the New Approach was being prepared at the Community level.

The most difficult part of the agreements was the requirement for every national standards

---

"The most difficult part of the agreements was the requirement for every national standards organization to adopt the agreed upon European Standard— even if an organization voted against it—and to withdraw all conflicting standards from its standards collection."

---

organization to adopt the agreed upon European Standard—even if an organization voted against it—and to withdraw all conflicting standards from its standards collection. The experience in CENELEC, which had implemented such a rule about a decade before, made its acceptance easier.

The arrival of mandates (i.e., official requests) from the Community for joint development of European Standards made necessary, especially between 1985 and 1990, the massive establishment of European Technical Committees for a large number of sectors. Their encouraging results stimulated further stakeholder interest in entirely voluntary standardization efforts (i.e., work not having a connection with the European Union's mandates or legislation). Today, according to statistics made available by the European Standards Bodies, about two-thirds of their work are initiated and adopted independently of the European Union's mandates.

This change is not only quantitative. It contains a deep qualitative change in the approach for standardization by the national industry and other stakeholders' associations. They are abolishing the old-fashioned approach of working alone in their own corner. The internal market in Europe as well as the world market does not offer serious opportunities for "own" solutions. Politically seen, this change of behavior is the genuine implementation of the European ideal at the level of standardization. From the trade point of view, it can also be considered the result of what is now more visible through surveys and other means in Europe (i.e., that national standards are potential—if not already real— technical barriers to trade).[11]

This also explains the position of Europeans regarding the international standards bodies (ISO, IEC, and ITU).[12] They have traditionally supported international standards bodies loyally, seriously, and consistently implemented the results of their work to their fullest potential and continue to support them.

As a result, the European Union now has the privilege and advantage of having all of its national standards bodies, including those being traditionally recognized as "big powers" in their area and those from co-operating nations (EFTA), working together. They represent one-fifth of ISO's membership and a very important part of the world in terms of trade.

The "exposure discomfort" of standardizers

Standards bodies have, at least morally, the obligation to serve the wider public interest. However, as standards began to play an important role in supporting European legislation, it

---

"Standards bodies in Europe who want to reach their full potential must now actually demonstrate that they can meet their wider obligations to society."

---

was no longer enough to merely have *declared* this obligation. Standards bodies in Europe who want to reach their full potential must now actually *demonstrate* that they can meet their wider obligations to society. They need to practically show that they take steps to include all stakeholders, work to achieve consensus, and are open and transparent in all their activities. In other words, these organizations became accountable not only to their membership but to the public authorities and societal stakeholders.

The standards bodies do not seem to have prepared themselves for this qualitative (and, seen from certain aspects, also quantitative) change. Over the twenty or so years that the New Approach has operated, no significant and visible structural change has been made to the standards bodies in Europe. The changes only focused on effectiveness and efficiency; they were not influenced by the need for wider accountability.

This inertia of the standards bodies has, in some cases, created stress in their relationships with the public administrations, who are responsible for the overall accountability and quality of the system, as well as mistrust from some of the bodies representing European level societal stakeholders (e.g., the environmental interest groups). The efforts of the standards bodies to remedy the situation are still considered by these societal partners either as "not enough" or "much too slow." However, in some of their positions, these societal stakeholders ask for changes that, while creating their ideal system, would not maintain the character of real standardization.

The standardizers discomfort created by this exposure—an exposure for which they were not prepared—limits the areas where standardization could be used by the European legislator in a "New Approach-style" legislation or may delay their introduction. Addressing this issue is one of the most important challenges they have to face in the coming years.

Accelerating the "production" of standards

After the first difficult years of adaptation to the new situation, European standardization is now at a cruising speed. The European collection already serves as a "critical mass" and it is unlikely that European standardization is vulnerable from the point of view of standards content. However, risks exist and new challenges are faced daily.

Current efforts to improve the efficiency of the European standardization system must consider conflicting factors. On one hand, the quality of consensus building and the requirements of openness and transparency imply that there is a minimum amount of time needed. On the other hand, ever decreasing product life cycles demand speedier standards production. This is why there is a need to focus efforts on applying sound project management to the development of each standard, and the bits that are controllable should be well managed. For example, from the start one needs to think carefully about the impact, users, and purpose of the standard; planning and thinking about problems that may occur during development is needed (for example, will there be a laboratory validation needed of the test method). Only when this is done will we have standards that are needed, reflect market needs, and are within the timescales desired by the market.

However, the method of European standards development, especially in the framework of CEN, does not seem very efficient. Every subject of a European Technical Committee is mirrored by national technical Committees, which are established by the majority of CEN members. In these Committees, national stakeholders discuss every document under consideration by the European Technical Committee. As a result, these Committees essentially provide the "national instructions" that delegations must follow to participate at the European level. Whilst in some areas with controversial proposals or a rather large population of interested parties (e.g., small and medium-sized enterprises) this would be acceptable, it multiplies (potentially by a factor of close to 30!) the human resources and costs devoted to standardization. In addition, it discourages some important players who, under these circumstances, would need to visit every country to defend their positions.[13]

In ETSI, the system is more straightforward— ETSI Committees, composed by member representatives, establish the documents. Their final acceptance for becoming a European Standard (EN) is based on a weighted voting system, identical to that of CEN and CENELEC, where delegations are formed on a country basis.

CEN is also starting to experience success in their "workshop-style" standardizing activities; recently, a "CEN Workshop Agreement" addressing the area of electronic signatures has been officially recognized.

It is obvious that speed is higher in sector-based standardization organizations, as is the case for CENELEC and ETSI. However, speed brings with it the risk that the resulting standards collection will be incoherent.

The "selling less and influencing more" paradox

The major source of the national standards bodies income is the sale of their documents. Since all European standards have to be implemented as national standards with identical content, European Standardization has, by definition, resulted in the creation of fewer standards overall. With the exception of the need for translations (something extremely important in Europe for the accessibility of small and medium size enterprises), the national standards bodies, as the sole distributors of their standards, obviously sell less. On the other hand, the adoption of a European standard in a given subject brings with it the possibility of more broadly influencing not only intra-European but also international trade.

A paradox is therefore created: the volume of the standards sold is decreasing while their

---

"the volume of the standards sold is decreasing while their influence (and through them that of the relevant technology) is increasing significantly."

---

influence (and through them that of the relevant technology) is increasing significantly. But the (national) standards bodies cannot live on influence; they have to sell in order to stay alive and continue to serve their constituencies. The added influence of the resulting standards does not seem to be transformed into an additional financial contribution from their (qualitatively)

better-served constituencies. This seems to be a failure on behalf of their management.

A similar situation, although caused by different reasons, also exists elsewhere. The Standards Developing Organizations (SDOs) in the USA also survive on their sales. Their standards are, very often, of high quality and serve as "carriers" of important technologies. However, in cases where their standards are considered appropriate to become International standards (and logically, to be exposed to broader "ownership"), the SDOs hesitate because of the risk sales losses. The paradox here is that in an effort to prevent some income loss, they limit the potential for the technologies represented in the standards to become more influential. In order to stay alive, they have to limit the influence of the technologies embedded by their constituencies in their standards.

It is obvious that in both cases we are facing a serious problem—the standardizers are obliged, in order to survive, to avoid loyally serving their constituencies. There is a clear role here for both the governments using these standards and especially the standards bodies' constituents who receive better service when their standards are more influential. A way has to be found to transform this influence into resources and someone has to provide them.

Reference to Standards in "Traditional" European Legislation

Standards are not only used in the framework of the "New Approach-based" legislation. Hundreds of references to standards are made in the European legislative corpus. Ironically, very few of them are European standards.[14] Most of them are national standards that are often superseded or withdrawn. Furthermore, a large number of cases even refer to standards that do not originate in Europe.

The most important problem for these references is the constant need for updating. A recent document published by the European Commission exemplifies this problem clearly. [15]

It is obvious that Europe must still do important work to develop a more organized system and monitoring technique for this extra "New Approach" use of standard. This would not only help the quality of the legislation but also facilitate its synchronization with technology.

A Way Forward?

The European Standardization system has to be prepared for changes. In its present organizational form, it cannot fully satisfy the need for speed and efficiency. With the exception of ETSI, where only the constituency directly elaborates on the standards and checks against "weighted national acceptance" at the final stage, the systems of CEN and CENELEC[16] are more oriented to a "national delegations negotiating mode."[17] This implies that the standards are negotiated at least twice—once at national level in the relevant mirror committee among the (nationally organized) stakeholders and a second time between national delegations, briefed by their relevant mirror committee.

This means that a sector-based organization of the work (but not necessarily sector-based *separate bodies) will become inevitable.*[18] However, if the resulting standards have to satisfy the principle of coherence, there is still further need for strong, central coordination of standardization programs and control of the resulting standards coherence. [19]

Strengthening the international dimension will be another challenge for the European standards bodies. They are currently facing an odd situation in the framework of the International standards bodies (ISO and IEC)—some other national standards bodies are criticizing them for having seriously worked in and been loyal to the International bodies for decades! This risks undermining the importance of these standards bodies in which the Europeans have invested heavily. They have to create strong alliances and offer their know-how to other countries (for example through technical assistance) to convince them to provide further support for ISO and IEC. But this, again, needs strong political support and resources. And the support and resources can only come from their constituencies and users of their standards. The European Union has constantly supported the International Standards Bodies (ISO, IEC and ITU) in the framework of the WTO/TBT discussions and it will continue to do it for the foreseeable future.

But, as it was said earlier, there is also promising potential for the "New Approach" in Europe. While this is mainly up to the prerogative of the legislators, it also depends on the success with which standardization will face its current challenges. If this extension (and there are already signs of it in the area of environmental protection) turns into reality, the weight and pressure on standardization will become even larger. This is why the key is in the hands of the standardizers. The question is: Are these standardizers willing and talented enough to successfully face this challenge...

Notes

[1] Council Directive of 19 February 1973 on the harmonization of the laws of Member States relating to the electrical equipment designed for use within certain voltage limits (73/23/EEC), Official Journal of the European Communities, N° L77, page 29 ff, 26 March 1973, also accessible at http://europa.eu.int/comm/enterprise/electr_equipment/lv/direct/73-23.pdf

[2] Abbreviation for the French title : « Comité Européen de Normalisation Eléctrotechnique »

[3] Judgment of the Court of Justice of the European Communities delivered on 20 February 1979 in Case 120/78, ECR 1979 p. 649 ff., also accessible at: http://europa.eu.int/smartapi/cgi/sga_doc?smartapi!celexplus!prod!CELEXnumdoc&lg=en&numdoc=61978J0120.

[4] For more detail and relevant explanatory texts, see http://europa.eu.int/comm/enterprise/tris/about/index_en.htm

[5] Abbreviation for the French title : « Comité Européen de Normalisation »

[6] Abbreviation for the English title : « European Telecommunication Standards Institute»

[7] See "Completing the Internal Market," a white paper from the Commission to the European Council COM (85)310 at http://europa.eu.int/comm/off/pdf/1985_0310_f_en.pdf

[8] See Recommendations on Standardization Policies, Recommendation L, UNECE, ECE/TRADE/17/Rev.4 page 21, New York, Geneva 2002. Available at www.unece.org/trade/tips/WP6/WP6_major.htm

[9] "The New Approach: *Quo Vadis?*" *See (together with other relevant documents of this Seminar):* http://www.europa.eu.int/comm/enterprise/newapproach/seminar/index.htm

[10] AFNOR: Association Française de Normalisation (France); BSI: British Standards Institution (UK), DIN: Deutsches Institut für Normung (Germany)

[11] It is important to note here that, according to a DIN study, the trend for the creation of national standards on one hand and International/European on the other in Europe has been inversed within practically a decade!

[12] ISO: International Organization for Standardization; IEC: International Electrotechnical Commission; ITU: International Telecommunications Union

[13] The possibility cannot be excluded that this practice has made the consortia type standardization bodies (which in any case are not legally recognized in Europe) more attractive to companies who are active in a large number of countries.

[14] See Falke, Dr. Josef, "International Standards for the elimination of barriers to trade," Kommission Arbeitsrecht und Normung (editor), KAN Bericht 29, Available also for download at http://www.kan.de/content/englishcontent/frameset.htm

[15] See [Leibrock, Gero], "Methods of referencing standards in legislation with an emphasis on European Legislation," in Enterprise Guides, European Commission, Enterprise Publications, 2002. Available also for download in http://europa.eu.int/comm/enterprise/standards_policy/index.htm

[16] It has to be recognized that the CENELEC mode is, in most cases, even more advantageous; CENELEC preferably works first at the international level and then brings the results of the international work to Europe. This is the reason why two-thirds of CENELEC standards are identical to international standards.

[17] See also *supra in "Accelerating the 'production' of standards."*"the volume of the standards sold is decreasing while their influence (and through them that of the relevant technology) is increasing significantly.

[18] This method of organization of work was already introduced by CEN at the end of the 1980s. The results were unequaled for the sectors involved. Instead of using the best practice approach and seriously evaluating the system, CEN just abolished it in the mid-1990s.

[19] This would imply the establishment of a powerful central service modeling the internal service of DIN called "Normenprüfstelle." This service is the basis for the traditional high quality of German standards.

11

A Call to Action Addressing the Impact of Standards and Technical Regulations on Trade

U.S. Commerce Secretary Evans' Standards Initiative to Strengthen U. S. Competitiveness

PHILLIP J.BOND
Undersecretary for Technology
U. S. Department of Commerce

Abstract: *Phillip J. Bond, Under Secretary for Technology, U.S. Department of Commerce examines standardization as a key to U.S. competitiveness in the international marketplace. In recognition of the growing importance of standardization, Commerce Secretary Donald L. Evans has created a more aggressive approach to addressing standardization and regulation needs in the overseas markets. Essential to this plan are the input and needs of industry. This paper discusses the Secretary's Standards Initiative, examines the role of NIST in international standards efforts, and concludes with a list of questions for industry.*

In the last volume of *The Standards Edge* and at the "Nature and Future of ICT Standardization" conference a year ago in Boston, a clear and convincing case was made that while standards can facilitate cooperation among competitors in the hopes of creating larger markets and accelerating the market uptake of technologies, standards can also serve as a competitive weapon used to propel technology from a particular company or a country into the forefront, capture new markets, and leave the competition behind to play catch up. United States businesses are certainly well aware of this fact. Standards, however once esoteric and cryptic they may have been years ago, are now a driver in the development of corporate strategy and business models for American commerce and competitiveness in all overseas market sectors, especially information and communications technology (ICT).

For the ICT sector, a number of companies are finding the status quo for standards development a challenge. There is an urgent need for

> *"Standards, however once esoteric and cryptic they may have been years ago, are now a driver in the development of corporate strategy and business models for American commerce and competitiveness in all overseas market sectors, especially information and communications technology (ICT)."*

speed, effectiveness, and interoperability, and for standards that support these characteristics. U.S. customers want new technology and systems immediately, and they want those systems to be interoperable across a broad range of applications. Emerging homeland security needs present an additional impetus for interoperable, robust systems.

Survival in the ICT sector is predicated on the development of new technologies. Formal standards may not always be applicable. On the other hand, standards are the new field of competition – both domestically and in foreign markets.

Accordingly, U.S. businesses are pressing for an international standards development process that mirrors our strong and diverse tradition of developing and using voluntary standards with transparency, openness, and due process. These voluntary consensus standards for products, processes, and services underpin our nation's economy and are crucial factors in our international competitiveness. Yet, our nation faces new challenges in combination with increases in competition from other countries.

Standards and standards-related technical regulations are pervasive features for global

> *"Standards and standards-related technical regulations are pervasive features for global commerce, affecting an estimated 80 percent of world commodity trade. "*

commerce, affecting an estimated 80 percent of world commodity trade. These technical specifications make up much of the vocabulary in the exacting language of industry, consumer protection, and government regulation. As such, foreign standards and methods used to assess conformity to standards can facilitate efficient international trade and its benefits – or they also can be used intentionally or unintentionally to impede access to foreign markets.

Internationally, this is a very real concern for United States businesses and trade associations, and they have personally urged Commerce Secretary Donald L. Evans to take a more aggressive, coordinated approach to addressing standards and technical regulations in overseas markets. Many in industry view foreign standards and technical regulation as a principal non-tariff barrier in markets around the world. Divergent standards, redundant testing and

> *"Divergent standards, redundant testing and compliance procedures, and unilateral and non-transparent standard setting exercises are now recognized as major impediments to free trade."*

compliance procedures, and unilateral and non-transparent standard setting exercises are now recognized as major impediments to free trade.

United States businesses want a fair and equitable standards playing field and Secretary Evans has directed the Department to assist them in achieving that balance where standards ideally would be judged solely on their technical merits without regard to other tangential factors. As a result, on March 19, 2003, Secretary Evans announced an initiative to enhance the Commerce Department's standards activities. The Secretary's Standards Initiative consists of eight points.

The Secretary's Standards Initiative is aimed at developing a coordinated strategy between the various parts of Commerce that are already working on standards-related issues. The framework for the initiative includes:

- **Developing a Department of Commerce global standards activity assessment**

  The Secretary of Commerce has tapped the Technology Administration, through the National Institute of Standards and Technology (NIST), to conduct a standards activity assessment of all existing Commerce Department programs and efforts to reduce standards-related barriers in foreign markets. The Department will also work with other Federal agencies to include an inventory of existing government programs and initiatives to ensure greater coordination in Federal standards activities.

- **Reinforcing expertise in key markets**

  The Commerce Department has standards representatives in Europe, Latin America, Asia, and the Middle East to assist U.S. businesses and foreign governments in their standards development. A new, redesigned, intensive training program for standards liaisons posted abroad is being developed by the Department of Commerce.

- **Devising an effective training and outreach program**

  NIST and the International Trade Administration (ITA), in cooperation with U.S. standards development organizations and with U.S. industry, will develop a standards training program for members of the Commerce Department's Foreign Commercial Service officers so that all U.S. officers posted around the globe have sufficient understanding and knowledge of the importance of standards and international trade.

- **Creating a best practices database**

  Working with its offices abroad, other government agencies, and industry, the Commerce Department will assemble a database of "best practices" with useful information relating to standards, technical regulations, and market access in foreign markets.

"The Commerce Department will assemble a database of "best practices" with useful information relating to standards, technical regulations, and market access in foreign markets."

- **Expanding the early warning system**

  The Commerce Department will strengthen and expand "Export Alert," a free, web-based service to disseminate market intelligence and information on standards developments in key priority foreign markets in Europe, Asia, and Latin America.

- **Partnering with the President's Export Council on standards leadership**

  The Commerce Department will support the development of a dialogue on standards within the proposed President's Export Council subcommittee on technology and competi-

tiveness. The subcommittee would provide advice and suggestions on global standards issues for the Council's consideration to include in its overall recommendations for U.S. policy.

- **Outreach to U.S. industry**

  The Department of Commerce has hosted a number of industry-specific roundtables to gather input from U.S. industry on the most pressing standards issues and priority foreign markets. Information and transcripts from the roundtables will be shared with NIST and other interested parties in the development of the Standards Activity Assessment and related recommendations in action.

- **Appointing a liaison at the International Trade Administration**

  A senior official has been named to act as a Standards Liaison at the Commerce Department's International Trade Administration. This liaison will work with U.S. industry to coordinate the activities within the International Trade Administration, including its Foreign Commercial Officers posted overseas. This individual will ensure that industry's priorities on standards are promoted through the Department of Commerce's international policies and programs, and will work closely with the Office of the United States Trade Representative and other U.S. Government agencies on how to address these priorities in U.S. trade agreements.

  The underlying goal of the Secretary's Standards Initiative is to increase the Department's

---

"The underlying goal of the Secretary's Standards Initiative is to increase the Department's outreach efforts to industry and better understand some of the challenges that U.S. businesses face in overseas markets."

---

outreach efforts to industry and better understand some of the challenges that U.S. businesses face in overseas markets. In doing so, we can more effectively leverage our Commerce Department staff, both here in the United States as well as at our posts worldwide, to help tackle these challenges.

At the heart of the Department's standards activities is the National Institute of Standards and Technology (NIST). NIST, established in 1901 as the oldest U.S. national laboratory and a part of the Commerce Department's Technology Administration which I head, is the Federal government leader in standards. NIST has also been engaged to reduce standards-related barriers to trade.

NIST's technical programs support global recognition of U.S. standards, as well as harmonization of standards to avoid barriers to trade. These programs take advantage of synergies with Commerce Department trade-related programs and with the private sector. These programs are critical to U.S. industry's access to export markets.

NIST works closely with the International Trade Administration's industry and regional desks, and Trade Compliance Center (TCC). The TCC is the U.S. Government's one-stop shop to help American exporters facing foreign trade barriers and to assure that foreign countries comply with their trade commitments. NIST and TCC management collaborate on standards-related trade barrier issues and on the development of Department policy positions in this area.

NIST also works in partnership with the Department's Foreign Commercial Service to sponsor three standards experts on location in key foreign markets. These experts support Embassy commercial and economic staffs in identifying and resolving trade issues involving standards-related barriers. NIST itself has two contractors—one in Riyadh, Saudi Arabia and one in New Delhi, India—covering standards issues.

Improving the U.S. position in key international standards developing organizations, such as ISO and IEC, is another key strategic goal of the U.S. National Standards Strategy, which was developed under ANSI sponsorship and recognizes the need for a sector-specific approach to standards issues. NIST is working with other government agencies and with ANSI and its members to target critical activities in ISO and IEC and other standards organizations to avoid adoption of international product standards that are technical barriers for U.S. exports.

NIST staff represents U.S. interests in some 180 international standards committees and international industrial consortia. Focus areas include health care, information technology, building and construction, manufacturing, and telecommunications. NIST is responsible for establishing traceability of measurement results to NIST and to the International System of Units. This traceability underpins a wide range of tests and measurements conducted to meet regulatory agency and U.S. business needs, both nationally and internationally.

NIST conducts comprehensive workshop and training programs for foreign officials, targeted at key U.S. export markets. This program demonstrates the value of U.S. standards, technology, principles, and practices. Since 1995, NSIT has trained over 1,000 officials from the Americas, Asia, Russia and the Newly Independent States, and the Middle East. Contacts with foreign officials built through these workshops and through our standards experts have facilitated

---

"The U.S-European Union Mutual Recognition Agreement covers some $40 billion of two-way trade."

---

acceptance of U.S. products in key markets.

NIST is also actively involved in implementing three major trade agreements – with Europe, Asia, and the Americas – that provide for mutual recognition of tests and product approvals in regulated areas, particularly telecommunications and IT equipment. The U.S-European Union Mutual Recognition Agreement covers some $40 billion of two-way trade.

Additionally, NIST operates as the inquiry

point for the World Trade Organization (WTO) Agreement on Technical Barriers to Trade and disseminates information on proposed foreign technical regulations for comments by U.S. interests.

The Department's International Trade Administration has worked closely with NIST, USTR (Office of the United States Trade Representative), and regulatory bodies such as the Federal Communications Commission among others on standards and regulatory issues to address market access concerns as well as monitor countries' compliance to the WTO Agreement on Technical Barriers to Trade.

Given the important role standards play in trade, the Department has also worked very closely with industry to ensure that we are advancing industry's position on these issues when we meet with foreign governments on a bilateral or a multilateral basis. For example, the Department has discussed standards within APEC's Telecommunications and Information Working Group, where deliberations have resulted in the APEC Mutual Recognition Agreement. On a bilateral basis, we have co-organized activities with industry and foreign governments in Russia, China, and Brazil under our bilateral working groups.

As part of the Secretary's Standards Initiative, the Department of Commerce conducted a series of 12 standards roundtables over a span of six months in 2003 in order to gain U.S. industry's insight into how foreign standards and related technical regulations affect their competitiveness overseas. Additionally, a Federal Register notice to solicit feedback from industry on the Secretary's Standards Initiative was sent. At each of the roundtables, the Department asked for U.S. industries' views on national standards issues. Specifically, industry was asked to comment on:

- What are the highest priority standards issues facing your industry?

- Are there adequate national and/or international standards to satisfy your industry's trade/export-related needs?

- Does your industry experience standards-related problems in specific countries or regions, or do these problems affect multiple regions?

- Do your industry's problems result primarily from the technical requirements contained in standards or technical regulations that adopt such standards? Please describe specific examples where the technical requirements resulted in market entry problems in your industry.

- Do your industry's problems result from how compliance with technical requirements is assessed? Do you have examples of cases where either the technical requirements or the assessment process resulted in market entry problems for your industry?

- Has your industry been able to take an effective approach to address international standards issues? What steps have produced the most benefit? Could other industrial sectors benefit from using these approaches?

- Has your industry been able to take an effective approach to address national standards issues? What steps have produced the most benefit? Could other industrial sectors benefit from using these approaches?

- Do you have examples of a problem experienced by your industry where the federal government has been effective in resolving the issues? What steps taken by federal government officials were effective in resolving the issue, and why were they effective? Would such steps or approaches be applicable in other cases or were their successes unique to a specific problem? What steps were ineffective or less effective, and why do you think that this was so? Was it the unique nature of the problem, or would such steps have been equally ineffective in most cases?

- What actions would you recommend the Department undertake following this and similar roundtables? Would your industry be willing to help to improve the situation encountered with respect to problems associated with standards and conformity assessment?

Industry input will be used for the following: (1) Outlining a roadmap for future action by DOC, based on some of the major concerns and issues raised by industry and based on areas where the Department's efforts are either supporting or not supporting industry's most important needs; (2) Determining standards-related programs and strategies for Department activities; and, (3) Informing Commerce offices on the current status of industry issues and on industry perspectives, and ensuring that their concerns are heard by a broad cross-section of the Department, including at senior levels.

In January 2004, a report will be presented to the Secretary on his Standards Initiative. Input from the roundtables as well as an update on all actions taken to date will be included in the report. I am looking forward to the upcoming report and its recommendations. The report, expected to be one of the most comprehensive documents on standards assembled by the Federal Government, should provide a roadmap on the future of standards activities at the Commerce Department.

Conclusion

The Bush Administration remains committed to promoting competition and opening new markets for U.S. goods. Standards and testing are key to our international competitiveness. Yet, more and more, U.S. businesses state that foreign standards and testing requirements are keeping American products out of foreign markets. This approach is troublesome as it reduces efficiencies, limits competition, and increases prices for consumer goods. Secretary Evans' Standards Initiative is an effort to create a more level playing field around the world. In addition to the Secretary's Standards Initiative, the Commerce Department is already actively engaged in a number of activities related to standards. These include ensuring recognition and use of globally relevant and internationally recognized standards domestically and in the global marketplace, promoting worldwide acceptance of U.S. test and calibration data to facilitate the marketing of U.S. products, and providing assistance to other government agencies, industry, trade associations, exporters, and standards developing organizations.

12

Standards and the Congress

REPRESENTATIVE MARK UDALL
REPRESENTATIVE ZOE LOFGREN

Abstract: *This article serves as a call for action to both Congress and industry to work together towards creating a stronger standardization system. Drawing upon historical examples, we theorize that Congress mainly addresses standardization issues only when faced with an emergency. By involving themselves in the standardization process more regularly, Congress and industry can be better prepared to meet public needs—whether those needs are market driven or disaster driven. We end the article with a suggested action plan that requires the collaborative effort of Congress and private industry to succeed.*

One of the few explicit responsibilities that the Constitution gives the Congress is to "...fix the Standards of Weights and Measures" (article I, section 8, #5). Despite this Constitutional mandate, it took more than one hundred years for Congress to establish the National Institute of Standards and Technology (originally the National Bureau of Standards). Created in 1901, after strong advocacy by leading scientists and industrialists who endorsed the concept of a national standards laboratory, NIST was charged principally with meeting the needs of electrical instrument makers and manufacturers.

However, it was not until three years later that the need for standards was made clear to Congress and the public. In 1904, more than 1500 buildings (seventy city blocks) burned down in Baltimore, Maryland because of a lack of standard fire-hose couplings. When firefighters from Washington and as far away as New York arrived to help douse the fire, few of their hoses fit the hydrants. "If there had been nozzles enough, we could have flooded the burning district," the Baltimore Fire Chief said afterward, for at no time was there any shortage of water. Although NIST had collected more than 600 sizes and variations in fire-hose couplings in a previous investigation, the Baltimore fire galvanized action and NIST participated in the selection of a national standard.

We use this example to highlight two points: that the Constitution provides for a federal role

> *"...there is little recognition in Congress that standards of all sorts are the lubricant that allows for widespread commerce as well as the adoption and dispersion of new technologies."*

in the development of standards and measures, and that Congress rarely pays any attention to this responsibility except in the wake of some public disaster. The most recent example is Congress's authorization for NIST to conduct a thorough investigation of the structural collapse and evacuation of the World Trade Center and to make recommendations for improving building codes and evacuation/emergency response procedures.

For the most part, Congress has little understanding of standards, the standards development process, and the role of the federal government through the National Institute of Standards and Technology. Generally, standards are viewed as the basis of the health, safety, and environmental regulatory structure. But there is little recognition in Congress that standards of all sorts are the lubricant that allows for widespread commerce as well as the adoption and dispersion of new technologies.

In addition, there is little understanding of the "private-sector" nature of standards development in the United States. It has been our experience that many of our colleagues believe that the federal government is the standards-setting body in the United States, rather than the more than six hundred standards development organizations that currently exist. Nor is there knowledge of the consensus-based, voluntary nature of standards development in the US.

From NIST's creation in 1901 until the 1980s, the commerce and trade aspects of standards received very little attention from Congress. There were many reasons for this inattention, but the result was that NIST developed a good rapport with industry and a reputation for working with industry for industry's benefit. NIST was viewed as one of the few federal agencies that was neither politicized nor had any regulatory goals. The standards development organization (SDO) community continued to develop voluntary, consensus-based standards in support of industry needs.

Starting in the 1980s, a marked increase in international trade led many segments of the business community to realize that standardization was a key to unlocking markets across the world. Coincident with the formation of the "single-market" in the European Union, there were accusations that standards were being used as non-tariff barriers (NTBs). For the first time, Congress became focused on the commerce and trade aspects of standards. One result of this new attention to standards was that differences were highlighted in the standards development processes in the United States and Europe. Both the US and the EU recognized the importance of standards in developing markets. As a result, there was active and lively discussion about whose standards system was the best. Because of the centralized, government-based standards development system in the EU and its member nations (especially Germany), the EU was able to develop and implement a standards strategy to address the globalization of the marketplace and economy.

At the same time that the importance of standards to global competitiveness was recognized, the pace of technological change in the marketplace was increasing. Nowhere was this more

---

"Because of the centralized, government-based standards development system in the EU and its member nations (especially Germany), the EU was able to develop and implement a standards strategy to address the globalization of the marketplace and economy."

---

apparent than in the information technology industry. Product horizons began to be measured in months, not decades or years. Traditional standards organizations in both the U.S. and Europe struggled to keep abreast of rapid technological changes. As a result, a new type of standards process was developed to fill this void, and consortia-based standards were born.

This globalization of the marketplace has also added a complication to the standards process: companies can choose the standards development process in which they want to participate—a traditional U.S. SDO process, a consortia-based process, or an EU-based process.

What this means for the standards process writ large remains unknown. Will large multinational companies migrate to more internationalized standards setting processes such as the International Organization for Standardization or the European Union? Will consortia-based standards dominate the standards process in the information technology industry? If so, what will be the impact on traditional US-based standards development organizations? While the answers remain to be seen, we can gain some insight from testimony by the Department of Defense before the House of Representatives Committee on Science. The Defense Department noted a reduction in federal agency participation in the SDO process that was mirrored by a reduction of industry participation.[1]

A recent development has been the entry of the judicial branch into the standards process. Two cases in particular have the potential to significantly alter the standards process in the US. The Veeck case deals with the issue of who pays for standards and revolves around this question: If standards are specifically designed to be incorporated into the legal code, can citizens then be required to purchase these standards in order to comply with the law? The current court decision says no, but the standards development organizations have appealed the decision to the Supreme Court. SDOs view this decision as a serious threat to their existence because they sustain themselves through the sale of their standards. A separate case revolves around the issue of intellectual property incorporated into a standard. The most publicized example of this, the RAMBUS case, has a decision pending at this time.

Given this confluence of factors—the importance of standards to global competitiveness, the growing number of alternatives to traditional US-standards development organizations, and the complex legal issues arising around standards—we believe that concerted private sector and government action is required.

First, we need a comprehensive and objective assessment of the current standards landscape – both domestically and internationally. Such an assessment must include all sectors of industry that rely on standards, U.S.-based standards development organizations, and representatives of consortia-based standards groups. Second, we need a comprehensive tally and description of all federal agencies that are involved in the standards arena. This needs to run the gamut from participation in the standards development process to agencies that represent US-developed standards in international negotiating fora.

Once this is completed, industry, standards development groups, and federal agencies must develop a strategy and implementation plan that best utilizes the unique strengths of the U.S. standards infrastructure within the harsh context of global reality. We believe that the National Institute of Standards and Technology is perfectly positioned to lead this initiative. It has a reputation for objectivity and thoroughness. In addition, it has established relationships with industry, standards development groups, and other federal agencies involved in the standards process, as well as international standards groups.

We realize that in the late 1990s, the American National Standards Institute (ANSI) released its National Standards Strategy, and in March 2003, Secretary of Commerce Don Evans announced the Standards Framework Initiative. Although

---

"It is time for industry to once again educate Congress on the importance of standards to commerce and their importance to the strength of the U.S. economy."

---

these are steps in the right direction, we feel that they lack the breadth, and more importantly, the required resources to ultimately be successful.

The recommendations we have made will only be successful if they have the total commitment of all involved parties—especially the private sector. During our years in Congress it has been rare that industry representatives ever mention standards or the National Institute of Standards and Technology. Indeed, we often spend time fighting for adequate NIST funding because there is so little broad understanding of what NIST does and the importance of its activities. This leads us to our final recommendation.

It was a little more than 100 years ago that industry convinced Congress to establish the National Institute of Standards and Technology.

By any assessment, NIST has been an outstanding success. It is time for industry to once again educate Congress on the importance of standards to commerce and their importance to the strength of the U.S. economy.

Notes

1 Gregory E. Saunders, Defense Logistics Agency, Department of Defense. Standards Conformity and the Federal Government: A Review of Section 12 of P.L. 104-113. Subcommittee on Technology, Committee on Science, U.S. House of Representatives. March 15, 2000. "There are some understandable reasons for reduced participation. ... While we are concerned about the decline and continue to monitor the situation, we have also noted significant declines in industry participation – for many of the same reasons."

13

Government/Industry Interactions in the Global Standards System

ROGER B. MARKS
National Institute of
Standards and Technology

ROBERT E. HEBNER
The University of Texas at Austin

Abstract: *We review the evolution of the global standards system and its relationship to industry. We then discuss some of the approaches that governments have taken in order to modify the system for the benefit of domestic and worldwide economic development. We use as an example an effort of the U.S. National Institute of Standards and Technology to encourage voluntary consensus standards for interoperable broadband wireless access systems.*

NOTE—This manuscript is an update of an earlier paper [1] and an earlier summary update. [2]

Introduction

Globalization of the economy has in turn led to globalization of standardization. Governments play a strong role in shaping the global standards system. They have explored many approaches to optimize the system to meet their economic and social needs. However, governmental activity sometimes conflicts with the interests of other governments or of local industry.

Standards are critical for the marketplace success of many technological solutions, particularly in fields such as telecommunications. Standards that are adopted worldwide are especially powerful due to economies of scale. Telecommunications standards adopted globally offer additional benefits by virtue of the interchangeability they offer to users. This flexibility is most obvious in the case of roaming communications devices, but, even with generally stationary equipment, global standards distinctly enhance the value of technologies and reduce testing and certification costs.

Appropriate globally applicable standards are economically efficient and offer significant benefits to end users. Effective global standards, however, are difficult to achieve. Sometimes, local political needs have moved national administrations to use standards as a means of aiding local industry. Similarly, multinational

> *"Recognizing the burden that fragmented or inappropriate standards can impose on the global economy, international organizations, backed by sovereign nations, have moved to improve the standardization process and the resulting standards."*

corporations can use the system to impede competition from smaller companies. Recognizing the burden that fragmented or inappropriate standards can impose on the global economy, international organizations, backed by sovereign nations, have moved to improve the standardization process and the resulting standards.

In the evolving environment of world trade, the World Trade Organization (WTO) has been the convening body bringing nations together to develop international trade rules. Historically, WTO members have recognized that tariffs have been a primary barrier to global trade and have therefore concentrated on that issue. However, as tariffs have fallen in response to WTO agreements, other non-tariff issues continue to unnecessarily hinder global trade. Inappropriate or unnecessarily differentiated national and regional standards have emerged as one of the major non-tariff trade barriers.

Benefits of Standards

The benefits of standards in a modern economy have been classified into four categories: [3]

- Quality and reliability – Standards may define an acceptable level of performance. The standards dealing with boilers and pressure vessels that have been promulgated by the American Society of Mechanical Engineers are good examples. Governmental regulators have sometimes made these standards legally binding to assure a minimum level of public safety.

- Information – Standards may provide evaluated scientific and technical information. For example, in the construction industry, the latest research, from concrete handling to earthquake protection, is evaluated and incorporated into standards. The construction crews and engineers who use these standards can thereby exploit advanced technical information without independent knowledge of all recent research.

- Compatibility and interoperability – Standards may provide agreed-upon interfaces so that systems can operate with parts from different manufacturers. Examples are commonplace and include nuts and bolts, railroad gauges, electrical plugs and outlets, and interoperability standards for computer and telecommunication systems.

- Variety reduction – Standards may limit the number of possible variants of a product or process. Such reductions lead to economies of scale and can also stimulate economic growth. Standardizing the size of a bread slice led not only to an economy of scale for commercial bakers but also to inexpensive toasters and plastic sandwich bags.

As a result of benefits like these, standards have proliferated. About 200,000 exist, [4] with broad implications in industry and society.

Key Factors Forcing Changes in Standards Development

Two key interrelated factors are stimulating changes in the system by which standards are developed and promulgated. The first is the end of the Cold War. During the Cold War, the world was divided into two adversarial camps plus a group of nonaligned nations. In this environment, global trade was constrained, and standards tended to be largely national or harmonized among allied trading partners when convenient. With the end of the Cold War, a truly global economy began to emerge. With increasing mobility of capital, investment flowed to countries with low inflation, a nearly balanced national budget, a strong private sector, deregulated trade and investment, and economic competition. [5] In this environment, the existing system of differentiated standards emerged as a key barrier to trade.

The second factor is the increasing rate at which new technologies are introduced into the economy. During the 1980s and 1990s, many companies demonstrated the economic benefits of aggressively bringing new technology to market. This fact, paired with exponential improvements in microelectronic technology, dramatically shortened some product life cycles to periods measured in months. Short product life cycles create problems for the standards process. [6] Standards are reached by consensus, and development times of five years have been common for complex standards. Inefficiencies in development and information transfer cause some of this delay. These issues are being addressed by many standards-developing organizations through increased use of automation and streamlined procedures. However, some factors behind the delays are less responsive to a technical fix. The development of a consensus standard requires people to agree. Different participants in the process have different expectations and concerns to be identified and resolved. All participants recognize, however, that a standard whose development period exceeds the life of the product is of little use.

Industrial Response to Global Changes

As the geopolitical barriers to global trade were removed, industry moved to compete in and profit from a global market. This trend had implications in the standards arena. For example, in 1995, the Transatlantic Business Dialogue was established "to reduce barriers to transatlantic trade and investment." [7] This organization brought together leaders of companies with headquarters in Europe and the United States to work closely with government officials

In the area of standards, a guiding principle became "approved once, accepted everywhere."

in finding creative means to remove trade barriers. In the area of standards, a guiding principle became "approved once, accepted everywhere."

Industry also modified its own standards-developing organizations. For example, the American National Standards Institute (ANSI) developed and disseminated the "National Standards Strategy for the United States." [8] This document, discussed in more detail below, culminated an industry-led process to clearly define which elements of the existing standards system needed to change and which needed to be preserved.

Industry was also taking direct action to bypass the traditional standards process that leads to *de jure* [9] standards. Such changes

were driven partially by a perception that the accredited standards process was too slow and partially by a perception that an aggressive approach could lead to huge returns. This attitude was captured in *Wired* magazine's "encyclopedia of the new economy"[10] which asserted:

"Companies used to compete by making things and selling them. In the new economy, the game is often over by the time the first product emerges from the factory. Sometimes it's because a… first entrant effectively sets… the standard. In other cases, winners (and losers) emerge from backroom bargaining over the technical details that enable complex technologies to work together…"

Geoffrey Moore [11] identifies Microsoft, Intel, and Cisco Systems as companies that have benefited by *de facto* standards.

Economists have recently focussed on network externalities and "lock-in" effects that result from *de jure* or *de* facto standards. Such economic network effects are exemplified in hardware that, once widely deployed, offers a ready market to software developers and stimulates further hardware sales. Telecommunications networks also provide excellent illustrations of such effects. Examples of exceptional success based on lock-in have become widely known. As these economic models have become better understood, strategies for their exploitation have become increasingly popular. Varian and Shapiro have published a book on the topic, advising: [12]

"A go-it-alone strategy typically involves competition to become the standard. By contrast, participation in a formal standards-setting process, or assembling allies to promote a particular vision of technology, typically involves competition within a standard. Don't plan to play the higher-stakes, winner-take-all battle to become the standard unless you can be aggressive in timing, in pricing, and in exploiting relationships with complementary products. Rivalry to achieve cost leadership by scale economics and experience, a tried and true strategy in various manufacturing contexts, is tame in comparison."

An important strategy in the lock-in game is to price aggressively to win early market share in the hope that profit will follow later, once customers find change to be expensive. As we wrote in 2001,[1]"This approach may require large capital investment and years of losses. Whether the capital markets will remain as kind to this strategy as they were in the 1990s remains to be seen."

Industry's approach to standards has been driven not only by the economy but also by the regulatory environment. For example, consortia specifications flourished in the 1990s. A 1999 estimate indicated that, in the U.S., approximately 3500 consortia organizations were developing specifications, compared to approximately

> *"A 1999 estimate indicated that, in the U.S., approximately 3500 consortia organizations were developing specifications, compared to approximately 250 accredited standards-developing organizations."*

250 accredited standards-developing organizations.[4] Cooperative research and development consortia were given great antitrust leeway in the U.S. under the National Cooperative Research Act of 1984 (amended as the National Cooperative Research and Production Act of 1993). [13] Under the Act, certain types of activities ("such as, arguably, the development of standards" [7] are protected from the risk of treble damages and liability for a plaintiff's legal fees.

Technical Barriers to Trade Agreement (TBTA)

Given the economic benefit of standards, most countries want to assure that the standards process does not harm their industry and, if possible, boosts it. An important early step to adapt the world's standards system to global trade was the Technical Barriers to Trade Agreement (TBTA),[14] concluded during the 1994 Uruguay round of multilateral trade negotiations under the auspices of the World Trade

Organization (WTO). A specific motivation for that agreement was to "encourage the development of... international standards... systems." Sections 2.4 and 2.6 impact government relationships with standards organizations. In Section 2.4, signatories—national governments—agreed to use international standards as the basis for regulations whenever possible. As detailed in Section 2.6, the WTO signatories have also agreed to become participants in the preparation of international standards by "appropriate international standardizing bodies." This last term was undefined. Many organizations have defensible claims to be appropriate international standardizing bodies for various industries, technologies, or classes of products or processes. Annex 3 of the TBTA [15] establishes process attributes for use by national and regional standards developing organizations in the development of sound and fair standards. These attributes, including consensus, openness, and transparency, are further detailed in Annex 4 of the TBTA Second Triennial Review, [16] which references transparency, openness, impartiality, consensus, effectiveness, relevance, and coherence as the hallmarks of effective international standards development. These attributes are process-oriented rather than outcome-oriented. As

> *"As global standardization matures, outcome rather than process may be recognized as the more effective gauge of standardization."*

global standardization matures, outcome rather than process may be recognized as the more effective gauge of standardization.

The TBTA explicitly recognizes the legitimate need for technical regulations, standards, and procedures for assessing product conformity with standards. Thus, it recognizes the rights of governments to adopt the regulations and standards that they consider appropriate to protect health, safety, or the environment, to meet essential security needs, or meet consumer interests in their countries. The Agreement's provisions are designed to preserve the ability of governments to act in this area but guard against use of arbitrary or scientifically unjustified measures to protect domestic industries.

As a result of Sections 2.4 and 2.6 of the TBTA, national regulations may now be determined partially by industry and, because of Section 2.6, partially by outside governments. This is consistent with the trend [3] of decreasing local autonomy in the global economy.

U.S. Response to TBTA

The U.S. standards system has its roots in private industry. Over the last century, it has successfully met marketplace needs on a sector-by-sector basis. It has developed the rules for consensus, transparency, openness, and due process that were adopted by the World Trade Organization as bedrock principles. [2]

The United States' WTO commitments, including conformance with the commitments embodied in the TBTA, were incorporated into U.S. law through a 1994 amendment to the Trade Agreements Act of 1979. Furthermore, many of the principles of the TBTA were echoed in the 1995 National Technology Transfer Advancement Act (NTTAA). [17] The NTTAA has three major implications for the relationship between the government and standardization: (1) government procurement, (2) government regulations, and (3) government participation in standards development.

Under the NTTAA, federal agencies are directed to rely on voluntary consensus standards wherever feasible and appropriate in their regulatory, procurement, and policy activities. In particular, "Federal agencies and departments shall use technical standards that are developed or adopted by voluntary consensus standards bodies, using such technical standards as a means to carry out policy objectives or activities determined by the agencies or departments." Unless the use of a private-sector standard is "inconsistent with applicable law or otherwise impractical," its use in specifying procurement criteria for a given purchase is mandatory. [18] In parallel with Section 2.4 of the TBTA, the

NTTAA also applies to government agencies in their regulatory activities; wherever possible, Federal regulations are to be consistent with voluntary consensus standards.

In parallel with Section 2.6 of the TBTA, the NTTAA also requires that Federal agencies "shall, when such participation is in the public interest and is compatible with agency and departmental missions, authorities, priorities, and budget resources, participate with such bodies in the development of technical standards." This clause provides a route for direct government involvement in private standardization through voluntary consensus-standards bodies. We discuss this issue in greater detail below.

The United States interprets the term "appropriate international standardizing bodies" broadly, to include any voluntary consensus standards organization implementing the principles of TBTA Annex 4 and whose documents are used globally. At the same time, U.S. industry continues to experiment with different structures. The current government position was developed during the Clinton Administration and reflected in the 1998 Office of Management and Budget (OMB) Circular A-119, [19] which implements the NTTAA with specific policy and language. Circular A-119 specifies that each federal agency "must use voluntary consensus standards, both domestic and international, in its regulatory and procurement activities in lieu of government-unique standards, unless use of such standards would be inconsistent with applicable law or otherwise impractical." A-119 defines "voluntary consensus standards" using language far more specific that that of the NTTAA, in accord with the TBTA Annex 4 principles and, generally, with ANSI accreditation rules. [20] This definition excludes many consortia-developed standards, a fact that has been criticized by some in U. S. industry, including in testimony before the U.S. House of Representatives. [21] Circular A-119 has had specific regulatory implications. For example, a number of comments filed before the U.S. Federal Communications Commission (FCC) have referred to Circular A-119, and the agency has, in at least one case, taken note of the accordance of its decision with A-119. [22]

So, following the TBTA, U.S. law has moved towards a domestic position parallel to that defined by the TBTA. One significant difference is that, while the TBTA puts "appropriate international standardizing bodies" in a key position, the U.S. has "voluntary consensus standards," sometimes defined according to ANSI accreditation policies, in a parallel position. Since "international standardizing bodies" are generally driven to a large degree by national interests while "voluntary consensus standards" are more representative of private interests, this distinct approach is in accord with the U.S. tradition of private-sector standardization. U. S. industry supports both an ANSI-accredited system and a significant consortium activity.

European Response to TBTA

Compared to the U.S., Europe's standardization tradition involves a greater degree of government involvement. Furthermore, Europe has been integrating its economic activities since the 1990s. Perhaps as a result of these factors, the European response to the Technical Barriers to Trade Agreement has revolved around coordination of efforts regarding the more formal "international standardizing bodies." One noteworthy effort was the effective development of the European Committee for Standardization (CEN) and the European Committee for Electrotechnical Standardization (CENELEC) within Europe. Both of these organizations, which trace their roots to the 1960s or earlier, attempt to harmonize standards throughout Europe. With the development of open trade within the European Union, the European Union decided it was important to eliminate arbitrary standards-related trade barriers. The importance they attributed to this issue is underscored by the fact that about 40 % of CEN's budget is covered by the European Union. [23] CEN and CENELEC are multinational, though not international, standards organizations. As such, they have made agreements that, if managed properly, can be used to assist industry within the

European Union. The Vienna Agreement [24] and the Dresden Agreement[25] provide a mechanism for European harmonization to proceed nearly concurrently with international harmonization through the International Organization for Standardization (ISO) and the International Electrotechnical Commission (IEC). The ISO and the IEC are Geneva-based nongovernmental standards-developing organizations that aspire to be truly global in their influence.

In the case of telecommunications, Europe has also engaged with the International Telecommunications Union, an international treaty organization linked to the United Nations. The Geneva-based ISO, IEC, and ITU each assign one vote to each country's representative, typically cast in the ISO and the IEC by a private-sector national committee. This approach gives particular strength to well coordinated alliances such as the European Union and its coordinating organizations. Funding, such as that provided by the European Union to CEN, CENELEC, and the European Telecommunications Standards Institute (ETSI), can support such alliances. If the funding and the shared vision is sufficient, such an organization has the potential of influencing the agenda of the ISO, IEC, or ITU and of accelerating or slowing the process for the benefit of the alliance. If, for example, companies operating within the alliance are not generally at the leading edge of technology, the alliance may seek to slow the standards process and adopt standards that impede the introduction of the latest technology. Conversely, an alliance of high-technology countries could assist domestic companies to increase their market share by accelerating the standards process and thereby speed the introduction of new technology. So, the current ISO, IEC, and ITU rules offer potential benefit in alliances.

The U.S. National Standards Strategy

Partially in reaction to European initiatives, many in the U.S. have called for a more coherent approach to standardization. ANSI's

U.S. National Standards Strategy [6] articulates these concerns:

"The European Union is aggressively and successfully promoting its technology and practices to other nations around the world through its own standards processes and through its national representation in the international standards activities... Emerging economies with the potential for explosive growth are looking to ISO and IEC for standards. In some sectors these standards do not reflect U.S. needs or practices... The exclusion of technology supporting U.S. needs from international standards can be a significant detriment to U.S. competitiveness. The U.S. will lose market share as competitors work hard to shape standards to support their own technologies and methods. Equally important, standards are the basis for protection of health, safety and the environment. When our standards in these areas are not accepted elsewhere, we all lose."

U.S. governmental policy has evolved along the lines of these industry concerns. For example, in the "Memorandum of Understanding between the ANSI and the [U.S.] National Institute of Standards and Technology (NIST)," [16] the two organizations "agree on the need for a unified national approach to develop the best possible national and international standards, as reflected by the U.S. National Standards Strategy adopted by ANSI." NIST has not reached a similar agreement with the less centralized group of consortium standards setters.

One important implication of the cooperation between ANSI and the U.S. government regards the definition of "voluntary consensus standards" and therefore the legal position of traditionally developed standards as compared to consortia-promoted specifications. The ANSI National Standards Strategy states that "U.S. interests strongly agree on the principles necessary for the development of national or international standards to meet societal and market needs." Among these principles of "successful standards processes" are consensus, open participation, balance, transparency, and due process. While the strategy applauds the benefits of consortia-based specification development, it encourages coordination among consortia and traditional standards developers. It also requests the U.S. government to "encourage more use of the principles embodied in accreditation by recognizing the ANSI process as providing sufficient evidence that American National Standards (ANSI) meet federal criteria for voluntary consensus standards." These federal criteria may trace back to the definitions of voluntary consensus standards in the NTTAA and in OMB Circular A-119. Because of the relationships among NIST, ANSI, consensus standards-developing organizations, and market-driven consortia, the details of the NTTAA and A-119 directly affect regulatory matters. [26]

U.S. Governmental Role in Standards Development

According to Circular A-119, federal agencies "must consult with voluntary consensus standards bodies, both domestic and international, and must participate with such bodies in the development of voluntary consensus standards when consultation and participation is in the public interest and is compatible with their missions, authorities, priorities, and budget resources." Agencies are authorized to contribute funds as well as personnel. Furthermore, "Agency representatives serving as members of voluntary consensus standards bodies should participate actively and on an equal basis with other members, consistent with the procedures of those bodies, particularly in matters such as establishing priorities, developing procedures for preparing, reviewing, and approving standards, and developing or adopting new standards. Active participation includes full involvement in discussions and technical debates, registering of opinions and, if selected, serving as chairpersons or in other official capacities. Agency representatives may vote, in accordance with the procedures of the voluntary consensus standards body, at each stage of the standards development process unless prohibited from doing so by law or their agencies."

Many voluntary consensus standards have relevance to one or more federal agencies, typically due to an agency's procurement requirements or regulatory authority. Circular A-119 outlines conditions under which those agencies participate in standards development. However, one agency has a unique mission related to standards. The mission of the National Institute of Standards and Technology, an agency of the United States Department of Commerce, is "to strengthen the U.S. economy and improve the quality of life by working with industry to develop and apply technology, measurements, and standards." NIST lacks regulatory authority, and its procurement needs are rather small. However, NIST's standards mission has always been carried out through involvement in voluntary standards activities, particularly where measurements important to commerce are incorporated in standards. Circular A-119 provides encouragement for NIST staff members to participate directly in the development of voluntary consensus standards if such standardization will improve the economy and quality of life.

An Example of Proactive NIST Action in Standards Development

Standardization is a key driver in telecommunications. Regarding wireless communications, the U.S. in 1994 began taking the position that spectrum would be auctioned to private users, who would then be largely free to decide on its use. Following years of regulated specifications, the wireless communications industry was slow to develop the traditions of consensus standardization. In the 1990s, Europe's broadly supported GSM standard developed a strong position in the world market for "second-generation" cellular telephones, while the U.S. market remained fractured. The standards wars of "third-generation" cellular were fought by many companies and consortia and ultimately in the International

Telecommunications Union (ITU). As a treaty organization, the ITU voting policy is one vote per country.

In 1998, NIST began looking at a different wireless application: fixed broadband wireless access providing high-speed network access to businesses, homes, and other stationary sites, generally through rooftop antennas. [27] NIST found little evidence of U.S. or worldwide efforts to standardize such services, although an early program in the European Telecommunications Standards Institute (ETSI) had begun. This application seemed ripe for standards,[28,29] but industry needed a catalyst. NIST assumed the role and called a meeting to discuss the topic in August 1998. With the participation of 45 attendees, a plan was crafted to initiate the standardization process.

The plan developed by this group did not follow the traditional telecommunications model of creating one or more national standards and then moving toward an international standards competition. Instead, the plan was to follow the traditions established in data communications that had led to the global standards underlying the Internet. These standards had yielded a vibrant business in which customers were delighted with dramatically declining prices while manufacturers enjoyed accelerating unit sales growth.

Following that model, the NIST-initiated group, after considering possible consortium development, elected to proceed with standardization through the ANSI-accredited IEEE Standards Association (IEEE-SA), which is the standards developing arm of the Institute of Electrical and Electronics Engineers (IEEE), a transnational nonprofit technical society of over 350,000 members.[30] In particular, that group approached the IEEE 802 LAN/MAN (Local/Metropolitan Area Networks) Standards Committee. IEEE 802 is the source of the ubiquitous Ethernet standards that define local area networks and that have rapidly turned new technology into readily available commodity equipment. IEEE 802 has also taken the lead in wireless data networking, with an active and successful project in the IEEE 802.11 Wireless LAN standards as well as a more recent effort developing the IEEE 802.15 Wireless Personal Area Network standards. [31, 32]

In two months, the NIST-pioneered effort to create standards for fixed broadband wireless access led to an IEEE 802 Study Group chartered to develop a standardization plan. Four months later, this plan was approved, and the IEEE 802.16 Working Group on Broadband Wireless Access [33] was created and chartered to develop its first standards project. The project attracted broad global interest, eventually drawing members from 13 countries. Holding bimonthly weeklong sessions, it moved quickly. The core standard defining the WirelessMAN® air interface was approved as IEEE Standard 802.16 in 2001.[34,35] Four additional standards to enhance the applicability of the work and aid deployment of the systems have also been published, with several more under development. Active work continues, with attention aimed at expanding the specification for mobile applications and at publishing a set of conformance test documents as standards.[36] Industry activity supports the standardization efforts, and the Worldwide Interoperability for Microwave Access (WiMAX) Forum is preparing to support compliance tests. Companies, small and large, are currently implementing the standard into commercial equipment.

NIST has actively participated in IEEE 802.16 activities. After initiating the project, a NIST staff member (the first author of this paper) was elected 802.16 Working Group Chair, leading the activities, driving the development of standards, and representing the group to its superior bodies. The same staff member has served as Technical Editor of standards, organized a number of sessions, and provided many other services to maintain the group's progress.

This activity fulfills NIST's mission in several ways:

1. By encouraging standardization through the voluntary consensus standards process, the work supports the goals of the NTTAA,

OMB Circular A-119, and the ANSI National Standards Strategy.

2. By encouraging the development of standards in an open, global, technically based, consensus process, the project ensures that all participants, large and small alike and regardless of nationality, can, if they have the resources, have access to the process so that the resultant outputs are likely to be of high quality.

3. By accelerating standardization, the work moves broadband wireless access closer to widespread deployment. This will expand opportunities for equipment vendors and service providers.

4. By leading to wider deployment, standardization will offer more broadband access alternatives to a wider range of U.S. consumers and businesses, including those in locations that may otherwise be poorly served by more conventional broadband access networks.

5. By enhancing the deployment of broadband services, the work will expand the applicability of the Internet and its positive effect on the economy.

6. By developing standards with global participation, the project will increase the chances of a uniform global result with broad export market opportunities for manufacturers in all countries.

NIST has also contributed its unbiased technical expertise to IEEE 802 standardization projects. In support of further such contributions, NIST has also planned to develop the National Wireless Electronic Systems Testbed (N-WEST) for use in measurements that contribute to effective standardization and compliance testing.[37, 38] Such an undertaking will require significant investment.

Balancing Interests: Manufacturers versus Users

When seeking to boost their own economies, governments may wish to consider the full range of voices within their constituencies. For instance, standardization is often driven most strongly by manufacturers and other product vendors. These voices may argue that government action on standards should be driven, within WTO obligations, by the goal of enhancing production and profits among manufacturers. However, governments should not overlook the economic interests of the users of the technology. Interesting case studies might come from the fields of computer networking, including the most popular standards for wired and wireless networks developed by the IEEE 802 LAN/MAN Standards Committee. For instance, the success of Ethernet has been so strong over the past 30 years that the technology's primary inventor, Bob Metcalfe, considers it not so much a technology standard but a business model. [39]

"There are four business models out there today. The first is the vertical model... The second, which dominates today, is the horizontal model... The third is the Linux/open-source business model. And the fourth is the Ethernet business model. It's based on *de jure* standards with proprietary implementations of those *de jure* standards, and it is unlike open source in that competitors don't give their intellectual property away. The competition is fierce, but there is a market ethic that products will be interoperable. And the standard evolves rapidly based on market engagement in such a way to value the installed base. There is a heavy value placed on sustaining and maintaining the installed base. That's the Ethernet business model."

Clearly, deployment of these standards-based networks has had enormous impacts on economies. For example, IEEE 802.11 networks are widely used in the United States, with significant economic impact, even if most 802.11 equipment is manufactured elsewhere. Would the United States as a whole have benefited more from a policy of supporting, through standards policy, the U.S. manufacturing industry? Perhaps not.

Conclusions

The world standards system has undergone rapid change and restructuring. The role of governments in the emerging system is taking shape. Widely different models for government engagement exist in different regions of the world. Europe is oriented primarily toward interaction with formal international standardization bodies. In the United States, government and industry are agreeing that government should play an active role in encouraging and accelerating voluntary consensus standardization. As NIST is demonstrating through its participation in the IEEE 802.16 Working Group on Broadband Wireless Access, this role can constructively contribute to the economy and quality of life.

Acknowledgements

The authors acknowledge the manuscript review provided by Mary Saunders of NIST and appreciate her insights into the standards process.

Notes

[1] R. B. Marks and R. E. Hebner, "Government Activity to Increase Benefits from the Global Standards System," 2001 IEEE Conference on Standards and Innovation in Information Technology (Boulder, Colorado, USA), pp. 183-190, 3-5 October 2001 <http://ieee802.org/16/docs/01/80216c-01_13.pdf>.

[2] R. B. Marks, "Governmental Approaches to Standards in World Trade," *MediaView* magazine (in Chinese language), pp. 39-40, April 2003 (in English at <http://emarks.net/mediaviewstds>).

[3] G. Tassey, *The Economics of R&D Policy*, Quorum Books, Westport, CT. USA, 1997.

[4] R. Hebner, "Standards and Trade—Who Really Cares?" in *Technology Standards and Standardization Processes: Their Impact on Innovation and International Competitiveness*, pp.3-16, Stanford University Press, 1999 (see also <http://fuji.stanford.edu/seminars/fall98/sep24-p/sld001.html>).

[5] T. L. Friedman, *The Lexus and the Olive Tree*, Anchor Books, New York, 2000.

6 Desi Rhoden, "Real-Time On-Line Standards, the Ever Changing JEDEC, and other Standard Topics," in *Technology Standards & Standardization Processes. Their Impact on Innovation & International Competitiveness*, pp.32-41, Stanford University Press, 1999 (see also <http://fuji.stanford.edu/seminars/fall98/oct8-p.pdf>).

7 Transatlantic Business Dialogue <http://www.tabd.com>.

8 *National Standards Strategy for the United States*, The American National Standards Institute, 2000 <http://web.ansi.org/public/nss.html>.

9 Andrew Updegrove, "Forming and Representing High-Technology Consortia: Legal and Strategic Issues," *The Computer Lawyer*, March 1994 <http://www.lgu.com/pubs/cons47.htm>.

10 John Browning and Spencer Reiss, "The Encyclopedia of the New Economy," *Wired*, Aug. 1998 <http://hotwired.lycos.com/special/ene>.

11 Geoffrey Moore, "Standards and the Gorilla Game: The Dynamics of Setting Standards in High-Tech Markets" in *Technology Standards and Standardization Processes: Their Impact on Innovation and International Competitiveness*. pp.117-134, Stanford University Press, 1999 (see also <http://fuji.stanford.edu/seminars/fall98/dec3-p/sld001.html>).

12 Carl Shapiro and Hal R. Varian, *Information Rules*. Harvard Business School Press, 1999.

13 Sean P. Gates, "Standards, Innovation, and Antitrust: Integrating Innovation Concerns into the Analysis of Collaborative Standard Setting," *Emory Law Journal*, Volume 47, Number 2, Spring 1998 <http://www.law.emory.edu/ELJ/volumes/spg98/gates.html>.

14 "Agreement on Technical Barriers to Trade," The World Trade Organization, <http://www.wto.org/english/docs_e/legal_e/17-tbt.pdf>.

15 "Code of Good Practice for the Preparation, Adoption and Application of Standards," The World Trade Organization <http://www.jurisint.org/pub/06/en/doc/16.htm#16.a3>.

16 Annex 4, "Decision of the Committee on Principles for the Development of International Standards, Guides and Recommendations," World Trade Organization Committee on Technical Barriers to Trade, Second Triennial Review of the Operation and Implementation of the Agreement on Technical Barriers to Trade, G/TBT/9, 13 November 2000.

17 National Technology Transfer and Advancement Act (Public Law 104-113), <http://ts.nist.gov/ts/htdocs/210/nttaa/113.htm>.

18 Andrew Updegrove, "U.S. Government Initiative Boosts Standards," The Technology Law Bulletin, July 1996 <http://www.lgu.com/pubs/cons50.htm>.

19 "Federal Participation in the Development and Use of Voluntary Consensus Standards and in Conformity Assessment Activities," Office of Management and Budget (OMB) Circular A-119, February 10, 1998 <http://www.dsp.dla.mil/omba119.htm>.

20 "Memorandum of Understanding between the American National Standards Institute (ANSI) and the National Institute of Standards and Technology (NIST)," <http://ts.nist.gov/ts/htdocs/210/nttaa/ansimou.htm>, December 2000.

21 Carl F. Cargill, "The Role of Consortia Standards in Federal Government Procurements in the Information Technology Sector: Towards a Re-Definition of a Voluntary Consensus Standards Organization," testimony before the House Science Committee's Subcommittee on Technology, Environment, and Standards, June 27, 2001.

22 <http://www.fcc.gov/Bureaus/Wireless/Orders/1999/fcc99085.txt>

23 "Annual budget for the CEN Management Centre (1999)," European Committee for Standardization <http://www.cenorm.be/aboutcen/whatis/corporate/budget.htm>.

24 "Agreement On Technical Cooperation Between ISO and CEN (Vienna Agreement)," 1995 <http://isotc.iso.ch/livelink/livelink/fetch/2000/2123/SDS_WEB/sds_dms/vienna.pdf>.

25 "IEC - CENELEC Agreement on Common Planning of New Work and Parallel Voting," European Committee for Electrotechnical Standardization, 1996 <http://www.iec.ch/cenelec.htm>.

26 "Market-Driven Consortia: Implications For The FCC's Cable Access Proceeding (Working Draft)," The Center for Regulatory Effectiveness, July 20, 2000 <http://www.thecre.com/action/whitepaper.html>.

27 R. B.Marks, "Broadband Wireless Access for the First Mile," National Science Foundation "Last Mile Panel," April 8, 1999 <http://nwest.nist.gov/first_mile.pdf>.

[28] R. B.Marks, "Standards Make Wireless Work," *Applied Microwave & Wireless Magazine*, pp. 101-102, February 1999 <http://nwest.nist.gov/editorial_amw.html>.

[29] R. B.Marks, "Cooperative International Wireless Standardization," European Institute Roundtable: Spanning the Spectrum of Communications Policy, May 6, 1999 <http://www.standardsresearch.org/standards-discuss/0006.html>.

[30] R. B.Marks, "IEEE Standardization for the Wireless Engineer," *IEEE Microwave Magazine*, pp. 16-26, June 2001 <http://WirelessMAN.org/docs/01/80216c-01_09.pdf>.

[31] R. B.Marks, Ian C. Gifford, and Bob O'Hara, "Standards from IEEE 802 Unleash the Wireless Internet," *IEEE Microwave Magazine*, pp. 46-46, June 2001 <http://WirelessMAN.org/docs/01/80216c-01_10.pdf>.

[32] R. B.Marks, "Advances in Wireless Networking Standards," *Pacific Telecommunication Review*, pp. 30-37, 4th Quarter 2002 <http://WirelessMAN.org/docs/03/C80216-03_03.pdf>.

[33] <http://WirelessMAN.org>

[34] IEEE Standard 802.16-2001 ("IEEE Standard for Local and metropolitan area networks—Part 16: Air Interface for Fixed Broadband Wireless Access Systems") <http://ieee802.org/16/published.html>.

[35] Carl Eklund, R. B.Marks, Kenneth L. Stanwood, and Stanley Wang, "IEEE Standard 802.16: A Technical Overview of the WirelessMAN Air Interface for Broadband Wireless Access," *IEEE Communications Magazine* , pp. 98-107, June 2002 <http://ieee802.org/16/docs/02/C80216-02_05.pdf>.

[36] R. B.Marks, "IEEE Standard 802.16 for Global Broadband Wireless Access," ITU Telecom World 2003, Geneva, October 12-18, 2003 <http://ieee802.org/16/docs/03/C80216-03_14.pdf>.

[37] R. B.Marks, "The National Wireless Electronic Systems Testbed: Initial Development," MTT-S European Topical Congress on Technologies for Wireless Applications, Amsterdam, pp. 220-223, October 7-9, 1998 <http://nwest.nist.gov/eumc.html>.

[38] Submission of Testimony for the Record by Raymond G. Kammer, Director, National Institute of Standards and Technology, before the House Science Committee's Subcommittee on Technology (Standardization of Wireless Internet Technologies), April 11, 2000 <http://www.nist.gov/testimony/2000/wireless.htm>.

[39] CNET News.com, "30 years of Ethernet Gains," 21 May 2003 <http://news.com.com/2102-1082_3-1008450.html?tag=ni_print>.

14

Testing: A Key to Building Trust and Confidence in IT Systems

Dr. Susan F. Zevin

National Institute for
Standards and Technology

Abstract: *Computers now touch every aspect of human life. This has occurred because of the promise of improving the quality of life. Maintaining trust and confidence in information technology is central to keeping that promise. This is difficult when most information technology systems fail to meet key user expectations; are difficult to use, fail unexpectedly, contain hidden security vulnerabilities, and are delivered full of bugs. Building the trust of users of IT systems requires a significant new focus on techniques and tools to improve IT systems, from hardware, to system and application software, and to the interactions between the system and the user. Developing the connections between expectations and measurable system attributes enables the user to better understand and establish the level of trust that can be placed in an IT system. NIST concentrates on the development of measurement technologies and testing programs commensurate with life-cycle phases of software development to foster this understanding. Testing methods range from simple code checking to formal validation and certification programs conforming to international standards for laboratory testing programs. Future work must address testing beyond component development to the interoperation of components in integrated systems. And, as systems become more complex, dynamic, scalable, and changeable, new testing paradigms must be developed.*

Building Trust is Essential

Most information technology systems fail to meet key user expectations. Systems are full of bugs or fail unexpectedly. They contain hidden, unknown, unintended, and even sometimes intended security vulnerabilities. While some IT systems are easily set up by the user initially, the underlying software components may create problems during future operation of the system. These problems may be caused by poor documentation or usability, and they may fail to meet performance expectations; they may fail to interoperate with other components. More often, it is

> *"...productivity gains that are supposed to be achieved through automation are diminished by the costs and effort of installation, disappointing functionality, and lack of interoperability with other systems."*

difficult for a user to understand what complementary components, devices, and other software may be needed in order to enable the system functionality that is wanted. Or a user simply may be overwhelmed by the number of product choices available with little guidance as to the criteria with which to choose. Thus, productivity gains that are supposed to be achieved through automation are diminished by the costs and effort of installation, disappointing functionality, and lack of interoperability with other systems.

It is well known that additional testing performed by the software vendor can reduce many of these problems and save the user valuable time and resources. A recent study by the National Institute for Standards and Technology

---

"...the national annual cost of an inadequate infrastructure for software testing is estimated to range from $22.2 to $59.5 billion."

---

stated that "the national annual cost of an inadequate infrastructure for software testing is estimated to range from $22.2 to $59.5 billion. Over half of these costs are borne by software users in the form of error avoidance and mitigation activities. The remaining costs are borne by software developers and reflect the additional testing resources that are consumed due to inadequate testing tools and methods" (NIST, 2002). The costs to the user in dealing with "buggy" implementations is unknown; but, for example, the exploitation of buffer overflows, those avenues by which malicious code can be slipped into the computer and executed, and which are the most common form of security vulnerability (Schneier, 2000), have cost the world community $10s billions in clean up. The result is that because of lack of understanding of how systems work and their potential fallibility, many consumers simply become reluctant or afraid to use them.

Yet, the promise of these technologies pushes business and economic sectors toward greater utilization. Individuals and society as a whole are becoming more dependent upon information technology to enhance speed, utility, and connectedness of communications and computations. Pervasive, wireless, and embedded devices create extraordinary capabilities and opportunities to enhance our everyday lives. As systems become more complex and extensible, users are demanding reassurance that they can trust the operation of their systems and have confidence in the information delivered. People ask:

- Is the system doing what I expect?

- Am I acquiring the relevant data?

- Have the data been tampered with?

- Are there people listening who should not be listening?

- Will the information be available when I need it?

- Are my measurements provably correct?

Measurements and Tests are Key

The National Institute of Standards and Technology develops measurement science and technologies in order to answer such questions. In IT metrology, we seek quantitative and measurable ways to specify how well computers should function, perform, fail and be restored, how well a computer or network should process data, and how fast these operate under different circumstances. Among the techniques for measuring IT components are modeling and simulating processes and functions against which actual operations can be measured, performance criteria and standard ways to measure functionality, reference data sets in which different algorithms can be compared with known results, and testing methodologies. These measurement technologies allow the inter-comparison of like systems, like computers, and like software.

More frequently, NIST is being asked to help various communities of consumers meet needs for reassurance through testing—testing requirements through user validation, testing conformance to specification or standards, testing designs for performance, testing for accessibility and usability, testing code, components, and interoperability within system architectures, testing operations, information content, and upgrades. By making the testing methods widely known and available, NIST provides the capability for developers, integrators, and users to determine for themselves the goodness of the products and the weaknesses that require improvement. By using standard approaches to testing with well-accepted, rigorous, easily used and widely applicable methods, and ensuring results are available for review—either explicitly or through a certificate—vendors prove their commitment to quality and save money; consumers save money and time, and commit to product. Society and the economy benefit as a whole.

> *"NIST provides the core measurement and testing methods that enable the effective development, implementation, and utilization of standards by all parties."*

Individual industry vendors may set de facto standards and self-test mechanisms. However, seldom are these regarded by other industry members and competitors as unbiased. Standards Development Organizations provide formalized forums for consensus standards development (these are known as de jure standards), and consortia satisfy the need for tar-geted consensus approaches and solutions to the benefit of specific communities. NIST provides the core measurement and testing methods that enable the effective development, implementation, and utilization of standards by all parties.

Building Trust and Confidence Requires Measurements and Testing throughout the Life-Cycle of Software

In order to understand current testing techniques and paradigms, one might start with a picture of a conventional IT development approach (Figure 1). Generally, the process begins with requirements and specifications and proceeds through design and development of the component, tool or system, testing for conformance at various stages of development, followed by conformance testing, operation and maintenance, and finally upgrade or replacement. To this traditional model of development, we add the stage of data use (information utilization). This is to ensure that a system or component performs according to specification; if the specification is poor (if the specification is not precise, or is ambiguous or not testable), the information received from the system may be worthless.

Figure 1. Compentency-Based Model of Trust and Confidence

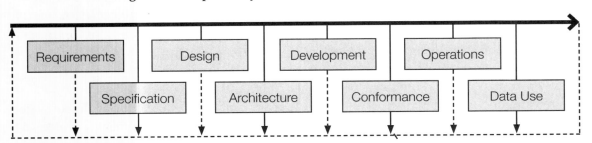

Source: Internal Planning Document

NIST concentrates its work on measurement technologies to support each particular stage from requirements through preservation. In the NIST IT measurement science program, globally recognized competencies include biometrics, speech and text searches, computer forensics, computer security, network modeling, and XML.

Table 1: Terminology of the Competency-Based Model of Trust and Confidence

Term	Definition	Level of Measurement Science Development
Requirement	Demanded, obligatory	Undeveloped
Specification	Statement of particulars	Underdeveloped
Design	Conceive in the mind, plan	Underdeveloped
Architecture	Science of building	Underdeveloped
Development	Act, process or result of developing	Underdeveloped
Conformance	Acting in accord	Underdeveloped
Operations	Performance of work	Developed
Preservation	Protect and maintain	Underdeveloped

For simplicity and breadth of understanding, definitions of terms used here are derived from those found in Webster's dictionary (see Notes) and synopsized in the column "Definition." A straightforward designation of the development level of enabling tools and technologies is included as a general baseline for our understanding of the state-of-the-art measurement science supporting IT development. Examples of applications and technologies to which NIST has contributed its measurement science expertise are: formal methods of specifications, object-oriented languages, service discovery protocols, architecture models and description languages, XML, computer security, networking, biometrics, and speech processing. Thus, for example, in the view of NIST scientists, there are few if any rigorous, objective, unbiased formulae, systematic, or semantic approaches widely available that would enable a user to articulate and formally generate requirements—there are no Requirements Description Languages like there are Architecture Description Languages that describe the relationships of distributed components or Extensible Markup Languages for marking text. The successful deployment of a computer program requires that each life-cycle stage be completed to the highest levels of accuracy and performance, implying there are

metrics to signify successful completion of the work in each life-cycle stage. These successes foster system development with closure of each life-cycle phase and initiation of the next in an integrated process.

Traditionally, testing is associated with debugging code. And, indeed, many software

> "The successful deployment of a computer program requires that each life-cycle stage be completed to the highest levels of accuracy and performance, implying there are metrics to signify successful completion of the work in each life-cycle stage."

errors could be thwarted during the software coding phase if the requirements are precisely and unambiguously defined in a formal specification, rather than by using spoken language. An alternative to developing a formal specification is to develop a specification in a semi-formal language like XML. Yet, the questions remain: What are the tests checking? How, and for whom, and for what purpose? Most software development approaches do not consider the testing and validation strategies needed to assure that the requirements are well defined and realized, that performance can be assured during operations, and that the information derived from the system is the information needed. Indeed, much remains to be done to strengthen testing for each stage in the life-cycle.

Testing Is for Everyone

As previously noted, testing normally is viewed as an iterative process used by the developer during coding. It may be completed using technologies as common as syntax checkers or as sophisticated as automatically-generated tests based on formal specifications or requirements. In this iterative approach, the developer is usually in charge of test design and execution, including bench, simulated, and field testing. Most often, the software is coded and corrected by the very same person who develops the tests, leading to potential conflicts of interest in finding errors. In contrast, formally written specifications provide a direct linkage between the specified functionality and the written code, providing a basis for objective and unbiased testing rules. However, the use of formal methods to define specifications long has been viewed as arcane; and only recently has XML been shown to be a good surrogate,

---

"The key to better software is through education of engineers in utilizing quality processes, like formal methods. But, university curricula rarely include such course work. "

---

though its widespread acceptance for this purpose is doubtful. The key to better software is through education of engineers in utilizing quality processes, like formal methods. But, university curricula rarely include such course work. Furthermore, formal methods will not help to debug legacy (already implemented) code since specifications for legacy code already are developed. So, it is assumed that the curse of "buggy" software will continue for many years to come.

Other methods for assuring conformance to requirements and specifications are available. Once a program or module is coded, the implementer, developer, or user may request a next level of testing. Conformance testing evaluates the adherence or non-adherence of an implementation, program, module, or component to a specification or standard. And, it may be carried out at various levels of formality, from self-tests, to structured validation and certification programs created and operated by user communities or mandated by legal authorities or government agencies. Validation is the process of testing for conformance by using an official test suite in a prescribed manner. Certification may follow validation as a formal acknowledgment that a validation has been completed and the certification criteria (established by the certifying organization) have been met (Rosenthal, et al, 2001). The international standard for setting up a formal conformance testing program is known as ISO 17025. According to this globally recognized process, a formal accreditation body, such as the NIST National Voluntary Laboratory Accreditation Program (NVLAP) or the American Association for Laboratory Accreditation (A2LA), helps to establish and oversee the work of testing labs that carry out the conformance testing. Labs must be reaccredited every so often, depending on the nature of the testing to be performed. The testing laboratories follow specific procedures, use specific testing software, and documentation to check for conformance. The results are provided to the developer and a report may also be sent to the certifying body (if certification is a part of the conformance program).

It is with more structured or formalized conformance testing that the greatest advances towards building trust and confidence in systems can be made. And, it is in the development of these conformance testing programs that NIST is seeing the greatest demand from user communities. Indeed, the greatest benefit can be achieved through the combination of formalized conformance testing programs with the voluntary utilization of conformance tests developed early on, before implementations get to market.

Conformance tests, developed early on have been used quite extensively to debug programs on a voluntary basis and improve the quality of the nation's software. For example, the NIST developed XML tests are used by all XML processors as a free quality assurance resource to improve their software. Conformance tests, developed early on, can be used in conjunction with formal testing programs. By providing these early tests, implementers can improve their software before being submitted for laboratory testing and validation, thus enabling a higher percentage of implementations to pass the conformance tests and obtain certifications.

In this spirit, the World Wide Web Consortium has adopted a conformance testing process using NIST-provided test suites. In the WWW scheme, before new standards are adopted, each feature or functionality must be demonstrated to have been implemented correctly. NIST also assisted the OASIS (Organization for the Advancement of Structured Information Standards) to build its certification and conformance testing infrastructure for electronic business XML (ebXML). In like manner, NIST is working with the American Telemedicine Association to establish formal processes and procedures for its own standards development and conformance assessment for programs in diagnostic retinopathy. In another example, the voting system community, represented by the National Association of State Election Directors, sponsored by the Federal Elections Commission, developed a conformance testing process, including test suites carried out by independent testing authorities and certificates issued by the NASED certification body. This was a major undertaking over many years by a small community of motivated users. In these examples, it is the user represented by an organization or community of interested parties, like a consortium, that is in control of developing, implementing, and overseeing the testing programs.

Sometimes, governments or legal authorities mandate conformance testing through regulation or law when the protection of the public is paramount. In the example of the voting sys-

tem standards conformance testing, the Help American Vote Act of 2002 establishes a formalized certification process; and with the assistance of NIST, the testing will be transitioned to an ISO 17025 certification program based on the initial efforts of the NASED and FEC. The accrediting body will be the new Election Assistance Commission, supported by NIST.

More often, government oversight of conformance testing is associated with computer security programs. The Cryptographic Module Validation Program (CMVP), a joint validation and certification program between the governments of Canada (Canadian Security Establishment, or CSE) and the U.S. (NIST and CSE, 2003), encompasses validation testing for cryptographic modules and algorithms against Federal Information Processing Standards (e.g., the Advanced Encryption Standard (NIST, FIPS 197, 2001) and Digital Signature Standard (NIST, FIPS 186-2, 2000)). Government oversight is deemed necessary in order to assure the highest levels of integrity and confidentiality in these most basic codes used for secured, confidential exchange of data. The testing program makes a difference: In an initial survey of the testing of the first 164 cryptographic modules and 332 algorithm validations that were validated, the question was asked if the CMVP testing and standards revealed any underlying flaws in completed ready to market modules that were submitted for testing. The results showed that of 164 cryptographic modules surveyed (during testing), 80 security flaws were discovered and 158 documentation errors were found; in the 332 algorithm validations tested, 88 security flaws and 216 documentation errors were found (NIST, 2003).

The National Information Assurance Partnership (NIAP) is a coordinated approach by the National Security Agency (NSA) and NIST to test the security levels of a broad range of software programs and modules. While NIAP encompasses traditional approaches to conformance, validation and certification of vendor products, the program also establishes baseline categories of security requirements that must be addressed according to the degree of security sought by users. These baseline requirements for specific functionality at targeted levels of performance are known as protection profiles. Thus, in NIAP, a vendor can request certification of a product at a specific evaluation assurance level; or, perhaps more importantly, a user can specify certain security needs and refer to a particular

---

"The protection profile establishes the direct link between the user requirements and the certified level of the vendor product."

---

protection profile for the goals and protection mechanisms that will help achieve the needed level of security. The protection profile establishes the direct link between the user requirements and the certified level of the vendor product. Conformance testing, validation, and certification provide assurance that the user gets what is required in the security module.

However, even government sponsored procedures do not cover all the aspects of testing needed to assure a quality implementation. NIAP conformance testing assures that the security module conforms to the functionality required. NIAP does not, however, guarantee that the system in which the module is embedded will perform flawlessly, nor does it assure the user that unintended consequences cannot occur or that vulnerabilities do not exist in the code. Furthermore, by their very nature of specialization, government mandated testing schemes traditionally have been costly in time and money. Thus, it is best to develop programs that balance the benefits of obtaining conformance versus the costs of creating and running a certification program (Rosenthal, et al, 2001).

New Testing Methods Are Needed for the Future

NIST is working with many sector-specific communities to address the life-cycle competencies applicable to their needs, to assist in the development of consensus–based, widely applicable, rigorous standards and specifications, and to develop community-controlled conformance testing programs. Thus, NIST works with the banking and financial community towards tests for trusted methods of data exchange and the interoperability of smart cards; with the business (ebXML) community to establish dictionaries, reference data sets, and registry of codes to test the interoperability of basic business software functions; with the health care community to set standards for and test conformance to the Health Insurance Portability and Accountability Act (HIPAA). However, the underlying goal of all of these efforts is to work towards consistent, cross-sector approaches that are applicable and adaptable for a variety of users, and applicable to many user operating environments (Figure 2).

Ideally, testing, like security, should be

Figure 2. NIST Works Across Industry Sectors

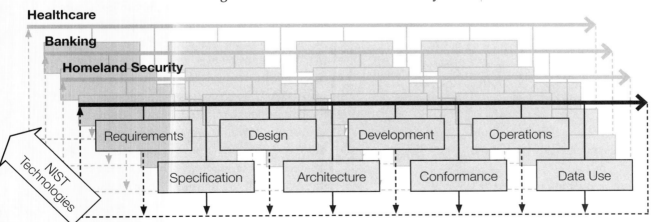

Source: Internal Planning Document

viewed as integral to the ongoing "health" of a program, component, or system to be applied consistently throughout the life-cycle in order to ensure continuous performance. This approach ensures that functionality is maintained when

> *"Ideally, testing, like security, should be viewed as integral to the ongoing "health" of a program, component, or system to be applied consistently throughout the life-cycle in order to ensure continuous performance."*

patches, updates, or upgrades to the component are applied; or when complementary, interacting, and interoperable programs are patched, updated, or enhanced. Whether it be a wholesale change in operating system, application of a new service pack, or upgrade to a co-functioning application, retesting for performance and conformance are essential. Validation and testing certifications normally will not automatically carry over to revised software except under policies set forth by the accreditation body. Unfortunately, few implementers or users understand this, and vendors have been known to change software AFTER conformance testing. Moreover, while there are numerous tests that can be applied to individual software programs or components,

> *"Current trends suggest that future software systems may appear as collections of distributed components that combine and recombine dynamically in response to changing conditions. Such dynamic environments will require new analysis approaches and tools for software design ."*

there are few formalized, objective third-party conformance testing programs for integrated systems.

Finally, there will be extensive research needed to develop future generations of tests for the complex systems of the future. "Current trends suggest that future software systems may appear as collections of distributed components that combine and recombine dynamically in response to changing conditions. Such dynamic environments will require new analysis approaches and tools for software design (Dabrowski and Mills, 2002)." Furthermore, complex systems and networks are becoming so difficult to understand, monitor, and predict in behavior, that the need is arising to include "smart code" in them, which mimics the behavior of human operators, maintainers, and builders. By studying the behavior of several sample complex systems (e.g., electronic health records, large scale building structures, Internet commerce), abstract models of complex systems can be developed that identify salient common characteristics. Once the characteristics of these systems are identified, meaningful metrics associated with these characteristics can be developed, facilitating new methods and tools to make complex systems easier to design, develop, test, and manage. New conformance testing programs and paradigms will need to be developed and adopted.

Summary

Many good testing methods and programs exist today. Users are beginning to be aware of and to demand such standardized approaches in order to build trust and confidence in the computers and networks on which society depends. The programs noted above are but a sampling of some of the better known implementations. Yet, there is much to be done to fill in some very significant gaps in the measurement science of testing. Testing methodologies need to be generic to many communities, individuals, business, and economic sectors. And, testing must be extended beyond the component level to the integration and interoperation of components as systems become more complex in the near future. Research is needed to understand the characteristics of these dynamic, sometimes ephemeral interconnecting components, and new paradigms of conformance testing programs will need to be designed.

Acknowledgements

The author gratefully acknowledges the support provided by Kirk Dohne, Information Technology Specialist, in preparation of this paper during several hours of discussion and in written comments on an earlier draft. Ms. Kathleen Roberts, Mr. Mark Skall, and Dr. Ronald Boisvert of the Information Technology Laboratory provided excellent editorial comments.

Notes

1. Certain commercial products or company names are identified in this report to describe NIST programs adequately. Such identification is not intended to imply recommendation or endorsement by the National Institute of Standards and Technology, nor is it intended to imply that the products or names identified are necessarily the best available for the purpose.

2. Webster's II: New Riverside University Dictionary defines the terms used in the Competency-Based Model of Trust and Confidence as follows:

- Requirement – to have as a requisite: need; to impose an obligation on: compel.

- Specification – an act of specifying; a detailed and exact statement of particulars, esp. a statement pre-scribing materials, dimensions, and workmanship for something to be built, installed, or manufactured.

- Design – to conceive in the mind: invent; to form a plan for; to plan by making a preliminary sketch, outline or drawing.

- Architecture – the art and science of designing and erecting buildings; design or system perceived by humans.

- Conformance – conformity; likeness in form or character: agreement; action in correspondence with prevailing customs, rules, or styles.

- Implementation – to put into effect: carry out

- Operations – a process or series of acts aimed at producing a desired result or effect; an action resulting from a single computer instruction.

- Data Use – use of factual information as a basis for reasoning, discussion, or calculation.

3. Information on the mentioned NIST programs can generally be found at http://www.nist.gov/ and http://www.itl.nist.gov/.

Bibliography

Dabrowski, Christopher, and Mills, Kevin, "Analyzing Properties and Behavior of Service Discovery Protocols Using an Architecture-Based Approach," *Working Conference on Complex and Dynamic Systems Architectures*, Brisbane, Australia, December 2001.

Harris, Shon, *All-in-One, CISSP Certification, Exam Guide*, McGraw-Hill/Osborne, Berkeley, California, U.S.A., 2002.

ISO/IEC 17025: 1999, "General requirements for the competence of testing and calibration laboratories."

Judge, Paul, editor, *Business Week Online*, Newsmaker Q&A, "The Guru of Zero-Defect Software Speaks Out; Watts Humphrey says his procedures could help developers cut costs in half. And if the U.S. hasn't yet taken notice, India sure has," March 1, 2000.

National Institute of Standards and Technology, *Cryptographic Module Validation Program, Frequently Asked Questions*, November 2003.

National Institute of Standards and Technology, *Federal Information Processing Standard, FIPS 197*, "Advanced Encryption Standard," February 2001.

National Institute of Standards and Technology, *Federal Information Processing Standard, FIPS 186-2*, "Digital Signature Standard," February 2000.

National Institute of Standards and Technology (USA), Communications Security Establishment (Canada), *Implementation Guidance for FIPS Pub 140-2 and the Cryptographic Module Validation Program (CMVP)*, pdf 9-11-03, http://csrc.nist.gov/cryptval, initial release March 3 2003, last update September 11, 2003.

National Institute of Standards and Technology, Program Office, Strategic Planning and Economic Analysis Group, *Planning Report, 02-3*, "The Economic Costs of Inadequate Infrastructure for Software Testing, " prepared by RTI, May 2002.

Rosenthal, Lynne, Skall, Mark and Carnahan, Lisa, "Conformance Testing and Certification Framework," NIST, http://www.itl.nist.gov/div897/ctg/conformance/ebxml-test-framework.pdf, April, 2001.

Schneier, Bruce, *Secrets and Lies, Digital Security in a Networked World*, John Wiley & Sons, Inc., USA, 2000, pp. 207-210.

15

Internet Technical Standard Setting Bodies: The Public Policy Venues of the Twenty-First Century

JOHN MORRIS, JR.
Center for Democracy and Technology

ALAN DAVIDSON
Center for Democracy and Technology

Abstract: *Technical design decisions about the Internet and the communications protocols on which it is based can have dramatic and sometimes harmful impacts on public policy concerns such as privacy and free expression. Most of the design decisions are made far from the public eye, in technical standards setting bodies such as the Internet Engineering Task Force and the World Wide Web Consortium. This chapter looks at the need to ensure that public policy concerns are appropriately considered and addressed within the standards bodies. To ensure that the Internet continues to develop with positive public policy impacts, there must be greater public and public interest participation in the standards processes, and the standards bodies themselves must move toward new procedures to consider and address the public interest. Both government and industry leaders should actively support the development of tools for public policy impact assessment.*

Introduction

It is now widely understood that technical design decisions about the Internet can have lasting impacts on public policy and individual rights. The concept that "code is law" has been most recently and most accessibly explained by Professor Lawrence Lessig, but it follows a rich literature on the impact of

technology on society and policy.[1] This reality raises a critical question: How can public policy considerations, and the public interest generally, be best accounted for in the development of the Internet's "code?"

This chapter suggests a multipart answer to this question. First and foremost, there is a critical need to promote increased participation of public policy experts and advocates in the technical standards setting bodies. But that participation alone is not enough—a more systematic approach is also needed to ensure that the public policy impacts are carefully considered. The authors propose moderate but important changes that can be made in the Internet standards development processes to maximize the possibility that public policy impacts will be recognized and considered early in the design process.[2]

Since 2000, the Internet Standards, Technology, and Policy Project of the Center for Democracy & Technology (CDT) has explored the public interest in information and communications technology (ICT) standards. The Standards Project has participated in the work of key Internet standards bodies, engaged technologists and policy experts, and undertaken to inform and educate other policy advocates and policymakers about the ICT standards processes. Based on the experience of the Standards Project, this chapter looks at approaches intended to ensure that public policy issues are appropriately considered in the standards setting process. By seeking to institutionalize the consideration of public policy concerns within standards development, the authors hope to ensure that the architecture of the future Internet is crafted with the public interest in mind. And critically, this approach to addressing policy concerns within the existing structures and processes of the standards bodies will allow the public interest to be protected without inviting legislative or regulatory intervention in the evolution and development of the Internet.

The Public Interest in Internet Standards

In terms of both substance and process, the public has a strong interest in the development of the technical standards on which the Internet is based. Many standards are highly technical and arcane, and have little direct impact on social values or public policy. But in a small but growing percentage of cases, standards can dramatically influence policy concerns. For standards with a direct impact on issues of public concern, the development process often does not fully recognize the potential public policy impacts, much less address those impacts adequately.

Policy impacts of technical standards

Technical standards, from building codes to "generally accepted accounting principles," can have important impacts on public policy concerns, and this is especially true in the field of information and communications technology (ICT) standards.[3] In the Internet space, standards are crucially important. Indeed, the very existence of the Internet itself originated in and is built on technical standards—the core concept of the Internet is that diverse and quite different computers and networks can communicate with each other through the use of well defined communications and network protocols.

Decisions about technical design standards are most commonly made in private bodies—such as the Internet Engineering Task Force (IETF) and the World Wide Web Consortium (W3C)—that set technical standards for the Internet. These and other key standards bodies operate largely outside of the public eye and with little involvement of public interest groups or policymakers. Once the sole province of engineers, academics, and industry, Internet and other ICT technical decisions can increasingly have far-reaching implications on property rights, personal privacy concerns, and the public's access to information.

The broad societal embrace of Internet technologies is fueling the public's interest in the Internet's future course of development. As the Internet is used by a wider segment of society for a wider range of uses, changes to the Internet have a correspondingly wider impact. The rapid pace of change in Internet technology also makes its standards of continuing importance and broad impact.

The example of IPv6 addressing

The development by the IETF of "Internet Protocol Version 6" or "IPv6" provides one example of the ways that technical design decisions can directly impact public policy concerns. In 1998, an IETF standard describing IPv6, a new protocol for Internet addressing, set off a major controversy about user privacy and anonymity.[4] Under IPv4, the predecessor to IPv6, Internet addressing allowed a reasonable amount of privacy and anonymity, because the numeric IP address (such as 206.112.85.61) was typically not tied to any particular machine or user. With IPv6, however, the standard provided that in many cases a user's IP address would be derived from a unique number embedded in that user's Ethernet network card. IPv6 would therefore enable greater monitoring of users' online behavior since their IP address would be tied to a unique identifier. Thus, for example, a particular laptop computer would be widely identifiable and traceable when it communicated online, no matter where or how the computer was connected to the Internet.

The privacy implications of the new IPv6 address scheme likely were not intended or even fully recognized by its original designers—the use of a unique hardware ID was a clever and efficient technical approach to generating unique IP addresses. But once the concerns were raised, significant debate ensued both in the public policy space and among technologists. The issue was ultimately resolved by the IETF with publication of an optional addressing scheme for IPv6 that added privacy-protecting alternatives to the original design.[5]

IPv6 provides just one example of the wide array of situations in which information and communications technologies standards setting affects public policy concerns. Other recent examples[6] of policy questions raised by technical standards include: (a) whether wireless location-tracking technologies will allow users to control who can track their location, (b) whether standards for electronic "e-books" will accommodate the needs of blind users, (c) whether "digital rights management" technologies to protect intellectual property will allow users to make lawful "fair use" of copyrighted content, and (d) whether third parties will be able to modify, without permission, Internet content as it is transmitted from the sender to the recipient.

Policy consideration within technical standards bodies

Public policy concerns do arise and are considered within standards processes, but almost always on an ad hoc basis. This ad hoc approach to public policy concerns presents at least two major problems—the lack of systematic analysis of public policy issues, and the lack of "public" or other outside input into the analysis that does take place.

Though many technologists within the leading standards bodies are public-minded, few have explicit expertise in policymaking or at interpreting the public interest. Standards organizations have typically (and appropriately) emphasized technical goals over broad societal

ones, but in the Internet's early history there was a significant overlap between the two. Openness, accessibility, anonymity, and robustness were all technical features of the network that became public values as well.

Additionally, since the Internet in its early days was small, the pressure for explicit analysis of public policy concerns was minimal—policy impacts deriving from technical choices would affect just a few people. The Internet's population and diversity of uses has grown enormously since the early days of the network, and technical design decisions now directly affect the online experiences and options of hundreds of

---

"Although many past standards were consistent with the public's interest in a robust and flexible new mode of communication, there is little to suggest that the coincidence will continue."

---

millions of users. Although many past standards were consistent with the public's interest in a robust and flexible new mode of communication, there is little to suggest that the coincidence will continue.

The risk of divergence between standards and the public interest is significantly heightened by the commercialization of the Internet. The introduction in the early 1990s of commercial traffic to the Internet began an influx of private interests to a standards community that had been largely research-oriented. The subsequent explosion in commercial use of the Internet prefigured a significant increase in privately motivated participants in the standards process. This in turn has subtly changed Internet standards-making: While many private sector participants make high-quality contributions to standards, the extent to which participants can be expected to agree about the network's architecture is diminished because of diverging market interests. And because of these changes, there is a growing risk that the public interest in standards could fade into the background of discussion among private interests.

*The value of early identification
of potential policy impacts*

In many cases, harmful impacts on public policy concerns can be avoided if they are considered early in the technology design process. Raising policy issues early is essential. The standards design process often takes between 18 and 36 months, and marketplace deployment may be months later. If policy concerns are not raised until after a standard is finalized, or after products are deployed, the chance of constructive change is very low. Legislative or regulatory fiat cannot inject into a service or product technical capabilities that were not designed in the first place, and can often at best only restart a lengthy standards design process. In many cases, post-design regulation is powerless to put a harmful technological genie back in the bottle.

From a public policy perspective, the key question is how to obtain an outcome in the standards design process that appropriately balances both technical/engineering considerations and public policy concerns. The effort to obtain a desirable outcome will in many cases, as discussed below, require the active participation of public policy advocates in the standards design process. But an even more threshold question is how can both the standards development and public interest communities even identify the design efforts that might impact public policy. Even the direct recognition of a potential policy impact is alone likely to improve the handling of the policy concern.

The Need for Public Interest Engagement with Internet Technical Standards

If standards bodies impact policy, and have few mechanisms for accounting for public interests, how can those interests be included? The model of direct government intervention and control over standards development is unlikely to promote the continued innovative development of the global Internet. Instead, the participation and intervention by representatives of public interest organizations is a more natural, and ultimately more effective, place to start.

Government mandate or control is not the answer

As a threshold matter, we note that—in the United States—direct government intervention in standards processes remains a controversial and, at least for now, a highly disfavored approach. Government engagement in technical standards has long been a subject of debate.[7] The problems of governmental control are aggravated in the Internet context.

Most critically, government intervention is suspect due to the complexity of the technical issues presented, the rapid pace of change, and the lack of government expertise. Traditional government decisionmaking venues and processes (whether administrative agencies or legislatures) are commonly too slow and too broad brush for the highly focused and technical design decisions that are made every day within the technical standards bodies. Moreover, the vast bulk of technical knowledge about the inner workings of the Internet resides in the private and academic entities that have had primary responsibility for the development of the network.

Equally critical is the fact that the Internet is a global medium, and its continued development should not be controlled or dominated by one or a few governments. Already we have seen global resistance to the role that the United States Department of Commerce plays in overseeing the management of the Internet's Domain Name System. Greater government intervention can only exacerbate this problem.

This is not to say that governments cannot productively participate in the work of technical design bodies. Although not without some culture clashes, governmental representatives have made important contributions, for example, to the work of the "Internet Emergency Preparedness" Working Group of the Internet Engineering Task Force.[8] Greater and broader government input (without any accompanying mandate) can only serve to increase the public policy robustness of Internet technical design standards.

Can public interest participation in technical standards setting be effective?

Compared to government mandates, the possible contributions of non-governmental organizations is more in synch with the private sector orientation of most ICT and Internet standards development. Over the past fifty years, public interest advocates and advocacy groups have played a vital role in the development of public policy. Historically, this advocacy has focused on traditional policy making venues of legislatures and regulatory agencies, in addition to advocacy in both the courts and the court of public opinion.

Technical standards setting bodies, however, are a radically different type of venue, and the traditional approaches used by public interest

---

> *"...the traditional approaches used by public interest advocates do not easily translate to the technical fora of the standards bodies."*

---

advocates do not easily translate to the technical fora of the standards bodies. Only recently have public interest organizations attempted to participate in Internet technical standards setting processes. That experience, including the work of CDT's Standards Project, indicates that direct public interest involvement in standards development efforts can be effective in identifying issues of public concern, spurring analysis of such issues, and promoting approaches and results that further the public interest.

In some cases, public interest participation has been a part of a technical design effort from its inception. In 1997, the World Wide Web Consortium (W3C) undertook to develop the Platform for Privacy Preferences (P3P) as a specification that enables web sites to express—in a machine-readable way—their practices with regard to users' personally identifiable information. P3P permits users to quickly interpret privacy policies whose complexity might otherwise be disarming, and to make informed choices about disclosure. Numerous members of the public advocacy community and Internet industry

participated actively in P3P's development, providing extensive input into the vocabulary P3P uses to describe all the various practices and implications for personally identifiable information. Since its release, P3P has been adopted by thousands of web sites, and is now built into the leading World Wide Web browser in use today. Public interest participation proved to be a critical element of the P3P development process.[9]

In other cases, public interest advocates have injected themselves into existing standards discussions to raise issues of public concern. In 2000 and 2001, the Internet Engineering Task Force (IETF) community struggled with the question of whether to charter a proposed working group on "Open Pluggable Edge Services" (OPES). The proposed OPES protocol would permit operators of servers in the middle of the Internet to modify content in midstream from a server to a user, raising significant questions about censorship, data integrity, and user privacy. In 2001, joining some critics within the IETF, public policy advocates submitted to the IETF extensive comments about the public policy issues raised by OPES. In response to the concerns raised, the Internet Architecture Board (which provides architectural guidance to the IETF), in late 2001, undertook an extensive review of the OPES proposals and recommended that any work on OPES include strong protections for data security and privacy. The input of public interest advocates in the OPES debate helped to crystallize the issues raised by the proposal, and made clear to the IETF community that outside groups shared many of the concerns raised by some within the IETF.[10]

In another interaction with the IETF, public policy advocates have played a major role in the development of a protocol for privacy protection in location-tracking and location-dependent services. Working within the Geopriv Working Group, public policy advocates have pushed the IETF to include strong protections for privacy in any transmission that sends location information. The way that users can express their location privacy and security preferences will likely have a broad impact on user privacy and control.

Although very much a "work in progress," the Geopriv effort shows the potential for cooperation between standards technologists and the privacy community.[11]

To be effective, however, public interest advocates must bring to a standards discussion a strong technical understanding of a proposed standard and its context. Moreover, advocates must be prepared to commit substantial investments of time and energy necessary to follow

---

"To the maximum extent possible, advocates must raise public policy concerns using the procedures and terminology of the standards body."

---

ongoing internal discussions about a given policy proposal. To the maximum extent possible, advocates must raise public policy concerns using the procedures and terminology of the standards body. When carefully done, public policy input into technical standards setting processes can make a significant contribution to the development of technology that is sensitive to public concerns.

Is public interest participation necessary?

Not only can public interest involvement make valuable contributions to technical standards design efforts, such involvement is essential over the long run. Although technologists within standards bodies do at times identify public policy concerns, public policy input is still needed for a variety of reasons:

- Just as technical issues can be subtle, policy concerns can also be subtle, and some concerns will be overlooked entirely without direct public policy consideration of a technical proposal.

- Although some policy issues are identified by the technical participants themselves, the resolution of the concern at times requires an added level of experience with the policy concern to be able to evaluate the gravity of the policy threat and the sufficiency of proposed solutions.

- Increasingly, private and commercial agendas are being pursued within technical standards bodies (attempting, for example, to push a technology through quickly without addressing inconveniences such as privacy considerations), and public concerns will be overlooked or inadequately addressed without participants whose primary agenda is the public interest.

- More generally, technologists are often quick to acknowledge that they lack expertise in legal or policy issues, and they are thus hesitant to address a public policy concern without direct input from experts in the field.

For these and other reasons, it is vitally important that public interest advocates continue and increase their level of participation in Internet technical standards setting bodies.

Is public interest participation sufficient?

Although public interest participation should be a vital element of the appropriate consideration of public policy concerns in technical standards bodies, it is not sufficient for a variety of reasons. With unlimited financial and human resources, direct involvement might be able to adequately address the public interest, but given the realities of funding and resources, public interest advocates alone are not sufficient. There are a number of factors that suggest that direct public interest involvement will always be inadequate:

- Ongoing and active participation in a standards working group requires a very significant commitment of time (with the general guideline that meaningful participation in a technical working group requires a baseline of approximately 20% of an individual's time).

- Effective public advocacy within the technical standards bodies requires the right mix of technical knowledge (or ability to learn) with public policy experience, which somewhat limits the pool of possible advocates.

- The time horizons for standards development efforts is very long, and may be too long to garner the dedicated attention of many public interest organizations that are balancing scarce resources and immediate policy crises.

- Many standards bodies have an institutional or cultural resistance to addressing public policy issues, often based on past experience with public policy advocates who failed to tailor their message to the forum.

- The sheer size, number, and diversity of technical standards setting bodies means that public interest advocates will not be able to "cover the whole waterfront" of standards bodies—there simply are too many standards working groups and task forces for the public interest community to cover.

In light of the importance of protecting the public interest in the development of technical standards, and the lack of capacity of the public interest community to accomplish that task alone, it is clear that the technical bodies should undertake concrete internal steps to identify and begin to address public policy issues that arise within their standards development efforts.

The Need for Systemic Change in Internet Standards Bodies to Address Public Policy

As described above:

- some, but not all, technical standards activities can have broad policy implications;

- there are major benefits to considering those impacts early in the design process; and

- participation by policy experts and interest groups is not alone sufficient.

Therefore, a more systemic approach to public policy issues is desirable. Such an approach is more likely to be effective at raising policy issues early in the design process, especially if it can be reasonably implemented within the existing procedures of standards bodies.

Corporate and governmental leaders should endorse systemic change

Historically some standards bodies have sought to avoid public policy issues and

debates, at least in part because some view policy debates as (in the vernacular of the Internet standards world) "ratholes" down which unlimited amounts of time and energy can flow. And recently, some corporate participants appear to prefer working in standards bodies thought to be less concerned about ensuring that a new technology is developed with public values in mind. Such views about whether or when to consider public policy concerns, however, are shortsighted.

In a great many cases, public policy concerns about a standard (or about products based on a standard) will arise sooner or later, and the concerns can be far more easily addressed if they are identified early in the standards design process (and well before the product design process). Although identifying and addressing public policy concerns may somewhat extend or complicate the development process, the resulting standard will likely meet with fewer post-development marketplace or regulatory obstacles. The investment of time and effort to address a policy concern early will likely pay off in terms of costs and delays avoided later.

"Cookie" technology introduced by Netscape in the mid-1990s provides a good example of technology that would have benefited from early consideration of public policy concerns.[12] Cookies enable a variety of convenient features, such as online "shopping baskets" and the storing of usernames and passwords needed for particu-

---

"Had personal privacy been considered when cookies were first designed, most of the convenience could have been achieved without all of the accompanying harm to privacy (and the ensuing regulatory response)."

---

lar web sites. But cookie technology can also be used to track web sites visited and other personal information, allowing advertisers and others to develop a broad profile of Internet users. Cookies were a critical contributor to the broad harm to online privacy over the past five years, leading to direct government regulation or legislative proposals aimed at bolstering privacy. Had personal privacy been considered when cookies were first designed, most of the convenience could have been achieved without all of the accompanying harm to privacy (and the ensuing regulatory response).

A proposal for "public policy impact assessments"

A system of "public policy impact assessments" could form the foundation of a strategy for standards bodies to identify and address public policy impacts. The core idea is fairly simple—that technical standards setting bodies should develop a procedure for a relatively brief but focused assessment of new technology proposals to identify whether public policy concerns might be affected. Specifically, such a procedure would ideally be executed internally, usually without the direct involvement of a public policy expert or advocate. Moreover, the key purpose of the public policy assessment is to *identify* policy concerns early in the design process, not to indicate how those concerns should be addressed.

To achieve these key goals, the public policy assessment must be one that looks at technical design issues from the perspective of *the technology designer, not the public policy advocate*. In other words, the assessment must be in terms that are well understood by the community of technologists in the standards body. For example, the public policy assessment process should not ask questions like "does this technology harm privacy?" Instead, the assessment process should break the technology down into components that themselves are known in some cases to harm privacy. Questions that would be more appropriate and constructive would be "does this technology expose information about an end user to a third party?" or "does this technology permit the retention of information about an end user?" Thus, to develop an effective system of public policy impact assessments, abstract public policy concerns must be broken into concrete and familiar technological elements that can be evaluated.

Because of the great diversity of standards bodies (in terms of their focus, structure, and procedures), a single one-size-fits-all (or even one-size-fits-most) public policy impact assessment process may not be effective, for at least two reasons. First, different standards bodies deal with different types of technologies, and thus the public policy issues most likely to arise within each standards body will be different. Similarly, the structure and procedures of different standards bodies may suggest quite different procedural options for actually implementing a public policy assessment process.

In mid-2003, the authors submitted to the Internet Engineering Task Force (IETF) a first draft of a public policy impact assessment for IETF-developed standards. The draft, titled "Public Policy Considerations for Internet Design Decisions,"[13] is considered a "work in progress" and has no official status within the IETF. A key goal of the proposal is to encourage members of the IETF community to think about the specific technical design elements that (a) have a significant potential to raise public policy concerns, and (b) are reasonably likely to arise within IETF standards. Among the design elements discussed are:

- *Bottlenecks and choke points.* Historically, the Internet does not have any single or limited number of points through which communications must flow. Any technology that creates such bottlenecks, even for narrow categories of communications, will create an opportunity for unintended third party or government censorship and control.

- *Discrimination among types of Internet traffic or classes of Internet user.* Historically, most communications on the Internet have received the same handling by the routers and networks that carry Internet traffic. Technology that allows certain traffic to receive priority over other traffic (such as some "quality of service" initiatives) might also be able to be used to discriminate against less wealthy or less powerful groups of Internet users.

- *Persistent identifiers.* Technologies under which individual users receive an identifier that remains the same over time can create concerns about users' anonymity or privacy.

- *Retention of user data.* Any technology that permits the aggregation and/or retention of data about users significantly increases privacy concerns.

The proposed public policy assessments certainly have limitations [14] and will depend in large part on the importance attached to the assessments. But even with limitations, an assessment process can help identify a broad range of public policy concerns, and thereby create the possibility that harmful policy impacts can be avoided.

Other possible innovations for Internet standards setting bodies

Public policy impact assessments would likely be beneficial within a wide variety of standards bodies. But such assessments are not the only steps that standards bodies can take to promote the appropriate handling of public policy concerns. Other approaches may prove beneficial, including:

- *Dedicated policy staff.* By building dedicated internal policy expertise, standards efforts can improve their ability to address policy considerations. For example, the World Wide Web Consortium has expressly structured itself to recognize and respond to the reality that standards affect social and public concerns. Among its components is the "Technology & Society Domain" that specifically seeks to create standards that advance a public purpose. Although the scope and size of the W3C's Technology & Society Domain – which has a staff of ten – may be beyond the capacity of many standards bodies, most standards organizations could follow the W3C's model and dedicate some resources to addressing public policy concerns. At a minimum, standards bodies could dedicate resources to implement and oversee a public policy impact assessment process.

- *Soliciting input.* More generally, standards bodies could make efforts to solicit the participation and input of public policy advocates and organizations in the design process. Some standards and industry bodies (such as W3C) have made such efforts. Other technical bodies (such as CPTWG— Copy Protection Technical Working Group) are so inherently focused on public policy issues that public interest participation naturally occurs. But standards bodies that do not already have public interest involvement could take concrete steps to facilitate such involvement.

- *Heightening sensitivities more broadly.* In the long term, the most effective approach to considering policy implications may be found in heightening awareness and sensitivity among the technologists developing new standards. Making technologists more sensitive to the social context and implications of their work has the potential to incorporate awareness about policy implications into many more technology development efforts. While an ambitious idea, it is one that is increasingly called for in a society so dependent on complex technical systems and facing so many difficulties translating between technical development and policy outcomes.

Conclusion

As we have outlined, in the complex and rapidly-evolving world of Internet and ICT standards, technical decisions can have lasting public policy consequences but are often made without full appreciation of those consequences. Significant social benefits can arise from consideration of those policy impacts early in the technical standards development process – and well before products are actually produced and are difficult or impossible to change.

Engagement by policy experts or public interest advocates is the critical first step towards identifying and addressing public policy concerns raised in the standards processes. But, while such engagement is essential to address policy concerns, it is limited by resources and of Internet and ICT standards efforts. Rather, more systemic approaches to raising awareness about policy are also needed.

A public policy impact assessment process could be a useful tool for many Internet standards bodies, especially where public policy issues are not a central focus or where strong public interest involvement does not already take place. In many cases, routinely asking a set of critical policy impact questions could go a long way towards identifying and addressing potential policy consequences early in the technology development life cycle.

But as noted, good policy assessments are hard to do and face many challenges. Other methods of raising awareness – including more sweeping changes in engineering education and the sensitivities of technologists – may be needed. And assessments are only a critical first step towards identifying public policy impacts before they occur. Assessments alone will not guarantee that public concerns, once identified, will be appropriately addressed. That will likely require direct involvement by policy experts in the design process – and remains a topic in need of greater research, understanding, and ultimately, funding.

Ultimately, both greater public advocate involvement in standards development and evolution of the standards processes themselves can together ensure that issues of public policy concern are recognized and addressed as the Internet continues to evolve—and addressed without the need for governmental control of or intervention into the technical design processes. By ensuring that public policy concerns are appropriately considered, technologists and policy advocates can ensure that the Internet will continue to be the most democratically empowering mode of communications ever developed.

The Center for Democracy and Technology is a nonprofit Internet policy and civil liberties group based in Washington, DC. John Morris is the Director of CDT's "Standards, Technology, and Policy Project," and Alan Davidson is CDT's Associate Director. This paper is based on work made possible through the generous support of the Ford Foundation. The authors wish to acknowledge: Jerry Berman, Matt Blaze, Scott Bradner, Carl Cargill, Lorrie Cranor, Sally Floyd, Becky Lentz, Alison Mankin, Jonathan Peizer, Allen Renear, and Stefaan Verhulst, among many others, for their input, ideas, and feedback on the work of CDT's Standards Project, much of which is found in this paper.

Notes

[1] *See* Lawrence Lessig, Code and Other Laws of Cyberspace (2000); *see also, e.g.,* Helen Nissenbaum, "Values in the Design of Computer Systems," Computers in Society, 38-39, March 1998; Langdon Winner, *Autonomous Technology: Technics-out-of-Control as a Theme in Political Thought* (1977); Lewis Mumford, *The Myth of the Machine* (1966).

[2] Many of the ideas in this chapter have been explored in greater detail in two papers presented by the authors at the Telecommunications Policy Research Conferences. See "Policy Impact Assessments: Considering the Public Interest in Internet Standards Development" (2003), at http://www.cdt.org/publications/pia.pdf; "Strangers in a Strange Land: Public Interest Advocacy and Internet Standards" (2002), at http://www.cdt.org/publications/piais.pdf.

[3] The field of information and communications technology (ICT) broadly covers a range of computer and networking technology, with Internet technology being only one segment of ICT. This chapter focuses on Internet standards development, but the points made here would apply equally to broader ICT standards efforts. For an overview of relevant standards processes, see Carl Cargill, *Information Technology Standardization: Theory, Process, and Organizations* (1989).

[4] *See* "Transmission of IPv6 Packets Over Ethernet Networks," RFC 2464, December 1998, at http://www.ietf.org/rfc/rfc2464.txt. IPv6 was designed, among other purposes, to alleviate a growing shortage of numeric Internet addresses under the current addressing scheme, IPv4. The Internet in 2003 is in a state of transition from IPv4 to IPv6, with the great majority of computers and networks still using IPv4 but a growing number converting to IPv6 (and for the present supporting both protocols).

[5] *See* "Privacy Extensions for Stateless Address Autoconfiguration in IPv6," RFC 3041, January 2001, at http://www.ietf.org/rfc/rfc3041.txt.

6 Other examples are detailed in the authors' submission to the 2002 TPRC Conference, see endnote 2 above, and in publications of CDT's Standards Project, see http://www.cdt.org/standards.

7 *See, e.g.*, Office of Technology Assessment, "Global Standard: Building Blocks for the Future" (1992), at http://www.wws.princeton.edu/cgi-bin/byteserv.prl/~ota/disk1/1992/9220/9220.PDF.

8 *See generally* http://www.ietf.org/html.charters/ieprep-charter.html.

9 The public advocacy involvement in P3P has been described in detail by one of the co-chairs of the P3P development process. See Lorrie Cranor, "The Role of Privacy Advocates and Data Protection Authorities in the Design and Deployment of the Platform for Privacy Preferences," available at http://lorrie.cranor.org/pubs/p3p-cfp2002.html.

10 For a more detailed discussion of OPES, the issues it raises, and CDT's intervention into the debate, see Standards Bulletin 1.02, August 7, 2002, available at http://www.cdt.org/standards/bulletin/1.02.shtml.

11 CDT's Standards Project has been actively involved in GeoPriv since the working group's first meeting in August 2001. Together with other privacy advocates and technologists from private industry, CDT has drafted a variety of documents addressing important privacy priorities for the new standard. *See generally* Standards Bulletin 1.01, May 28, 2002, available at http://www.cdt.org/standards/bulletin/1.01.shtml.

12 To be clear, cookies did not originate in a standards body, but in a single company. Cookies are nevertheless a good illustration of technology that spawned avoidable public policy problems. Details of the original cookie specification are available in "Persistent Client State: HTTP Cookies," <http://wp.netscape.com/newsref/std/cookie_spec.html>.

13 *See* http://www.cdt.org/standards/draft-morris-policy-considerations-00.pdf.

14 The limitations in the proposed assessments are specifically discussed in the authors' submission to the 2003 TPRC Conference, see endnote 2 above.

16

Architecture as Policy[1]

Dale N. Hatfield

Telecommunications Consultant and
Adjunct Professor; Interdisciplinary
Telecommunications Department;
University of Colorado at Boulder

Abstract: *The work of Professor Lawrence Lessig and others have drawn increased attention to the importance of network architectures in public policy. In this paper, I focus on the adequacy of existing institutional arrangements and processes for choosing such architectures in an increasingly complex, deregulated, and competitive telecommunications market. To illustrate the challenges to existing institutional arrangements and processes, I describe two national developments with important public policy implications: the transition from analog to digital television and the design and deployment of wireless E911 services. Drawing upon these two examples, I describe some of the advantages and disadvantages of two broad classes of solutions that might be used to choose network architectures and thereby encourage the more rapid evolution of networks and services that are important not only to our economic and social well-being but also to the safety of life, property, and to homeland security as well.*

In this paper, I address a topic that—as an engineer and telecommunications policy-maker or advisor—has been bothering me for several years. The topic relates to the challenges of network design in an increasingly complex, deregulated, competitive telecommunications market. More specifically, it deals with network architectures. Federal Standard FS-1037C defines a network architecture as the design principles, physical configuration, functional organization, operational procedures, and data formats used as the basis for the design, construction, modification and operation of a communications network. Note that a network architecture is not a detailed design. Rather, as the definition suggests, it is the set of specifications or framework—the broad outline of the network -- within which the detailed design is carried out.

Systems engineers are well aware of the importance of architecture in determining the technical and economic performance of a given network. But the choice of a particular architecture for a public network often has implications that stretch far beyond its internal technical and cost performance. For example, not only does the choice impact on the overall cost/performance delivered to the public, it can also influence the ability of different firms to compete using the network as a platform and thereby significantly influence the pace of innovation.

Of course, one has to look no further than the Internet to find an example of how the choice of an architecture can have broad and profound impacts on society. While a bit of the bloom is off the Internet rose, so to speak, there is no question that the Internet has had—and is having—an enormous effect on our personal, social, economic, and political lives. As a society, we generally believe that those effects are positive as exemplified by our concerns about the digital divide—ensuring that all of our citizens have access to this increasingly powerful tool.

For readers of this book, I hardly need to recite the interrelated notions of openness, modularity, and protocol layering, and the concept of "end-to-end" that define the Internet architecture. With an architecture built upon open and not closed or proprietary standards and with the intelligence and hence ability to create applications residing in user devices at the edge of the network, the Internet—in contrast to the closed, proprietary data networks that preceded it—facilitated, rather than hindered, the development of revolutionary new services such as the World Wide Web. It empowered developers ranging from teenagers working in basements to computer scientists working in the best equipped laboratories. It not only created a potent platform for innovation but also a platform for the wider creation, distribution, and consumption of information content as well—a powerful concept indeed. In short, the architecture of the Internet promotes not only our Nation's competitive policy goals but our free speech goals as well. The Internet clearly demonstrates the broader impact of a particular choice of a network architecture.

My own interest in the broader public policy implications of network architectures stretches all the way back to the Federal Communications Commission's Computer Inquiries starting in the 1960s. But it began in earnest with the Commission's efforts in Computer Inquiry III to influence the design of the incumbent local exchange carriers' networks to reflect Open Network Architecture principles. Those proceedings, in the mid- to late-1980s and lapping over into the early 1990s, largely focused on the architecture of the public switched telephone network—the PSTN. Those efforts to "open up" the existing monopoly local exchange network

largely failed but that is a story for another day.

Towards the latter part of this period, I was following the development of the Internet and I was generally aware of the basic technical advantages of packet switching and statistical multiplexing in the Internet versus the circuit switching and time division multiplexing of the PSTN. However—and I am now somewhat embarrassed to say—that it was not until the publication of the National Research Council report entitled "The Unpredictable Certainty" in 1996 that I really began to appreciate the power of the Internet architecture as I just described it.[2]

I was also influenced by the paper entitled "The Rise of the Stupid Network" by David Isenberg [3] which was released in roughly this same time period and by Kevin Werbach's paper "The Digital Tornado."[4] Only then did I fully appreciate the importance of the Commission's earlier attempts to influence network architectures in Computer Inquiry III and the importance of the network architecture choices made by the early designers of the Internet protocols.

More fundamentally perhaps, while I was well aware that policy and regulation influences network architectures, I was just beginning to appreciate that—as someone put it about that time—"architecture is policy." It was also at about this time that I returned for my second tour of duty at the FCC first as Chief Technologist and then as Chief of the Office of Engineering and Technology (OET) under then Chairman William Kennard.

What really drove home this idea of architecture as policy—for me anyway —was the publication of Professor Lawrence Lessig's book *Codes and Other Laws of Cyberspace* in 1999. [5] I

> "Network architectures truly are becoming an increasingly important component of public policy."

had heard Professor Lessig speak on several occasions—including at the FCC—and I began to more fully comprehend the significance of his idea that just as law—legal codes, markets, and social norms exercise control over individuals—so do network architectures, broadly defined. Network architectures truly are becoming an increasingly important component of public policy.

With this background, I could focus the balance of this paper on some specific, contentious issues involving network architectures—again broadly defined—that have recently been before the Commission. However, rather than focus on specific issues such as Internet Service Provider (ISP) access to cable systems ("cable open access") or Competitive Local Exchange Carrier (CLEC) access to the unbundled network elements (UNEs) of the incumbent local exchange carriers (ILECs), I would like concentrate on a somewhat broader issue.

Having established—hopefully at least—the importance of architecture as a component of national policy, I would like to focus on the adequacy of existing institutional arrangements and processes for choosing such architectures. From my perspective, these processes are coming under intense pressure due to increasing competition, convergence, greater complexity, and an increased reluctance on the part of regulatory entities to make specific technological choices, at least in some instances.

To illustrate the challenges that are facing us, I would like to talk about two national developments with which I have had some personal involvement. The first is the transition from analog to digital television (DTV) and the second is the development and deployment of wireless E911 services.

I first became involved in digital over-the-air television about fifteen years ago when I chaired one of the Working Groups associated with the Commission's Advisory Committee on Advanced Television Services (ACATS). In the intervening years, the importance of the DTV transition has become even more apparent. As a competitive matter, it is important for the over-the-air broadcast industry to make the transition from an analog to a digital network just as the balance of the telecommunications industry has done or is in the late stages of doing. From

a public policy standpoint, it is perhaps even more important because, as a society, we can no longer afford to have broadcasters use six Megahertz of precious radio spectrum—actually more—to transmit a single standard definition television signal.

When I returned to the Commission in 1997, the transition to DTV was going very slowly. There were—and still are—many reasons for the slow pace. For example, there may be strong public benefits from the transition in terms of the amount of valuable radio spectrum returned to the government and put to other, potentially higher-value uses as I suggested above. But to an individual broadcaster or television network, the transition may not produce enough additional advertising revenues to provide an adequate incentive to make the needed investment in new studio and transmitting equipment.

Another difficulty that has slowed down the pace of the transition relates to interconnection or, perhaps more accurately, compatibility issues. Interconnection issues—both between and among different networks and between networks and rapidly increasing types of end user

---

"...interconnection increasingly involves negotiations between competitors who may not have the same incentives or desired time frames for resolving disputes."

---

devices and equipment—are becoming more complex. Not only are there more networks and more entities involved in interconnection or compatibility issues, but the issues increasingly extend to all levels of the protocol stack.

Moreover, interconnection increasingly involves negotiations between competitors who may not have the same incentives or desired time frames for resolving disputes. With different parties controlling different parts of an end-to-end system, there can be a strong incentive to shift costs to someone else in order to lower your own costs. Or there may be incentives to control the intelligence in the network in such a way that others are reduced to supplying low value, commodity-like services or boxes. Similarly, some providers may attempt to close their portion of the network by using patents, copyrights, and trade secrets to prevent others from interconnecting with it. Also, parties may "game the process" in an attempt to gain a performance advantage at the expense of other service or equipment suppliers. The net result of negotiations made under these conditions is apt to be a network architecture that suffers in terms of added costs or decreased performance for society as a whole. In engineering terms, it can lead to a classic case of sub-optimization.

I should emphasize that the DTV network architecture I just referred to is not simply the architecture of any individual network—say the over-the-air terrestrial broadcast network, a Direct Broadcast Satellite (DBS) network, or a cable television network for delivering entertainment video—but rather the interrelated "network of networks" that comprise the entire system for producing, transporting, delivering and displaying such programming.

What I am really saying is that there is no "master architect" that can move us closer to the optimum system. Note that this example points to a well recognized social phenomenon that "centers on the problem that individuals in groups face with the choice of doing what is best for themselves or what is best for the group."[6] The "Prisoner's Dilemma" is a familiar academic example of the phenomenon. I will return to this issue of choosing architectures after I briefly describe wireless E911.

I first got involved in wireless E911 issues during my last tour of duty at the FCC. My office—OET—was involved in some of the narrow technical aspects of the topic, but in the latter part of 2001, after I had left the Commission, they retained me to lead an inquiry into the technical and operational issues affecting the deployment of Wireless Enhanced 911 Services in the United States. I initiated the inquiry in April, 2002 and submitted my report in mid-October of the same year.[7]

In most areas of the country, when you place an emergency call on the wireline network by dialing 911, the call is automatically delivered to a Public Safety Answering Point or PSAP. With Enhanced 911, the telephone number—the calling or callback number—and location information is also conveyed to the appropriate PSAP operator. The latter step requires that a query be made to a database that relates telephone numbers to street addresses. The wireline E911 service has proven to be an extremely important part of the Nation's emergency response system and is credited with saving many lives.

The regulatory interest in extending E911 services to wireless mobile subscribers began in 1993 and, in 1999, the federal Wireless Communications and Public Safety Act was enacted into law. Among other things, the Act established, as a matter of national policy, the goal of extending E911 capabilities to cellular customers. Extending E911 service to wireless subscribers has, among other things, required the development of appropriate location technologies and the modification of the existing E911 infrastructure to transport and process the geographic coordinates of the caller. The continued rapid growth in the number of wireless subscribers, the increasing fraction of all 911 calls placed from cellular phones, and the trend for some consumers to substitute a wireless phone for their traditional landline phone, has served to add further impetus to the Congressional finding. In retaining me to conduct the study, the Commission was concerned about technical and operational problems that might be slowing the deployment of wireless E911.

I won't take the space to summarize all of the findings and recommendations contained in my report. I do, however, want to point to one finding that relates directly to the topic of this paper, which is centered on the challenges of overall network design in an increasingly complex, deregulated, competitive telecommunications market.

In order to architect, design and deploy wireless E911 in the United States, cooperation is required not only of some 6,000 PSAPs but thousands of commercial stakeholders as well. These commercial stakeholder groups include, among others, (1) the Commercial Mobile Radio Service (CMRS) providers who are subject to Commission's rules on wireless E911, (2) hundreds if not

---

"In order to architect, design and deploy wireless E911 in the United States, cooperation is required not only of some 6,000 PSAPs but thousands of commercial stakeholders as well."

---

thousands of local exchange carriers, including both the Incumbent Local Exchange Carriers and the emerging Competitive Local Exchange Carriers, (3) a host of equipment suppliers, including not only the traditional suppliers of network infrastructure equipment to the wireline and wireless industry but also the developers and suppliers of wireless position location hardware and software and the Customer Premises Equipment utilized by PSAPs in the handling of E911 calls, (4) a large group of handset manufacturers, (5) a number of entities that offer aspects of wireless E911 services on a third party basis, and (5) a raft of systems integrators, consultants, and advisors that are employed in various capacities throughout the industry to support the rollout of wireless E911.

Within this complex environment, critical network architecture choices are being made that will have a profound and lasting impact on the public's interest in a robust and seamless E911 system. These choices will also have a major impact on the extent to which competition develops in the provision of E911 services and, hence, on the speed of innovation in emergency communications systems. The choice of network elements—both hardware and software—and the associated degree of modularity influences performance and the extent to which competition can develop. Similarly, network designs based upon open architecture principles and standardized rather than proprietary interfaces between network elements can facilitate competition but can also raise issues of diminished economic incentives, security, and privacy. Choices

as to who owns or controls the necessary intelligence (e.g., the processor-based logic used to provide E911 services) and the associated data bases (e.g., the automatic location information data base I alluded to earlier) and where that intelligence and information resides influence network performance, including network reliability and availability, in fundamental ways. Resolution of these questions of ownership and control will also influence the eventual development of competitive commercial location based services and telematic systems more generally.

This complex environment is in contrast to the early development of wireline 911 that occurred prior to the divestiture of the Bell Operating Companies from AT&T in 1984. During this earlier period, the necessary system engineering functions—the architectural choices if you will—were largely carried out within the Bell System in response to public safety requirements. Since only the local telephone companies and their public safety customers were involved and since provision of local telephone service was regarded as a monopoly service and regulated as such, the necessary systems engineering could be carried out *within* the Bell System under traditional regulatory oversight. Indeed, the Bell System—through Western Electric— even supplied most of the necessary equipment, further easing the coordination required.

"Once again, stakeholders are put in the position of choosing between what is best for them or what is best for the system (and the public) as a whole."

As I pointed out above, however, the situation today is much more complex. As in the case of DTV, not only are there more stakeholders involved, their interrelationships are much more complex and the stakeholders themselves have different incentives and varying degrees of ability to influence critical engineering choices. Once again, stakeholders are put in the position of choosing between what is best for them or what is best for the system (and the public) as a whole.

During my meetings with stakeholders and stakeholder groups while I was collecting information for my report, it was pointed out to me—often with a high degree of frustration—that there is no longer a single organization charged with the overall system engineering function. That is, to use the term I coined earlier, there is no "master architect." Various entities—such as standards-making bodies -- have important responsibility for parts of the system. I don't mean to imply otherwise.

However, there is no entity charged with examining how the parts fit together and how they might be redesigned or reconfigured to improve end-to-end performance or reduce the overall costs of meeting the requirements spelled out in the Commission's rules. Likewise, there is no single entity charged with carrying out the system engineering studies necessary to develop the means to accommodate changing technology and changing requirements at minimal overall cost.

Before I conclude by suggesting some possible solutions to this issue, let me briefly summarize my arguments so far. *First,* I have argued—as Larry Lessig and others have argued more eloquently than I—that "architecture matters." The architecture of public networks is a matter of public concern. Architecture is policy. I used the architecture of the Internet and its success to bolster my argument. *Second,* I have argued that the task of choosing network architectures is becoming increasingly difficult because of increasing competition, convergence, and greater complexity (e.g., in terms of the number of stakeholder groups involved). I have argued that the complexity can lead to classic forms of sub-optimization when stakeholders are put in the position of choosing between doing what is best for them or what is best for the system as a whole. I used the rollout of digital television and wireless E911 services as examples of where this complexity has led to—or at least contributed strongly to—the delay in the deployment of services that are important to our economic and social well being. *Third,* and this is the subject of the balance of this paper,

I have suggested that there may be a need for "master architects" or at least better processes that can respond to this increased complexity. The idea is that they would, in each instance, move us closer to "optimum" solutions—architectures—while facilitating a more rapid rollout of services that are important not only to our economic wellbeing, but also to the safety of life, property, and to homeland security.

As a threshold matter—and this shows some of my own policy biases—I think that any new processes should be centered in the private sector. After all, it is ultimately the private sector that will have to invest the capital and take the risks of any changes in architecture. However, as I pointed out in my two examples, individual stakeholders may lack the necessary incentives to take actions that benefit the network as a whole. Indeed, I have argued that they may have an incentive to shift costs to others or, if they have a degree of market power in one segment of the network, to adopt interconnection or other restrictions which improve their own competitive prospects at the expense of the network as a whole. Because of these and other factors, purely voluntary negotiations between and among stakeholder groups—often competitors—may not occur and even if they do

> *"The fundamental questions, then, become whether, and if so, when and how the government gets involved in choosing architectures."*

occur they may not move us toward an optimal architecture.

The fundamental questions, then, become whether, and if so, when and how the government gets involved in choosing architectures. Clearly, the government needs to get involved when some clearly understood public policy goal is being thwarted or unreasonably delayed by the private sectors failure to reach *purely* voluntary agreements because of the perverse incentives—or lack of incentives—that I described before. Because of the valuable radio spectrum involved in the transition to DTV and the impact of that transition on ordinary consumers and because of the critical role that E911 systems play in our Nation's emergency response system, I am convinced that both of them fall into that category. But my focus here is not on those two specific examples; rather it is on the more general issue of how the process of choosing architectures might be improved.

I can identify several alternatives for answering the "how" part of the question. Broadly speaking, these alternatives can be divided into two categories. For convenience, I will refer to the first category as informal and the second as formal. In the first approach, the government facilitates voluntary agreements among the stakeholder groups through informal means including the use of the "bully pulpit" or "jawboning." In the second approach, the appropriate government agency embarks upon a formal rulemaking process, perhaps supported by a public advisory committee established under the Federal Advisory Committee Act. In this formal approach, the necessary solutions—changes in architecture—would be legally mandated and then enforced in the normal way.

While the public interest and consumer welfare clearly favor the formal rulemaking approach in some situations, there are also a host of problems associated with it. First of all, by its very nature, the formal rulemaking process is time consuming and often resource intensive. Second, and on a related point, the inherent delays in the formal rulemaking process (which often encounter additional delays because of judicial appeals) make it difficult to change standards, for example, within a time frame that is compatible with today's product cycles. Third, because of budgetary and other constraints, it is often difficult for the regulatory agency to recruit and retain the necessary qualified personnel to make detailed technical decisions. Fourth, in certain situations at least, mandatory performance standards, for example, may prevent consumers from making desirable tradeoffs between cost and performance on a smaller scale and producers may regard them as a ceiling—

"all that the government requires"—rather than a competitive floor.

For these and other reasons, the alternative, informal or voluntary, approach would appear have a significant amount of appeal. Government facilitation of voluntary agreements can range from doing little more than suggesting that the stakeholders meet and negotiate to heavy government involvement in the meetings and intense jawboning. Despite its many advantages, the informal, voluntary approach has problems as well. First, it does not fundamentally change the underlying incentives of the stakeholders while the threat of an enforcement action under the formal approach does. Second, to be really effective, jawboning—getting stakeholders to take action that they would not otherwise like to take—assumes that the regulator has some authority over them. Without it, the stakeholder can simply ignore the informal entreaties of the regulator. For instance, the FCC does not have legal jurisdiction over some of the important stakeholders in either the DTV and wireless E911 examples that I described before. Fourth, the formal rulemaking process imposes certain procedural obligations on the agency—in terms of openness and transparency—that may not be present with informal jawboning. Hence, ordinary consumers or small firms, for example, may effectively be closed out of such negotiations with little or no recourse to normal procedural safeguards.

In actuality, of course, in both the DTV transition and the wireless E911 examples, the FCC has used combinations of formal and informal methods for influencing the respective technical choices and facilitating the rollout of the systems. However, when viewed from a broader "network of networks" perspective, they have been somewhat piecemeal. In the case of E911, I concluded in my report that the lack of a "master architect"—an entity charged with the responsibility for the overall system engineering function -- will create an obstacle to the efficient, timely, and cost-effective deployment of wireless E911 in the medium to long term. I also concluded that it will hamper the Nation's ability to extend E911 access to a rapidly growing number of non-traditional devices, systems and networks.

Because of the lack of an entity charged with the responsibility of the overall system engineering function and obstacles that this lack may present to achieving the vision setout by Congress, I recommended that the Commission establish—or cause to have established—such an entity. One possibility I suggested would be for the Commission to establish an advisory organization under the Federal Advisory Committee Act. Clearly the advisory committee would not have the power to dictate changes in network architecture and design. However, it could create a technical framework for the necessary changes, including changes to the network elements, interfaces, and data required to take advantage of improving technologies and changing requirements. I also suggested that, if resources were available, it might be desirable to provide the advisory committee with added analytical capabilities through an arrangement with an independent (of the stakeholders) non-profit entity such as Mitre or RAND.

However, the point that I want to conclude with is not what we as a Nation should be doing about the further development of E911—important as that issue is. Rather, I simply hope that I have (1) further sensitized you to the importance of network architectures in a broad public policy sense and (2) succeeded in getting you thinking about how critical network architectures should be chosen in an increasingly complex, deregulated, convergent, and competitive telecommunications market.

Notes

[1] An earlier version of this paper was presenteds a keynote speech entitled "Challenges of Network Design in an Increasingly Deregulated, Competitive Market" at the IEEE International Symposium on Integrated Network Management (IM 2003), Colorado Springs, March, 2003.

[2] NII 2000 Steering Committee, "The Unpredictable Certainty: information infrastructure 2000," National Research Council, National Academy Press, Washington, 1996 (Available at http://stills.nap.edu/html/unpredictable/index/html)

[3] Isenberg, David S., "The Rise of the Stupid Network," Computer Telephony, August, 1997 (pp. 16-26) (Available at: http://www.hyperorg.com/misc/stupidnet.html)

[4] Werbach, Kevin, "Digital Tornado: the internet and telecommunications policy," Federal Communications Commission, March, 1997 (Available at http://www.fcc.gov/Bureaus/OPP/working_papers/oppwp29.pdf)

[5] Lessig, Lawrence, Code and Other Laws of Cyberspace, Basic Books, New York, 2000.

[6] Felkins, Leon, "Introduction to Public Choice Theory," available at http://www.magnolia.net/~Leonf/sd/pub-choice.html. (Last visited 3/21/03.)

[7] Hatfield, Dale N., "Technical and Operational Issues Impacting the Performance of Wireless E911 Services," October, 2002 (Available at: http://gullfoss2.fcc.gov/prod/ecfs/retrieve.cgi?native_or_pdf=pdf&id_document=6513296239

Section 3

IPR Solutions

Eolas, Rambus, SCO…the very names bring up feelings of consternation or elation, depending on your point of view. Intellectual Property Rights (IPR) remain a tremendous issue in the ICT industry and their impact is increasing. With the recent Eolas ruling, which favored the IP claims of Eolas and the University of California over Microsoft, impacting Microsoft's core products including Internet Explorer and Windows, it is evident that not even the largest companies are immune to the proliferation of patents and lawsuits. If we are lucky, this case may spur industry into a concerted action to address the IPR problem once and for all. If we are not so lucky or do not drive this collaboration, the ICT industry will continue to strain under this severe dynamic tension, always looking back to detect potential lawsuits or hiding its head in the sand to try and avoid them, until plausible solutions are agreed upon.

Can standardization act as a tool to help manage this tension and bring it more into balance? Should governments be involved in setting national or international guidelines on IPR policies in standardization bodies to facilitate this? Should there be a single IPR policy for all standards setting organizations? What happens when an SSO's members adhere to its IPR policies, only to be undermined by a company outside of the process as in the Eolas case? Is innovation truly served when small companies are barred from entering markets because they can't participate in cross-licensing agreements? Are there other solutions besides RAND and Royalty Free? These are just some of the questions that the mere mention of the term IPR brings to mind; questions that impact the standardization system and that the ICT industry must successfully address if it is to flourish. While many of these issues are beyond the scope of this book, this section does look at IPR choices and strategies from a company and a government perspective, proposing changes and alternative solutions in addition to the more traditional approaches of RAND and Royalty Free.

Companies face a choice in how they manage their intellectual property. The traditional approach has been to protect it at all costs, using it to ensure cross-licensing agreements as well as generate revenues. In this section, Larry Johnson examines conditions in which this strategy can actually prove detrimental to companies and may produce a negative return on investment. Similar to the strategy of "letting go" described in the "Introduction" of this book, releasing certain intellectual property may actually prove more beneficial to its owners than protecting it.

No article in this book illustrates the concept of dynamic tension stretched too tight more than Tineke Egyedi's article on "IPR Paralysis in Standardization." By citing numerous examples that include GSM and JAVA™, Egyedi argues that compatibility serves the public good at least as well as IPR policies. And standards obviously play a significant role in facilitating compatibility. In fact, DIN found that "From a macroeconomic perspective, it is significant that standards make a greater contribution to economic growth than patents or licences, that export-oriented sectors of industry make use of standards as a strategy in opening up new markets, and that standards help technological change."[1]

Finally, Toru Yamauchi from Japan's Ministry of Economy, Trade, and Industry (METI), who is tasked with creating Japan's IPR policy, discusses the findings of several government reports and looks at possible IPR policy solutions. And Mitsubishi Research Institute, who is working closely with METI, takes a closer look at these reports before providing its own suggestions for IPR solutions.

IPR policies created around the world, whether in standards setting organizations or by governments themselves, will impact innovation, market size and acceptance, and even trade. If industry does not solve this problem, most assuredly government will. Without a solution, the ICT industry risks suffocating itself in a pool of its own lawsuits. With agreed upon solutions, the ICT industry can continue to grow with the confidence and reassurance that its innovations will be allowed to prosper. The best solutions are not directly evident, nor will they be arrived at in a single meeting. However, effort exerted now towards building a solid IPR framework in the information and communications technology industry—even if that effort creates more tension in the short term—will serve to protect the growth of that industry far into the future.

Notes

[1] DIN German Institute for Standardization e.V., April 2000, "Economic Benefits of Standardization: Summary of Results," p. 4.

17

A False Sense of Proprietary

LARRY L. JOHNSON

Enterprise Systems
Architecture Consultant

Abstract: *Organizations often resist standards in order to protect their proprietary information and processes. Protecting proprietary information is essential. However, enterprises often have a misplaced idea of what information is truly proprietary to their business. The protection of information has cost associated with it. While it is important to protect intellectual property, it is also important not to protect that which is part of the broad state of the art. Furthermore, some information increases dramatically in value when shared in a collaborative environment. This article explores the concept of a misplaced sense of what is proprietary, the business case for separating proprietary and nonproprietary information, and the value of standardizing the latter.*

It's Ours... All Ours... Protect It All!

It's a natural reaction. Our team works its fingers to the bone on some piece of support software and we want to protect it. After all, it's the safest thing. If we open ourselves up to the prospect of sharing some of our work, there is danger in making a mistake. The mistake can go one of two ways:

1. **The cat's out of the bag**—If information is shared that shouldn't be, the business can be damaged. Competitors can be given a leg up against us. We can see our developments being offered to our customers by someone else at ridiculously low prices. Our competitive edge can be compromised. The potential for disaster is clear.

2. **Mum's the word**—If information is not shared that could be, what can be the harm? If everything is protected, then all is safe.

So "Mum's the Word" then. With this approach we don't have to think through what could go wrong with sharing the information. "No" is the easy answer and is the knee-jerk reaction of many corporate managers and attorneys because it seems to carry the least potential for disaster.

"Protect it All" has been a common approach in protecting Intellectual Property, but overlooks several aspects of the issue:

1. What is the Cost of Protecting Information?

2. What are the Benefits of Sharing Information?

3. What is Proprietary? Once we decide to share *some* information, how do we decide what should be shared and with *whom*?

The Cost of Protecting Information

Protecting information is not free. There are costs associated with it.

That which is everything is nothing: If common commodity information is under the protection of an organization, employees become numb as to what is truly proprietary. It becomes difficult to recognize the difference between proprietary information and blanket "Mum's the Word" protection. Blanket silence can make it extremely difficult to have a conversation in public venues without stepping on proprietary information, resulting in difficult or impossible enforcement.

Barring the doors: Limiting access to information is a necessity in containing and controlling it. If there are too many "leak-points" in an organization, it is impossible to assess leak sources. If one cannot determine the source of a leak, then one cannot assign culpability. Consequently, all deterrents fail. A costly side-effect of limiting access is the interruption in the flow of information among employees. There is danger that information will not be available to the right people in the organization at the right time. Rapid response to the quickly evolving business milieu requires agility, which in turn requires timely access to information.

Hire more attorneys: A good way to protect innovation is through patents and copyrights, recognized by the courts. The downside of patents is that they must be protected. In order to protect the patents, research must be done to find infringements or to assure that there are none. When infringements are found, remedies must be found (often through the courts). All of this incurs expense.

In summary, the more information is protected as proprietary…

- the more workers must be kept ignorant of the information;
- the less communication among workers takes place;

- the more workers fall out of touch with the technological community; and,
- the more money is spent in detecting and prosecuting infringements on intellectual property.

Consequently, it is essential that only "truly proprietary" information is protected.

The Value of Information Exchange

Having argued the downside of protecting too much information, we have to ask if there is an upside in sharing information.

We can, of course, start with the converse of the above "downside" points…

- **That which is something is useful:** In knowing definitively what is proprietary and what is not, employees can participate freely in the conversations of public forums. This helps the organization keep up to date with developments in technology and with the evolution of their industry's business practices.

- **More open doors:** This leads to a more open flow of information within the organization as well, enabling employees to have maximal access to information needed to conduct day-to-day business and to respond rapidly to unexpected situations.

- **Lower legal and control costs:** With less information to protect, fewer resources need to be applied to controlling and protecting information, and defending patents against infringements.

- **Less is more:** A side-effect of loosening control over nonproprietary information is that the control over truly proprietary information is enhanced. Protection resources can be applied in a focused fashion avoiding the dilution introduced by protecting information unnecessarily.

… but the benefits of information sharing go well beyond this. In many circumstances information can actually become more valuable to an organization by being shared in collaborative efforts. These benefits are explored below in three case studies in collaboration.

But before we do that, we should look at the separation of proprietary and nonproprietary information.

> " In many circumstances information can actually become more valuable to an organization by being shared in collaborative efforts. These benefits are explored below in three case studies in collaboration."

A False Sense of Proprietary

In their book on collaborative research & development, Allen & Jarman write:

"The objective of a company's legal staff should be to provide a legal mechanism to enable you to do what you want in collaboration. However, legal and contracts experts in large manufacturing companies have been well educated and trained in the discipline, to protect the companies intellectual property and to err on the side of too much protection. To do this, they have built fortresses of firewalls and layers of protection around products and processes that come in contact with knowledge property deemed key to existence of the business. While companies must continue to protect and defend the real knowledge based jewels that have competitive value, they must also be flexible and clever enough to find ways to peel away the layers which are not critical, so that value adding operations can be performed. Today, companies choosing collaboration are faced with inflexible legal and contracts people who do not understand or believe in collaboration as a viable means of doing business. Aligning these departments as early as possible in the process is very helpful and time saving."[1]

Effective protection of intellectual property demands that "truly proprietary" information is identified and protected while allowing nonproprietary information to be shared. So how do we "peel away the layers that are not critical"? There is no pat answer. It can be a difficult task, which is why it is not widely done well. "Mum's the Word" seems safe, but of course ignores the cost/benefit issues discussed above, and the greater benefits of information sharing described in the collaborative case studies below.

In order to identify intellectual property, an organization needs to look at its prospectus, formal statements of goals, its business plan, etc. Information that constitutes or directly serves the business case of the organization is that which requires protection.

Part of the difficulty in separating proprietary and nonproprietary information is that there is no sharp boundary, but a continuum of information sensitivity that depends on the business

> "Today, companies choosing collaboration are faced with inflexible legal and contracts people who do not understand or believe in collaboration as a viable means of doing business. Aligning these departments as early as possible in the process is very helpful and time saving."

context. The same information may be protected in one context while not others. For example, information might be shared more freely with a partnering organization while protected from competitors. This sharing with partners needs special constraints if the partnering organization might be a competitor in another contract now or in the future.

An organization might develop elements of computing infrastructure that are not available in the commercial marketplace. Some organizations will protect this information while others may openly share it hoping to encourage the appearance of such software in the market.

Proprietary information must be re-assessed periodically. The proprietary nature of information generally decays over time. That which provides a competitive edge at one point, later becomes commodity technology as the technological approach is adopted throughout an industry segment.

Every organization is unique. It is beyond the scope of this article to provide a detailed formula for sieving information into proprietary and nonproprietary categories. The point is that each organization needs to carefully examine their intellectual property portfolios periodically to assure they are not wasting money by protecting common knowledge and to assure that they are reaping the benefits of information sharing and collaboration.

Case Studies in Collaborative Information Sharing

The most compelling case for correctly identifying and protecting intellectual property, and sharing information that is not intellectual property, can be seen in collaborative efforts for process improvements and research & development. The following three case studies from my experiences at Texas Instrument's Defense Systems Group (TI)[2] exemplify the copious benefits that can be accrued in sharing information. The case studies demonstrate progressive degrees of information sharing and collaboration in Product Data Management (PDM).

Benchmarking: a case study in simple information sharing

From 1982 through 1997 I worked for Texas Instrument's Defense Systems (TI), an aerospace company. TI was among the first to deploy a Product Data Management system. In the mid-1980s, there were no viable commercially available PDM products suitable for our use, so we developed our own system at considerable cost. The manager of TI's PDM Systems Group, Travis Mitchell, had an unusually enlightened approach to the proprietary nature of our PDM Technology… *It isn't*. His directive: "There is nothing we do in PDM that cannot be shared, and we will encourage our partners, competitors, and customers to share as well. We are in the business of making missiles, not in the business of Product Data Management."

His position fit perfectly with a "Benchmarking" program that was being instituted by the company in keeping with the most modern trends in business at the time. In benchmarking, a company establishes a relationship with a competitor or a firm in a similar business to compare notes on "the state of the art" in business areas that the companies have in common. Our benchmarking partner was another aerospace company. The principal difference between our companies was that we made missiles and they made airplanes ("targets" in our perspective).

During the benchmarking process we discovered that the differences in our approaches to PDM were not remarkable. We did some things better, while they did other things better; they did some things that we hadn't thought of and vice versa; but all-in-all things were very similar between the two companies.

Up to the point of benchmarking, both companies felt that their PDM systems were a competitive edge and protected their efforts as proprietary information. Why were the fruits of their efforts remarkably similar? On reflection, this is not all that surprising. The engineers were educated in the same schools, using the same text books. Furthermore, many had moved

---

"Businesses in a particular industrial sector are competing in the same marketplace and have similar requirements. This drives organizations to similar solutions to similar problems."

---

among multiple companies over the course of their careers. Businesses in a particular industrial sector are competing in the same marketplace and have similar requirements. This drives organizations to similar solutions to similar problems.

At the core of the situation… product data management was making the turn from advanced, proprietary practice to commodity technology and business practice, as validated by the emergence of a full and robust commercial market in PDM support systems within a few years. So Travis' position was validated. His call was correct and the company benefited by not suffering the cost of protecting commodity technology and also enjoyed the benefits of sharpening its processes (as did our benchmarking partner).

The benefit of this collaboration was that each company was able to take home plans for improvement in their PDM systems. Each company absorbed the best of each other's system. This enabled them to facilitate their respective business processes, and it is in the business plan and process that real competition takes place. Both companies expend less energy on support systems that are becoming the state of the general art, focusing on their core business plans. And, both companies gain a competitive advantage over companies who expend their energy protecting information that is not in the mainstream of their business case.

Closed consortium: a case study
in aggressive collaboration

Having enjoyed benefits in their benchmarking projects, TI entered into the first Advanced Technology Program issued by the National Institute of Standards and Technology (NIST), the Rapid Response Manufacturing Consortium (RRM).[3]

The RRM program objective was to shorten time-to-market, improve quality-to-cost, and enhance product reliability. The participants included two competitors in the defense industry and two in the automotive industry. The idea was to share information in order to produce "pre-competitive" technology to which each member of the consortium would have rights to develop further into proprietary technology and business processes.

One of the areas addressed in the RRM was Engineering Data Management. TI, Ford, and Oakridge National Laboratories brought their experiences in PDM to the table. By this time (circa 1994) TI had five different PDM systems in various areas of the organization... some commercial... some home grown. Each of the PDM systems had special features that provided special benefits to the department that deployed it. This precluded eliminating all but one vendor

(a simple, but ultimately costly strategy). However, there were many applications that needed to span all PDM data regardless of the system in which they resided.

Ford, TI, and Oakridge in particular shared this problem and teamed together within the consortium to address it. The "Interoperability Services Working Group" (ISWG) was formed to address the problem. In order to integrate disparate systems, the ISWG defined a reference architecture that was suitable for all of the companies. To do this, the consortium members shared their experiences and technical data on the application of PDM systems in the context of their business processes. As an underpinning, the ISWG defined a message-oriented architecture based on the Object Management Group's (OMG)[4] Common Object Request Broker Architecture (CORBA) specification, particularly well suited to the integration of pre-existing systems.

Using this reference architecture, the ISWG defined an operational PDM semantic that was common to all of the systems targeted for integration, using a paradigm of system federation in which systems are integrated without each being aware of the other.

The collaboration resulted in the ability to swap PDM applications among Ford, TI, and Oakridge, regardless of Product Data Management System and regardless of the CORBA vendor/implementation used, and solved the problems each company brought to the table. All of this was made possible through the joint efforts of companies in a collaborative framework... sharing information.

Open standards: a case study in
community collaboration

Just as the Rapid Response Manufacturing Consortium (RRM) was beginning to enjoy the fruits of its collaboration in Product Data Management (PDM), the Object Management Group (OMG) issued a Request for Proposal (RFP) for a "PDM Enablers" specification. RFPs in the OMG are different from those in general industry. To respond to an OMG RFP is to actually do the work... not propose to do it. What is proposed is an actual specification.

The RRM members Ford and TI had the same PDM vendor, Structural Dynamics Research Corporation (SDRC, the Metaphase PDM product provider at the time, eventually became a late joining member of the consortium). Focused on the business requirements of these three members, the ISWG undertook an analysis of the desirability of responding to the standard and came up with the following compelling business cases for going forward:

Vendor's Business Case:

- With a standard semantic and Application Programming Interface (API), the vendor's PDM "engine" can be used with any application written in compliance to the standard.

- Customers are attracted to an open standard that protects their investment should their initial vendor disappear.

- The only thing standardized is the common commodity operations required by all businesses. How it is done is still proprietary. The vendor can differentiate itself in terms of performance, scalability, stability, price, product architecture, etc.

- A variety of client programs can be developed that will work with the vendors own PDM engine or with the engine of other vendors.

- Developing a standard API in conjunction with major customers reduces risk inherent in developing software. The vendor is reasonably assured that its product will meet its customers' needs and that there will be a market for the product.

End User's Business Case:

- The company can develop applications specific to its business process that will work with any PDM Vendors system.

- The investment in PDM is preserved beyond the failure of vendor.

- Organizations that were writing an integration layer over diverse PDM systems (such as the TI and RRM stories) will have their work reduced dramatically by having much of the capability provided as part of any product compliant with the standard.

Given the analysis, the Rapid Response Manufacturing Consortium (RRM), (through a membership acquired by the National Center for Manufacturing Sciences (NCMS), partnered with Structural Dynamics Research Corporation (SDRC) to submit a proposed specification for the PDM Enablers to the Manufacturing Domain Task Force (MfgDTF)[5] of the Object Management Group. Through an intense collaborative effort, the consortium submitted an Initial Submission through SDRC to the Object Management Group. This submission joined four other initial submissions by IBM and Matrix; Sherpa; Digital Equipment Corporation; and Fujitsu.

The MfgDTF evaluated the submissions, provided their comments, and suggested that the submitters come together to form a single joint submission team. The submitters agreed to do so and the RRM was asked to chair the Joint PDM Submission Team (JPDM). This broadened the collaboration further. The result was an extremely intense collaboration wherein 2 ½ day face-to-face workshops were held once a month, telephone conferences once a week, and a constant stream of email.

The fruit of the collaboration was the PDM Enablers Specification, which successfully met

---

" *This reduced the costs of infrastructure and allowed each company to focus on their direct business case.* "

---

the requirements of each of the member companies of the RRM as well as many other companies. This reduced the costs of infrastructure and allowed each company to focus on their direct business case. The broad collaboration possible through an open standards organization such as the Object Management Group enabled the standardization of commodity aspects of product data management while preserving the intellectual property of the firms implementing the mechanics of the generic capabilities.

Summary

Protecting information unnecessarily …

- dilutes and weakens the protection of truly proprietary information,
- impedes information flow within the organization,
- impedes information flow into an organization from the community at large, and
- increases the cost associated with information protection.

Organizations need to assess their proprietary information portfolios to assure they are not protecting information that:

- does not serve the direct business case,
- is stale information that no longer requires protection, or
- is commodity information.

Organizations need to look for collaborative opportunities in which they can:

- share the costs of pre-competitive development, and
- co-develop support software with vendors, customers, and competitors that address commodity needs, enabling the organization to focus on its core competitive business practices.

Notes

[1] Allen, Gene, and Jarman, Rick, *Collaborative R&D, Manufacturing's New Tool*, Wiley, May 1999

[2] Texas Instruments Defense Systems Group is now Raytheon Systems Company.

[3] The RRM was a $65M Advanced Technology Program (ATP) issued by the National Institute of Standards and Technology (NIST). It was established as a five-year collaboration (1993-97) involving four manufacturing companies – Ford Motor Company, General Motors, Raytheon Systems Company (formally Texas Instruments Defense Systems Group), and United Technologies Corporation/Pratt & Whitney; a National Laboratory – Lockheed Martin Energy Systems (Oak Ridge Y-12); and six software development companies – the MacNeal-Schwendler Corporation (Aries Technology was the initial participant and acquired by MSC in 1993), Cimplex, Concentra (previously ICAD and now Knowledge Technology International), Spatial Technology, and Teknowledge (previously Cimflex Teknowledge). The program was administrated by the National Center for Manufacturing Science (NCMS).

[4] The Object Management Group (OMG) is an open membership, not-for-profit consortium that produces and maintains computer industry specifications for interoperable enterprise applications. Its membership includes virtually every large company in the computer industry, and hundreds of smaller ones. Most of the companies that shape enterprise and Internet computing today are represented on its Board of Directors. The OMG now includes over 500 members, including: (1) Platform-oriented Software Vendors providing support for Model Driven Architecture, CORBA Object Request Brokers and other OMG middleware support and modeling services; (2) Application-oriented Software Vendors who offer Model Driven Architecture based solutions to wide varieties of business problems; and (3) End User Companies who participate in partnerships with vendors to define the requirements and roadmaps of the standards to be supplied by the Software Vendors. More can be found at http://www.omg.org/gettingstarted.

[5] The Manufacturing Domain Task Force (MfgDTF) later became the Manufacturing and Industrial Systems Task Force (ManTIS). See http://mantis.omg.org/.

18

IPR Paralysis in Standardization: Is Regulatory Symmetry Desirable?

Tineke M. Egyedi

Delft University of Technology

Abstract: *Fear of legal claims on Intellectual Property Right (IPR) sometimes paralyzes standards processes. IPR procedures of standards bodies address such problems. However, by default, unresolved problems will be addressed by the legal regime. The process of Java™ standardization, which is a thread throughout this article, well illustrates what may happen. In case of conflict between IPR and compatibility interests, the legal regime is such that mostly IPR interests preside. Should we strive for more symmetry between IPR and compatibility interests? The usual rationale for IPR regulation is that it stimulates innovation. I argue below that the public is equally served by compatibility. I analyze to what degree the public interest in compatibility is institutionalized in European, United States, and international regulation and end with questions that are meant to fuel policy debate.*

Introduction

The difficulty of developing standards for information and communication technology (ICT) where companies claim intellectual property rights (IPRs) has been well documented. The cases include the development of the standard for Global System for Mobile communications (GSM) in the European Telecommunications Standards Institute (ETSI),[1]

the third generation International Mobile Telecommunications (IMT) 2000 standards series in the International Telecommunication Union (ITU),[2] and formalization of Sun Microsystems' Java™ de facto standard in ECMA, an international industry association for standardizing information and communication systems.[3] All three examples concern key-areas in ICT, where the economic stakes are high and the possible impact on future networking is significant. Sometimes IPR problems can be solved. In the case of GSM, the main problems were overcome by cross-licensing Motorola's essential IPRs with essential and non-essential IPRs of other companies. In the case of IMT 2000, the conflict between Qualcomm and Ericsson was solved by giving each other access to patents and Ericsson's take-over of Qualcomm's unprofitable production unit for mobile Code-Division Multiple Access (CDMA) devices. But in the case of Java™, the standards process was disbanded. Sun withdrew because its copyright on the Java specifications was not properly safeguarded by ECMA's IPR rules, according to Sun. Because the Java case will be used as an illustration throughout this article, Box 1 briefly indicates what was at stake. See Box 1.

Box 1: Java Technology and Compatibility

Java started as a programming language. One of Sun's maxims is "Write Once Run Anywhere" (WORA). That is, a Java software developer should not need to rewrite his or her software program for different platforms. Java programs are to be portable and scaleable. In order to achieve cross-platform compatibility, Sun has created a standardized application-programming environment. Each system and browser provider must fully implement the specifications of the Java Virtual Machine (JVM)[4] and Application Programming Interfaces (APIs)[5] of the standardized Java environment if WORA is to be achieved. Several system providers such as IBM and Hewlett-Packard have done so. Thus, Java has evolved into a programming environment.

Java became popular because—platform-independent—small Java programs could be downloaded and executed by web browsers. These moving, colorful applets triggered its breakthrough on the Internet. Java was well on its way to becoming a de facto standard when Sun Microsystems approached JTC1 to formally standardize the Java™ Technology. (JTC1 is short for the Joint Technical Committee 1 of the International Standardization Organization (ISO) and the International Electrotechnical Committee (IEC).) Sun became a recognized submitter of Publicly Available Specifications (PAS) in late 1997. However, it refrained from using its submitter status because there was a likelihood that its Java specs would be significantly changed during the PAS-approval procedure. In April 1999, Sun approached ECMA, an international industry association for standardizing information and communication systems, for the same purpose. Once an ECMA standard, the Java specs could be submitted to JTC1 by way of the Fast Track process (usually a yes/no decision in JTC1). However, after the first meeting of the ECMA standards committee, Sun withdrew. According to Sun, ECMA's IPR rules were not elaborate enough. Sun preferred to evolve its own procedures for the Java Community Process towards a more open multiparty development of the Java specifications.

Public Interest: IPR and Innovation

In these and other cases, the main problem is how to strike the right balance between interests of compatibility and IPR interests. (The term compatibility refers here to interoperability; or, more precisely, to "the suitability of products, processes or services for use together under specific conditions to fulfill relevant requirements without causing unacceptable interactions," according to the ISO/IEC Guide 2 of 1991. For practical reasons, I restrict the discussion on IPR interests to patents and copyright, although in the Java case Sun's trademarks are also important.) Both concern a mix of public and company interests. Focusing on the public interest, the rationale for IP law is that it stimulates researchers and inventors to put intellectual property in the public domain[7] and thereby encourages innovation. Researchers from the Massachusetts Institute of Technology therefore use intellectual property as a direct index for innovation. [8] Revenues from R&D need to be protected by IPR law to safeguard R&D investments. Society at large

> *"...the main problem is how to strike the right balance between interests of compatibility and IPR interests."*

benefits from the innovations that result from these investments, so the reasoning goes.

Although the assumed relationship is disputable and lacks clear evidence,[9] sometimes IPRs may work out that way. But IPRs are not a prerequisite for innovation, as proponents of the open source movement would argue. Moreover, IPRs may also paralyze technology development. Increasingly large ICT companies are settling market disputes in lawsuits. The latter are often based on intellectual property claims. In March 1999, for example, Xerox and Hewlett-Packard were involved in six lawsuits on patent infringement. Although potential IPR infringement seems to be part of strategic risk taking among multinationals, there is also some fear of inadvertent IPR infringement. For example,

> *"...IPRs are not a prerequisite for innovation, as proponents of the open source movement would argue. Moreover, IPRs may also paralyze technology development."*

during standardization of Java, an ECMA committee member hesitated about whether he should distribute certain information because having knowledge of it might work against the participating companies in a possible lawsuit. At stake was knowledge of the Java™ source code. Related, Hewlett-Packard had earlier cloned Sun's Java Compatibility Kit tests in order to test its own "clean-room" version of Java (i.e., a version that avoids using Java™ source code to circumvent Sun's IPRs). Any sign of having previous knowledge of the code could imply copyright infringement. Moreover, under Sun's Community Source license any developer could look at the source code, which made cloning of Java an even touchier business from the legal standpoint. Thus, to certain degree fear of IPR infringement stilted the standardization and diffusion of Java technology.

Problem: Regulatory Asymmetry?

Let us, for the sake of argument, accept the legal rationale that underlies IPRs. Then, like IPRs, compatibility could also be argued to benefit technology development. Compatibility leads to network and other externalities, which spur innovation. Examples are GSM and IMT

2000. They illustrate how *ex ante* standardization may open new markets. And, if the ECMA technical committee 41 had met its aim to "develop a standard for a cross-platform computing

> *"...there is a clear public interest involved in achieving compatibility, an interest that is closely tied to technology innovation."*

environment based upon the Java 2™ Standard Edition (J2SE) Version 1.2.2 specification," platform-independent computing—and the reallocation of R&D resources—could have been one step nearer. In other words, there is a clear public interest involved in achieving compatibility, an interest that is closely tied to technology innovation. Since a similar innovation rationale applies to IPR and compatibility, in this respect one would expect a similar judicial framework. However, are they similar? Of interest, which ideas underlie intellectual property protection in law and standards procedures, whether compatibility aims have a law-based status, and how current political developments address innovative technology development in relation to IPR and compatibility.

Juridification of the Standards Regime

Before continuing, the term *regime* refers to the way an actor network or an organization governs a particular field of interest.[10] By *standards regime* I mean the values, beliefs, rationales, rules, and agreements that govern consortia and formal standardization bodies (SDOs) (e.g., ideal of a democratic standards process, decisions should reflect consensus, etc.). [11]

Three interrelated regimes have immediate bearing on the questions raised above: the legal, the market, and the standards regime. The standards arena is not solely governed by the standards regime. It is part of the market and is thus also subject to the "rules" of the market. In the standards arena market strategies are evident that are tolerated by the standards regime in question. For example, the IPR strategies that companies use to protect their market will also be used in standards setting. Because there is a tension between the compatibility aims of standards bodies, on the one hand, and IPR protection of contributions to draft standards, on the other, most standards bodies have installed special IPR procedures. If conflicts remain, the legal regime will be invoked to solve them. The legal regime is the default regime for handling IPR issues in standardization. The IPR code of conduct, to which standards participants must comply in some standards bodies, aims to prevent the legal regime from being invoked. But, since the standards arena is part of the market arena, *juridification* of market conflicts (i.e., a process by which a judicial interpretation of and approach to events is taking over—is also affecting standardization). To an increasing extent, legal matters have permeated the standards setting arena. See Figure 1.

Figure 1: Juridification of the standards regime

IPR market strategies

Bekkers & Liotard [1] provide an overview of IPR strategies, which companies use and standards bodies must deal with. They mention (1) the licensing with a general declaration strategy (i.e., announcing ownership of the IPR and declaring that licenses will be available on fair, reasonable and non-discriminatory terms), (2) the licensing without a general declaration strategy, (3) the withholding strategy (i.e., not licensing the IPR), and (4) the nondisclosure or late disclosure strategy (i.e., not informing other parties of the existence of the IPR). The impact of these IPR strategies on standardization is large if *essential* IPRs are involved. That is, when "on technical (but not commercial) grounds it is not possible to produce, sell, import, use or operate products that conform to a certain standard without infringing on that IPR" [1, p.117]. Essential IPRs may cover patents (e.g., in the GSM and IMT 2000 case) as well as copyrights (e.g., Sun's copyright on the Java™ specifications).

IPR rules of standards bodies

Theoretically, the formal standards bodies of ISO and IEC have become more susceptible to direct company interests and their IPR strategies since the installment of the Fast-Track procedure for A-liaison members and the JTC1 PAS procedure. Both procedures allow externally developed specifications to be fed into the JTC1 process as a draft international standard, that is, without going through the prior stages of committee standardization. The Java case, however, suggests that in practice no real changes have taken place. Sun approached JTC1 in 1997 and ECMA in 1999. Both times IPR problems arose. Their IPR rules are examined to determine the way intellectual ownership, in this case patents and copyrights, has been institutionalized therein. (Notably, the ECMA is an A-liaison member of JTC1. This means that it can fast-track ECMA standards to JTC1 and, therefore, ECMA and JTC1 procedures are likely to be similar.)

Patents

Typically, standards bodies try to avoid the inclusion of patents in standards. The ISO/IEC rules treat their inclusion as an exception. This refers back to the idea that the standards process is itself an innovative technology development process and need not depend on other sources. It also echoes the belief that technical alternatives are generally available. The inclusion of patents is seen to be foremost in the interest of the IPR owners themselves (i.e., a standard result that makes the company's R&D investment worthwhile and gives it a head-start vis-a-vis competitors). Standards bodies therefore request that IPR owners provide patents under fair and reasonable terms. A statement to this

Figure 2: IPR and compatibility

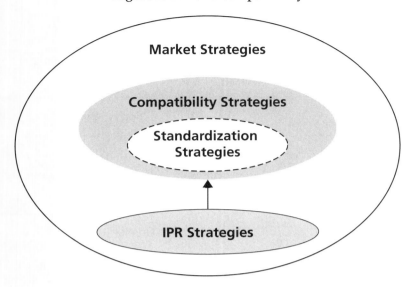

Figure 2 conceptualizes IPR strategies and compatibility strategies as market strategies. (I prefer to speak of compatibility strategies rather than standardization strategies, since there are also other ways to achieve compatibility.[4] Where I mention standardization strategies, I refer to multiparty consensus processes in standards consortia and formal standards bodies.) Companies use both—sometimes in combination—to further their interests. Most salient is the "misuse" of market strategies based on IPR-ownership in standards development (e.g., GSM and IMT 2000). Nevertheless, in some cases IPR strategies are used to safeguard compatibility (e.g., Java).

intent is requested of the patent holder. If this is withheld, the technical committee will not include the patented item. If a technical committee is not aware of any relevant patents during the standards process or if patents claims are made after publication of the International Standard, the ISO/IEC procedures disclaim authority on these matters. [12]

The ECMA has a *Code of conduct on patent matters*. In part, ECMA deals with patent claims on work covered by draft standards in the usual way, namely that such patents should be licensed on a reasonable and non-discriminatory basis or else the standard will not be approved. However, in case the patent belongs to an ECMA member, company participation in an ECMA technical committee and a yes-vote to the standard automatically imply compliance to reasonable licensing terms.

Copyright

The copyright on Draft International Standards (DISs) and International Standards (ISs) belongs to ISO and IEC. In respect to contributions, JTC1 has a procedure for *normative referencing*.[10] That is, a standards committee may want to incorporate specifications from sources outside ISO, IEC or ITU into an emerging standard by way of reference. Normative referencing differs from *informative referencing*, to which no restrictions apply. With normative referencing, the originator of the referenced specification must give written consent; or else the reference shall not be made.

ECMA standards and technical reports are available to all interested parties without restriction and without charge.[13] However, ECMA retains the copyright on ECMA standards. The copyright status of documents leading up to an ECMA standard is detailed in the table below.

Table 1: Copyright ownership in ECMA

Type of Document	Owner of the Document
Contribution from members of an ECMA group	The contributor
Drafts of formal documents	The ECMA group responsible for the document
Contributions to external organizations	The ECMA group responsible for the document
Final drafts submitted to the ECMA General Assembly	ECMA

When a contributor submits a document as input to an ECMA committee, the document is assigned a number by the ECMA secretariat for the purpose of referencing and archiving. Once this occurs, the contribution becomes an ECMA working document. (A working document is a "document (…) used by an ECMA Group, (…) distributed by the ECMA Secretariat and [that carries] one or more ECMA numbers."[11] Then, the copyright changes hands from the contributor to the ECMA Group. Alternatively, should the document on which a technical committee works be viewed as owned both by the contributor (extending its initial status) as well as by the committee (if viewed as an early version of the draft formal document)? The unclear copyright status of Sun's contribution was one of reasons to withdraw its Java specifications from the standards process. (See Box 2.) Sun subsequently also refused to agree with an ECMA standard that would be based on normative referencing to its Java specifications, something which posed no problem in a JTC1 context in 1997. (Sun agreed to normative referencing by the JTC1 standards committee for "Coding of Audio, Picture, Multimedia and Hypermedia Information." It held on to its IPRs but asked no fees.)[10]

In sum, standards bodies deal summarily with patent ownership. The patent holder can choose between reasonable licensing terms or no inclusion. More elaborate rules exist to regulate the inclusion of copyrighted mate-rial in standards. (See Table 1.) What could be the cause of this difference in IPR treatment? It could be that (a) standardizers see patent holders as competitors in technology development (idea-generators, see above), which leads to more straightforward go/no-go procedures while copyright holders work on the expression of an idea; (b) copyright owners are more prepared to negotiate and more easily waive their rights than patent owners, which would call for more subtle procedures; or that (c) standards procedures complement legal provisions, which would mean that patent law is more elaborate and needs less addition than copyright law. Additional research is needed to check these hypotheses.

Default legal regime

The discussion below is confined to the IPR laws regarding software in Europe and the US and to the influential *Agreement on Trade-Related Aspects of Intellectual Property Rights (TRIPS agreement) of the World Trade Organization (WTO). Of interest is the way they address IPR issues and whether compatibility interests are referred to in IPR regulation.*

European regulation [15]

Abuse of IPR is subject to EU competition rules. A European Directive of 1991 specifically addresses IPRs on software. It aims to curb the copying of computer programs. Copyrights are to be respected. The sole exception concerns

Box 2: Java in ECMA

Sun's reason to withdraw from the ECMA process was, according to its press release, that "(...) ECMA has formal rules governing patent protections; however, at this time there are no formal protections for copyrights or other intellectual property." Sun was under the impression that ECMA had agreed that Sun would retain copyright of the specifications during the standards process, and that ECMA would copyright the resulting standard. Although Sun would not claim copyright on the standard, it would hold onto its trademarked Java name and Java Compatibility logo, which had business value. During the first TC41 meeting, it appeared that the oral agreement on copyright, as Sun understood it, would not be upheld. Sun lawyers were taken aback by the ECMA Secretary General's (SG's) explanation of IPR rules regarding contributions to standardization. Regarding the copyright status of the Java specifications, Sun's contribution would become an ECMA document once it was assigned a technical committee (TC) document submission number – which it would receive at the start of the standards process. Sun protested and did not wait to see whether the ECMA SG could find an acceptable compromise.

The problem was that Sun and ECMA had a different view on what was previously agreed upon about the Java specifications' copyright. In addition, Sun attached two different meanings to the term copyright at that point. It differentiated between a copyrighted specification and copyright of the contents of the specification (i.e., roughly speaking, the difference between paper and software).[11] The latter copyright

interpretation was new to all concerned. In early December, before the negotiations could start, Sun announced its withdrawal.

The steps that Sun took in the following months gave credence to its official reason for withdrawal, namely concern about copyright protection. The European Information and Communication Technology Industry Association (EICTA), founded in January 2000, installed a Standards Policy Group (SPG) chaired by Sun. The policy group was to develop a position on the licensing terms of software technology embedded in standards that was to be protected by copyright rather than patents. Sun also planned to raise the issue at a meeting of the European ICT Standards Board, but ultimately decided not to do so. Lastly, Sun called together a Standards IPR Forum meeting during the Open Group Conference (April 2000, London). Its aim was to discuss copyright on submissions, among other things.

These initiatives, however, do not appropriately explain Sun's withdrawal from Java standardization. Possibly, proceeding with standardization would have had additional adverse consequences for the scope of IPR protection. As Stuurman[14] argues, de facto standards require resilience in respect to imitations. If they are formalized, they become more susceptible to infringement of IPRs because the difference between the expression of an idea (copyright) and the idea itself (patent) becomes unclear. However, the copyright conflict can also be a symptom of a struggle for power behind the scenes, as is argued elsewhere.[3]

---

the copying of information about interfaces when needed and used for the purpose of interoperability with an independently created program. "(...) An objective of this exception is to make it possible to connect all components of a computer system, including those of different manufacturers, so that they can work together." Although the Article 6 in question has been heavily debated, it indicates under which circumstances compatibility is deemed more important than ownership protection [12, p.459].

Different from the US, in the European Union

only the expression of a computer program is protected by law (copyright protection as a literary work). The ideas and principles which underlie programs are not (no patents). Patent-oriented R&D in the US and the need to comply with the international TRIPS Agreement (see below) led in 1997 to a Green Paper about the patentability of computer software in Europe. The follow-up document of 1999 noted that there were 13000 European patents on software,

---

"...there were 13000 European patents on software, despite the fact that computer programs were not patentable."

---

despite the fact that computer programs were not patentable. Apart from the need for a harmonized approach among member-states, the discrepancy with US and Japanese law pressed the Commission and the European Parliament to propose changes. The feeling was that software should meet the conditions of "novelty and industrial application" to be patented. Software patents would encourage companies to invest in R&D and would therefore stimulate innovation. The follow-up document made no mention of the problems that patents could pose for standardization or other issues of compatibility. A draft Directive on the patentability of computer programs was drawn up to complement the copyright Directive. However, it was voted down in November 2000. In particular open-source software advocates thought the Directive would hinder the development of new software programs. Programmers would fear infringing on someone else's patent. They referred to the situation in the US, where patent infringement claims kept software companies quite busy because the US patent and trademark organization had in the past not been very critical in assigning software patents.[16]

US regulation

US patent law allows companies to patent anything useful and non-obvious, including business methods and algorithms. Software patents are not explicitly discussed.[17] Nor are exceptions mentioned to patent infringement that could be related to compatibility interests.

US copyright jurisdiction appears to struggle with the compatibility issue, as the following examples will illustrate. They all concern *de facto* standards. The first example is that of Lotus vs. Paperback. Paperbacksoftware International copied the user interface of Lotus 1-2-3 because the latter was a *de facto* standard. Consumers would not agree to anything else, according to Paperback, and the company thus felt forced to infringe on the copyright of Lotus. Paperback argued that its actions furthered compatibility and were therefore in the interest of consumers. The judge rejected these arguments. There wasn't any prior jurisdiction which said that standardization, if not achieved through formal channels, was in the interest of the public at large. According to Judge Keaton (28 June 1990), "A moment's reflection is enough to disclose that the public interest in standardization is a sharply debatable issue."[12, p.461] In other words, copyright infringement could not be condoned for reasons of seeking compatibility with a *de facto* standard.

In the second example, the case of Lotus vs. Borland, Lotus accused Borland International of infringing on copyright of the menu structure of Lotus 1-2-3. In this case, the verdict was in

---

"The verdict suggests that compatibility arguments are not well institutionalized in US law. They need to be worded in terms of "competitive market" interests to be acknowledged."

---

favor of Borland: "to allow users to operate its programs in substantially the same way (…), Borland had to copy the Lotus menu command hierarchy." [12, p.462]

The third example, the case of Sun Microsystems vs. Microsoft, is discussed in Box 3. Here, the integrity of the Java platform was the central issue. Sun accused Microsoft of intentionally fragmenting the Java platform by means of mis-

Box 3: Sun vs. Microsoft

In 1995, Java was on its way to becoming a hype. As the Findings of fact in the anti-trust lawsuit against Microsoft indicate, Java's promise of platform-independent computing made Microsoft nervous. It undermined the fundaments of Microsoft's software market, the Windows platform. In that period, Microsoft approached companies such as Netscape and Intel to withdraw from activities that supported Java developments.

In March 1996, Sun and Microsoft signed a Technology License and Distribution Agreement (TDLA) for the use of Java. The document started with reciting the need for Java compatibility. Part of the agreement was that Microsoft would incorporate the JavaTM Technology into its Internet Explorer (IE) 4.0.

In late 1996, Microsoft released IE 3.0. In order maximize its use vis-a-vis Netscape Navigator, Microsoft decided that the next version would be more tightly integrated into the Windows operating system. Moreover, Microsoft started creating Java development tools and a Java runtime-environment in a manner that undermined the portability of Java programs and was incompatible with Sun's Java products. A lawsuit ensued and progressed as follows:

October 1997: Sun filed a complaint against Microsoft for copyright infringement

March 1998: The court granted Sun's request for a preliminary injunction—Microsoft was not allowed to use the Java Compatible logo unless its products passed Sun's test suites

May 1998: Sun filed an additional complaint for unfair competition

November 1998: The court ordered Microsoft to change its software and development tools. Microsoft appealed against the ruling. It argued that the punishment did not fit the crime committed. It pleaded guilty on "breach of contract," for which the TDLA stipulated a much lighter punishment than injunction

August 1999: The court granted Microsoft's appeal, upon which Sun protested

January 2000: A higher court confirmed that copyright infringement was not at stake. At stake was unfair competition by Microsoft

January 2001: The dispute was finally settled. Among other things, the TDLA was terminated and Microsoft agreed not to use Sun's Java Compatible logo anymore

using the Java name and the Java compatibility logo. It sued Microsoft for copyright infringement—and, at a later stage, for unfair competition. See Box 3. The court judged that only the "unfair competition" part could be sustained. The verdict suggests that compatibility arguments are not well institutionalized in US law. They need to be worded in terms of "competitive market" interests to be acknowledged.

The above cases illustrate that jurisdiction regarding copyright versus compatibility interests differs per situation. The Digital Millennium Copyright Act of October 1998 more clearly refers to the desirability of compatibility. The Copyright Act includes exceptions for circum-

venting copyright. One exception is reverse engineering for the purpose of interoperability.[18]

TRIPS agreement

The *Agreement on Trade-Related Aspects of Intellectual Property Rights of 1994* is, according to the World Trade Organization (WTO), currently the most comprehensive multilateral agreement on intellectual property. In respect to copyright, computer programs, whether in source or in object code, shall be protected as literary works (Article 10(1)). The agreement further only mentions that exceptions should be limited and does not specifically refer to compatibility. With regard to patents, "(…) Patents shall be available for any inventions, whether products or processes, in all fields of technology, provided they are new, involve an inventive step and are capable of industrial application," according to Article 27(1). This includes software. (There could be, implicitly, some leeway for unauthorized use of patents for compatibility purposes if such use would fall under "public non-commercial use" (Article 31 (b)).)

In sum, both European and US copyright law have a clause which says that copyright infringement is only allowed for the sake of interoperability (i.e., interface information for achieving interoperability with an independently created program, and reverse engineering for the purpose of interoperability, respectively). The proposed and implemented patent laws, respectively, include no such exceptions. (See Table1.) Thus, overall, intellectual property interests are well protected by the current dominant legal regime if compared to the public interest in compatibility. This means that the societal significance of technical compatibility will regularly need to be renegotiated. Compatibility will at best be a recurrent ad-hoc policy issue, subject to changing, short-term political forces.

Comparing copyright protection and patents, Kultti & Takalo note that only one patent can be awarded among similar innovations, "whereas copyright law permits independent discoveries. For instance, several papers on the same idea may be published (…)." [19, p.1] In this respect, copyright law appears to reflect R&D practice better than the patent system. Kultti & Takalo point out that similar inventions often occur simultaneously in different places. Their point is supported by Thomas Kuhn's paradigm

---

"Compatibility will at best be a recurrent ad-hoc policy issue, subject to changing, short-term political forces."

---

theory. Kuhn identifies communities of practitioners, who work in the same field, think along the same lines, and focus on the same sort of problems. They share the same paradigm. This heightens the probability that within a limited time-span similar inventions will be made in the same field of research.

Table 2: Degree to which IPR and compatibility interests are anchored in the standards and legal regimes

	Standards Regime		Legal Regime	
	Patent	Copyright	Patent	Copyright
IPR Interests	low (e.g., treated as an exception, code of conduct)	medium (e.g., Normative Referencing)	high (patent law)	high (copyright law)
Compatibility Interests	high (standardization procedures)		absent	partial (interoper. clauses)

Innovation: Intellectual Property vs. Compatibility

There are few studies that address the tension between IPR and compatibility from a social studies of technology angle. Interesting exceptions are Schoechle[8] and Iversen.[20] Iversen takes an evolutionary approach. He views the IPR regime as one in which variation of technology takes place. He likens the formal standards regime to a selection environment: during the standards process diversity is reduced. His analysis builds on three implicit assumptions: firstly, that the standards setting environment is generally not an innovative environment; secondly, that the phase of standards setting is of primary interest in relation to technology development; and thirdly, that standardization processes in the formal standards bodies well-illustrates the ways in which compatibility can be achieved.

In recent years, Iversen's first assumption, namely that past accounts of standardization have overemphasized the inventive quality of technical contributions, has gained support.[9; 21, p.38] Multiparty standards usually codify the state-of-the-art in a certain technical field. However, the crux of standardization is not that it leads to innovative standards. Innovative opportunities, for example, lie in the way specifications are implemented, occur because R&D resources are freed once compatibility is achieved, or lie in the exploitation of externalities. During standards diffusion, variation of technology takes place. The post-standardization phase is in respect to technology development at least as influential as the standards setting process itself is—to answer to Iversen's second assumption. Moreover, in respect to his third assumption, many strategies other than formal standardization improve technical compatibility. Examples in the field of software are licensing and open source strategies.[4] In particular, in the case of open source software development, where to date no distinction is made between forging compatibility (developing the "standard") and developing software, technology development shows a different pattern. It would

seem that innovations sometimes occur despite the IPR regime.

Discussion

This article raises a number of fundamental policy questions, which I will formulate as bluntly as possible in order to stimulate debate. The questions are:

- A regulatory asymmetry exists between IPR interests and compatibility interests. Current regulation anchors the primacy of IPR ownership and market competition in law, but it hardly recognizes the societal significance of compatibility interests (i.e., technical interop-

---

"Current regulation anchors the primacy of IPR ownership and market competition in law, but it hardly recognizes the societal significance of compatibility interests ."

---

erability). *Would it be desirable to legally anchor compatibility interests in a way similar to intellectual property interests?*

- There is a difference between the judicial treatment of patents and copyrights. The patent system, which is stricter than copyright protection, leaves no room for compatibility priorities whereas US and European copyright regulation does. Copyright law allows different people to write on the same subject. This approach is more consistent with the way R&D takes place—the near-simultaneity of inventions—than patent law. *Should patent law take the near-simultaneity of inventions into account?*

- Most standards bodies try to avoid the use of patented work for standards. The IPR rules treat their inclusion as an exception. *Should these standards bodies resign themselves to a non-innovative, process-oriented role and start thinking more in terms of "purchasing innovative technology" (i.e., incorporate patents more often)?*

- Standardization is one of the many compatibility strategies that companies can opt for. Software licensing and open source strategies, for example, may also enhance compatibility. Such strategies use various forms of IPR protection. O'Mahoney [22] lists the following types of software control: Copyhoarding, Licensing, Shareware, Copylefting, Freeware, Public Domain. *Should IPR regulation address these IPR approaches to software?*

Notes

[1] R. Bekkers and I. Liotard, "European Standards for Mobile Communications: The Tense Relationship between Standards and Intellectual Property Rights," *European Intellectual Property Review*, vol. 21, no. 3, 1999, pp.110-126.

[2] J. Ubacht, "UMTS: to boldly go where no one has gone before?" Presented at Congres Onderzoek in Nieuwe Media, 25 March 1999, Rotterdam, the Netherlands.

[3] T.M. Egyedi, "Why Java™ was - not - standardized twice," IEEE Proceedings of the 34th Hawaii International Conference System Sciences, January 3-6, 2001.

[4] I.e., software that runs on proprietary operating systems and is capable of interpreting compiled Java byte code.

[5] APIs comprise the standard packages, classes, methods and fields made available to software developers to write programs.

[6] T.M. Egyedi, "Compatibility strategies in licensing, open source software and formal standards: Externalities of Java 'standardization'," Paper presented at the 5th EURAS Helsinki Workshop on Standardization and Networks, VATT, Helsinki, 13-14 August 2000.

[7] M.B.H. Weiss and M.B. Spring, "Selected Intellectual Property Issues in Standardization," in: K. Jakobs (Ed.), *IT Standards and Standardization: A Global Perspective*, London: Idea Group Publishing, 2000, pp.63- 79.

[8] T. Schoechle, "Intellectual Property Rights and Emerging Technologies: Friends or Foes?" Submitted to the Minitrack on Standardization in Information Technology, HICSS-34, January 3-6, 2001.

[9] D.A. Hounshell and J.K. Smith, *Science and Corporate Strategy*, Du Pont R&D, 1902-1980 Cambridge: Cambridge University Press, 1988; Ph.A.Roussel, K.N. Saad and T.J. Erickson, Third generation R&D managing the link to corporate strategy Boston: Harvard Business School Press, 1991.

[10] V. Schneider and R. Werle, "Co-Evolution and Development Constraints: The Development of Large Technical Systems in Evolutionary Perspective," International Research Seminar: Large Technical Systems and Networks: Interconnection Processes, Governance Issues, Conceptual Development, Autun, France, 27-30 September 1995.

[11] T.M. Egyedi, "Institutional Dilemma in ICT Standardization: Coordinating the Diffusion of Technology?," in: K. Jakobs (Ed.), *IT Standards and Standardization: A Global Perspective*, London: Idea Group Publishing, 2000, pp. 48-62

[12] ISO/IEC sources: Reference to patented items, ISO/IEC Directives - Part 2: Methodology for the development of International Standards, Annex A, 1992; Procedures for the technical work of ISO/IEC JTC 1, 1999; The Normative Referencing of Specifications other than International Standards in JTC 1 International Standards - Guidelines for JTC 1 SCs, 1996-03-13, JTC1 N4046; ISO/IEC JTC1/SC29, 03-06-1997, N2082.

[13] ECMA sources: 'Code of Conduct in Patent Matters', 'ECMA By-laws, Promulgation of Standards and Technical Reports', Art 8.4, ECMA Memento 2000; Working documents and formal documents: rules for editing, recording and exchanging, Art. 2.11, ECMA, Feb. 2000; Minutes of ECMA CC 11-12 November 1999.

[14] C. Stuurman, Technische normen en het recht. Beschouwingen over de interactie tussen het recht en technische normalisatie op het terrein van informatietechnologie en telecommunicatie, Reeks Informatica en Recht, deel 17, 1995, Dissertation.

[15] Sources from the European Commission: Council Directive 91/250/EEC of 14 May 1991 on the legal protection of computer programs, Official Journal L

122 , 17/05/1991, pp. 0042 – 0046; Report from the Commission to the Council, the European Parliament and the Economic and Social Committee on the implementation and effects of Directive 91/250/EEC on the legal protection of computer programs, Brussels, 10.04.2000, COM(2000) 199 final; Promoting innovation through patents. The follow-up to the Green Paper on the Community Patent and the Patent System in Europe, Communication from the Commission to the Council, the European Parliament and the Economic and Social Committee, May 1999.

[16] M.L. D'Amico, "Europe considers loosening software-patent rules," *IDG News*, July 8, 1999; G. Lea, "US patent mess will get worse before it gets better," The Register, March 31, 2000.

[17] United States Code, 35 U.S.C. § 101 Inventions patentable; § 103 Conditions for patentability; non-obvious subject matter Patent Laws and Regulations, Jan. 18, 2000.

[18] L. Jamtgaard, "The U.S. Digital Millennium Copyright Act," International Legal Protection for Software, 1999, www.fenwick.com.

[19] K. Kultti and T. Takalo, "A Search Model of Intellectual Property Protection: Patent vs. Copyright," Paper presented at the 4th EURAS Helsinki Workshop, 1999.

[20] E.J. Iversen, "Standardization and Intellectual Property Rights: Conflicts between Innovation and Diffusion in New Telecommunications Systems," in: K. Jakobs (Ed.), *IT Standards and Standardization: A Global Perspective*, London: Idea Group Publishing, 2000, pp. 80-101.

[21] P. Mähönen, "The Standardization Process in IT —Too slow or too fast?," in: K. Jakobs (Ed.), *IT Standards and Standardization: A Global Perspective*, London: Idea Group Publishing, 2000, pp.35-47.

[22] B. O'Mahoney, "Software issues," 2000, www.benedict.com/news/resume.

19

A Perspective on Standardization and Intellectual Property

TORU YAMAUCHI

Ministry of Economy, Trade,
and Industry (METI)

Abstract: *In the current trend of rapid technology advancement, industries are facing a very difficult and complicated problem caused by two activities: standardization and intellectual property. This article focuses on the issues concerning patents included in standards, after analyzing the relationship between de jure standards and forums. It will also examine the similarities and differences between de jure and forum standardization bodies in terms of formation and rule setting in areas like patent policy. The recent situation in Japan on related issues is also described by introducing several government reports by the government. Finally, several concepts dealing with patent issues on standardization will be addressed.*

Classification of Standardization Activities

In recent years, several changes have occurred in standardization activities worldwide. First, in advanced technologies, standardization and acquisition of intellectual property rights now develop concurrently before new products or technologies come into the market. This is because standardization activity is closely related to the outcome of R&D. For example, draft proposals for international standardization organizations sometimes incorporate patents whereas, in the past, these standards did not include patents. Secondly, the significance of cooperation among companies in standardization is growing, even in competitive areas like information technology. In this situation, people categorize standardization activities into two types: de jure and de facto. However, I think that we should recognize a new type of standardization activity based on *inter-corporate* cooperation. Inter-corporate standards are growing, especially in IT fields where many companies own their patents. For example, in the area of IT security, the role of de jure standardization is becoming more closely related to inter-corporate activities. Under these circumstances, relationships between diversified standardization bodies are rapidly becoming complex.

To begin, it is important to define the three standards categories: de jure standards, inter-corporate standards (including forum standards and consortium standards), and de facto standards. *De jure standards* are developed through a public procedure, such as those in international standardization organizations (ISO/IEC/ITU-T). *Inter-corporate standards* are produced by a group of private companies and can be regarded as a new type of standardization in the sense that it isn't included in either de jure or de facto. Within this group, consortium standards might be regarded as different from forums in some extent of market competition. The term *consortium* is often used when one refers to a standardization body that focuses on joint research and development by several companies for its member companies, while competition among multiple groups of companies still exists. The term *forum* is often used when one describes standardization for a unique technology by all the major companies in a certain product field. Forums are developed to avoid incompatible systems that sometimes confuse consumers and prevent the market from developing. A forum usually has to be checked according to competition laws as to whether or not it weakens market competition beyond any rational benefit of standardization.

De facto standardization occurs when the market share of a product or a technology is dominant due to the outcome of competition. In this article, de facto will not be discussed because it is regarded as irrelevant to the issues concerning standardization and patents.

De jure standardization bodies, such as national standardization bodies (NSBs) or international standardization organizations, are trying new ways to attract industries because companies in the fields of advanced technologies often prefer forums or consortia to traditional de jure international standardization organizations in the terms of speed. In general, people think that de jure standards and forum standards are completely different, and companies view them in different ways.

Relationship Between De Jure Standards and Forums

I point out the hypothesis that forum standards are similar to de jure standards in terms of the way they handle patents, whereas consortium standards are similar to de facto in terms of market competition. Forums usually set their own patent policies, like international standardization organizations (ISO/IEC/ITU-T). This means that de jure SSOs and forums are facing very difficult and complicated issues in patents included in standards. In addition, forums usu-

ally declare an openness and transparency in both participation and standardization procedures. And, they are sometimes submitted for approval as international standards. For example, the DVD forum was established in 1995 so that consumer electronics producers could standardize a DVD format as soon as possible. Here, I would like to point out that some DVD standards were proposed to and approved by ISO/IEC JTC1/SC23 later. For example, the physical layers such as the diameter and thickness of disks were approved as international standards. We might imagine that producers expected to strengthen their standards by making them de jure standards. Clearly, there are some complementary relationships between forum standards and de jure standards.

Before entering standardization, competition and/or adjustment occurs among major players. Specifically, the players will reach a decision on whether to choose de jure or forum standards through a strategic approach. As an example, people might recall the competition between VHS and Betamax for VCRs.

Interface Between Standardization and Patents

Patents serve as a guarantee that companies may use the outcome of their R&D activities exclusively. In recent years, it is becoming difficult for one company to own all the patents for new products in a certain field where technology advancement depends on the R&D accumulation by concerned parties. In particular, the ability to interface between specific technologies when the patents for those technologies have different owners is needed in a systematized field like IT. In order to deal with relevant patents, companies sometimes collect them and bundle the intellectual property into a "patent pool" so that they can deal with it like a package. By making a patent pool, it is much easier for both licensers and licensees to negotiate how much money should be paid to patent holders. Patent pooling is one of the ways to deal with a number of patents held by multiple companies. The main feature of a patent pool is that it should not include more than the essential patents to avoid violation of competition law.

The role of a standard is to determine which patents are essential to a standard technology in the field like IT. The defined patents can then be pooled as essential patents for collective licensing. In other words, a standard has a crucial role of determining which patent holder enjoys the fruits from its R&D outcome in this context. So, international standardization activities are becoming important for industries worldwide. In the next stage, new technologies or new products are developed according to the standards, and market competition occurs among various products. Determination of standards is crucial for this cycle of new technology.

The characteristics and similarities of de jure and forum standards are interesting points. RAND (Reasonable and Nondiscriminatory) terms and conditions are usually applied to forum rules, which is why forum standards are similar to de jure standards in terms of intellectual property rights. The patent policies by itself are very important in the sense that they might influence the forum rules.

A patent pool based on a standard is usually not managed by SSOs or forums. Non-standardization bodies like patent pooling companies are often founded. Recent examples of patent pools based on standard technologies are as follow:
  – MPEG LA
  – Patent pools for DVD: 6C and 3C
  – 3rd Generation Platform

Issues Concerning Patents Included in Standards

Determining how to deal with patents included in standards is a global problem. Neither a government nor a region should set its rules without taking harmonization into consideration. This problem has seen especially crucial in the IT fields, where business relationships are expanded worldwide and standardization activities are getting more and more important.

In Japan, two policy papers were reported in public concurrently in the summer of 2003. One is "Strategy for Intellectual Properties (recommendation)," which was written by The Council for Science and Technology Policy. The other, "Strategic Program for Creation, Protection and Exploitation of Intellectual Property," was written by The Intellectual Property Strategy Headquarters. These papers point out the importance of standardization in intellectual property strategy in the context of intellectual property utilization. The papers propose several measures to activate Japanese international standardization activities through traditional SSOs as well as forums. The need for rule setting to ensure the legal stability of forums is indicated. Patent pooling is affirmatively regarded as a vehicle to utilize patents within standards. Some studies will be done on how to support patent pools based on standards by relevant government agencies under the framework of the intellectual property strategic program.

Currently, we are facing three problems in patents concerning standards, and we should seek a direction for a solution for each issue.

First, we should ensure that there are incentives for patent holders to participate in standardization, especially in some fields where rapid standardization is needed such as IT security or IT government procurement. As discussed previously, industries are watching both SSOs and forums at the same time. Sometimes, forum standards are made into international standards through organizations such as ISO, IEC, and ITU-T. Standardization people in the de jure system should recognize this and utilize forum activities as justified procedures if necessary. In this context, it might be a good idea to focus on the reform of the patent policies of SSOs. For example, forums often refer to patent policies of de jure SSOs like international standardization organizations (ISO/IEC/ITU-T) in order to create their rules for dealing with patents.

In terms of SSO patent policy, two points need to be discussed. One is the establishment of a clear definition of "reasonable" terms and conditions from RAND. SSOs have to ensure that they offer incentives for patent holders to participate in standardization while avoiding excessive royalties that lead to the collapse of standards utilization. Because the path is very narrow, a practical answer doesn't exist so far. It is hoped that meaningful experiences will be accumulated so that people make use of concrete terms and conditions for licensing. The other point is how to utilize and reform patent policy. For example, some people who work for ISO/ IEC standardization are sometimes unfamiliar with ISO/IEC patent policy. I once heard that a Japanese expert was told that patents should not be included in international standards by people on a technical committee. It is said that some secretaries (who are sometimes engineers) are not accustomed to legal matters. Particularly, there are no guidelines for how to utilize the ISO/IEC patent policy, like ITU-T, although the development of such guidelines should be considered. The cooperation among international standardization organizations (ISO/IEC/ITU-T) will be needed for the harmonization of patent policies.

Secondly, we must think about the stability of patent pools based on standards. First, patent pools are always facing the risk of violating competition law. As patent pools are evolving and diversifying—reflecting a new technological paradigm (e.g., 3G patent platform)—the need for ensuring legal stability is growing. Recently, prior consultation schemes of competition law authorities have been utilized on a case by case basis in order to reduce such risks. As far as I know, there is no legal guideline for a patent pool based on standards in technologically advanced countries. It is hoped that the competition law authorities in industrialized countries will study the necessity of such a guideline.

Patent pools usually include only essential patents so that they don't violate competition laws. How do they establish mechanisms to define essential patents for a standard? Do they need a third party to define essential patents? Has a common rule on cost sharing among concerned parties been established? Is there a third

party that is capable of coordinating concerned parties in terms of defining essential patents? In Japan, we lack the jurists for investigating the essential patents of standard technologies compared with the United States and European Union. The Japanese government is now seeking a way to educate lawyers for these kinds of jobs in the intellectual property strategic program.

Depending on a patent statement by a patent policy, some companies might declare too many patents to SSOs without justifying the need for them in the standards—and, they might claim royalties for them. This might make the utilization of standards difficult. I recommend a special

---

"...the operation of patent pools will work to eliminate unessential patents."

---

amendment of patent policy for a possible linkage with patent pools in some fields. Even if a patent statement is made with a big list of unjustifiable patents they will claim in the future, the operation of patent pools will work to eliminate unessential patents. In addition, the stipulation of participation in a possible patent pool in the patent statement of SSOs could relieve patent holders who wonder if competitors are staying outside patent pools.

Third, we should consider how patent holders who claim excessive royalties for standards should be dealt with. This is usually called a holdup problem. We see claims for unreasonable license fees by patent holders. Dell Computer's case in the 1990s is well-known. Recently, it has been reported that some electronics companies suffer from JPEG patent claiming. We can foresee the possibility of this kind of problem expanding from IT to other advanced technologies like biotechnology or nanotechnology in the near future.

It is rational to deal with this problem separately in two stages: before and after the publication of standards. Relevant parties need to consider measures to collaborate closely and effectively utilize them in both stages.

*Dealing with excessive royalties
before the publication of standards*

In the first stage, SSOs play an important role in reducing the possible number of excessive royalty cases before the publication of standards. I recommend the following four measures:

1) Public announcement asking latent patent holders to identify themselves

SSOs should create a situation in which most concerned parties worldwide understand a specific standardization activity before a final draft in order to decrease outsiders who hold essential patents. It might work well to publicly announce that an SSO is asking latent patent holders to declare the licensing terms and conditions (RAND, Royalty Free, none of them, etc.) as well as the comments on the draft standards. This kind of measure should be studied when international standardization organizations (ISO/IEC/ITU-T) reform their patent policies.

2) Patent search by SSOs

In general, SSOs do not conduct patent searches even in the participant companies of standardization. This may be because of a lack of resources. However, they should investigate the possibility of conducting patent searches in specific fields where latent patent claiming is foreseen by industries. It might be a good idea to examine the application of IT tools for patent searches.

3) Record of discussion on patents

Companies often argue about whether they were in the position to know about the existence of latent patents during the standards development process. So, it is recommended that records of discussion on patents in technical committees/subcommittees be kept. This might be included in the SSO's guidelines for their patent policies in order to help concerned people utilize the patent policies effectively.

4) Linkage with patent pools

While SSOs usually have no formal interaction with the patent pools, which should be able to provide relevant patent information, they should at least recognize whether or not there is the need for patent pools based on standards. In addition, SSOs may consider patent pooling to be a way to reduce the occurrence of a holdup problem. Special amendments of patent policy that allow a possible linkage with patent pools in some fields are a kind of measure for this. As written in the stability of patent pooling, these types of special amendments might prevent a holdup problem from occurring because they decrease the number of outsiders claiming excessive royalties.

After the publication of standards

In the second stage, it is generally assumed to be too late to change the contents of standards because a product or technology has been diffused in most cases. So, the possible applications of legal frameworks such as competition laws and/or intellectual property rights laws will be utilized, because SSOs usually have no authority to arbitrate disputes between companies. The utilization of Alternative Dispute Resolution (ADR) might work well in this stage, because it is a more flexible and rapid system than a trial. In any case, the situation will be discussed between industry and legal authorities in each county/region. However, it should be emphasized that legal frameworks have to be harmonized as much as they can because the relationship between standardization and patents is a global issue.

Conclusion

Standardization and intellectual property (patents) are closely related, especially in advanced technologies. Problems in patents concerning standards are becoming crucial to industries worldwide, because there is the possibility that this kind of problem will expand from IT to other advanced technologies such biotechnology or nanotechnology in the near future. Both SSOs and forums are facing very difficult and complicated issues on patents that are included in standards. They should ensure that incentives are provided for patent holders to participate in standardization, especially in some fields like IT. The legal stability of patent pools based on standards is becoming an important issue. SSOs should also consider how to deal with patent holders who claim excessive royalties for standard technologies. It is hoped that concerned parties examine how to improve the SSOs' rules including patent policies in order to prevent "ex post facto" excessive royalty claiming. These parties around the world need to consider measures that enable close collaboration and the effective utilization of these patent policies. This article is written based on personal perspectives and it does not reflect any view by the government or other entities.

References

Strategic Program for Creation, Protection and Exploitation of Intellectual Property, Intellectual Property Strategy Headquarters (2003), Japan (in Japanese)

Strategy for Intellectual Properties (recommendation), Council for Science and Technology Policy (2003), Japan (in Japanese)

Section: Influencing IPR Policies, *The Standards Edge*, edited by Sherrie Bolin, 2002, Bolin Communications

Policy issues in efficient collaboration through a patent pool, Sadao Nagaoka, Hitotsubashi University, for Taipei, 2003 International Conference on Competition Policies/ Laws-The Future Development of Competition Framework

20

Standardization and IPR—Global Situation, Japanese Challenges

HIDEHISA TANAKA
TORU TAKAYA
AYATO SUSAKI
Mitsubishi Research Institute

Abstract: *In recent years, standardization has been addressed not only by public standard-setting organizations (SSOs) under the initiative of governments, but also by forums voluntarily convened by private bodies. Meanwhile, companies' increased attention to protection of intellectual property rights (IPR) has led to some cases in which standardization, intellectual property rights, and competition policies conflict. These include cases in which companies protect the IPR of technologies that should be included in a standard or demand licensing fees for the use of technologies included in standards. This article intends to identify challenges that we are facing in propelling standardization while protecting IPR in de jure and/ or forum standards and considers necessary measures to support such goals.*

Preface

In this report, we summarize discussions from two study projects:

(1) "The Trend and Issues Concerning Relationship Between Development and Standardization of Advanced Technologies," conducted by Mitsubishi Research Institute, Inc. on behalf of the Ministry of Economy, Trade, and Industry of Japan

(2) A study group on standardization and intellectual properties, under the chairmanship of Professor Sadao Nagaoka of the Institute of Innovation Research, Hitotsubashi University, Japan—hosted by the same ministry.[1]

The study group continues to discuss the issue in FY2004, and it has to be noted that this article should be referred to as an interim report.

Changes in the Environment Surrounding Standardization

The environment concerning standardization has seen the following changes over the past few years.

> *"Whether a company's proprietary technology becomes a part of an international standard has become crucial to the success of business development in the global market."*

Increased importance of international standards

Whether a company's proprietary technology becomes a part of an international standard has become crucial to the success of business development in the global market due to the following background:

- While standards are what the public share in common, adoption of proprietary technologies in standards is of strategic importance for companies, since owning such technologies should bring competitive advantage in the market.

- The WTO/TBT Agreement (World Trade Organization's Agreement on Technical Barriers to Trade) stipulates that a standardizing body should use international standards, or the relevant parts of them, as a basis for the standards it develops.

Standardization in parallel with R&D

In the past, standards were often developed after products had already become widely available in the market. It is now common for standardization and R&D to be pursued concurrently under the following circumstances:

- Intensified competition and advancement of information technologies require even shorter cycles for developed technologies to be put to practical application, commercialized, and diffused in the market.

- Since the importance of international standards is continuously growing as noted earlier, it has become essential for companies to develop or win standards as early as possible.

- The more enormous and complex technologies become, the greater the cost grows to develop products and put them into the market. Therefore, standard setting after product commercialization would disadvantage those companies that had made efforts to incubate products with specifications different from the adopted standards.

Intensified activities of forums and consortia

In the past, standard setting was generally conducted by public Standards Setting Organizations (SSO). In recent years, however, private companies owning technologies are actively creating voluntary forums or consortia to develop standards. The following are some trends that underlie such movements:

- As technologies become more complex, companies tend to strengthen joint projects with external organizations for R&D or product development.

- The accelerated pace of technology innovation requires expedited approaches to standards development.

- Deregulation and privatization in an area that used to be under strict government controls are encouraging the participation of private companies in standardization.

Furthermore, some standards that public SSOs adopt are confirmations of those developed under forums or consortia, instead of those formulated on their own.

Collisions between standardization and protection of intellectual property rights

While standards have certain binding power, it is important that accessibility to them for the public is ensured. Meanwhile, along with the stream of pro-patent policies, companies tend

---

"While standards have certain binding power, it is important that accessibility to them for the public is ensured.."

---

to place more emphasis on IPR claims to their proprietary technologies. Therefore, in recent years, technologies adopted for standards tend to include those with IPR claims. Such claims in some cases have actually resulted in building barriers to the development, implementation, and dissemination of standards.

For example:

- Certain requirements for licensing essential technologies that owner companies impose may obstruct standardization.

- Complex interests arising from companies' intentions to gain competitive advantage by winning standards that include their proprietary technologies may hinder integration of such technologies as a standard.

- There have been some cases in which a

company claimed IPR after the development of standards containing its proprietary technologies.

Promotion of patent pools

Adoption of technologies covered by IPR in standards has been raising problems such as increased cost for license negotiations and cumulative licensing fees. One solution may be the establishment of so-called patent pools, which undertake the collective licensing of essential technologies.

Challenges Concerning Standardization

The changes in the environment as mentioned above have generated the following issues to address.

Standardization in the process of R&D

As more R&D and standardization take place in parallel, we face challenges on how to define and proceed with standard setting in R&D projects conducted within a company, under joint initiatives among companies, or with government support.

Coordination of IPR and standardization in companies

There are cases in which a company's interests in IPR policy and standardization contradict. To overcome this, those companies need coordination between the IPR and standardization departments so that they can opt for and execute the most effective strategies.

Development of IPR policies during the process of standard setting

Adoption of technologies with IPR claims in standards is now inevitable. To optimize the functions inherent in standards, SSOs need to develop IPR policies that clearly stipulate how to handle IPR during the process of standard setting.

Barriers obstructing access to standards containing IPR

At times, the existence of IPR may limit access to standards. Cases particularly concerned include the refusal of some companies to offer reasonable licensing terms for technologies adopted in standards and the demand for a prohibitive amount of licensing fees after the diffusion of standards.

Issues concerning patent pools

A patent pool benefits both licensors and licensees, since it deals with licensing fees for IPR in standards. Yet, the formation and management of a patent pool entail issues such as those

---

" ...the authorities dealing with patent law, antitrust law, and standardization must identify what roles respective organizations should play and how they should cooperate in this area."

---

concerning the definition of essential patents, incentives for company participation, distribution of royalties, and potential risk of violating competition law.

Policymakers' missions concerning the patent law, the antitrust law, coordination among different agencies, and supporting measures

In order to overcome the challenges mentioned above, the authorities dealing with patent law, antitrust law, and standardization must identify what roles respective organizations should play and how they should cooperate in this area.

Suggestions and Challenges

While we will continue to study this topic in FY2004, we have made the following suggestions in our FY2003 interim report.

Focus on standardization in the process of R&D

Standardization should already be addressed during the R&D phase. Not only companies but also public institutions and universities need to reinforce their R&D system to deal with standardization. Some suggestions include incorporation of standardization programs in

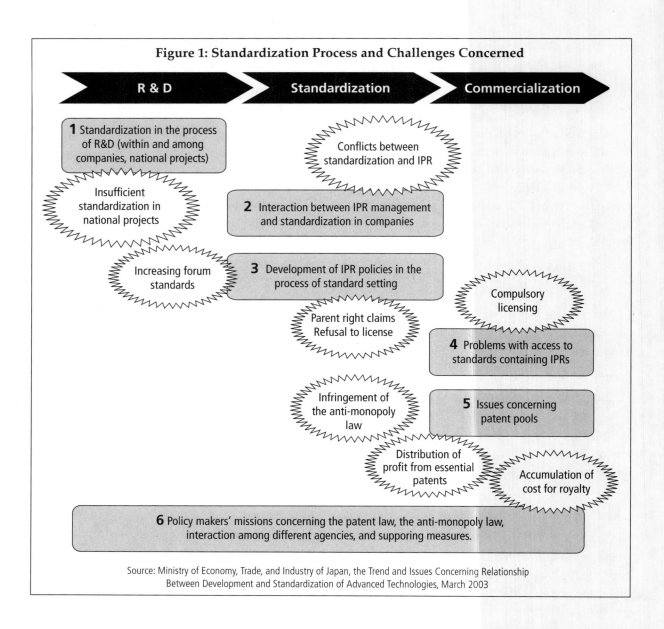

Figure 1: Standardization Process and Challenges Concerned

R & D → Standardization → Commercialization

1 Standardization in the process of R&D (within and among companies, national projects)

Insufficient standardization in national projects

Increasing forum standards

Conflicts between standardization and IPR

2 Interaction between IPR management and standardization in companies

3 Development of IPR policies in the process of standard setting

Parent right claims Refusal to license

Compulsory licensing

4 Problems with access to standards containing IPRs

Infringement of the anti-monopoly law

5 Issues concerning patent pools

Distribution of profit from essential patents

Accumulation of cost for royalty

6 Policy makers' missions concerning the patent law, the anti-monopoly law, interaction among different agencies, and supporing measures.

Source: Ministry of Economy, Trade, and Industry of Japan, the Trend and Issues Concerning Relationship Between Development and Standardization of Advanced Technologies, March 2003

R&D projects and securing budget and human resources dedicated to standardization.

Encourage coordination between protection of IPR and standardization in companies

Protection of IPR and standardization may have contradicting interests. Companies who include their IPR in international standards may benefit greatly from market diffusion, even when required to sacrifice the short-term profits that IPR may generate. Under such circumstances, companies need to construct systems under which IPR and standardization departments interact to promote strategic activities.

Although Japanese companies often regard standardization as an ancillary task, it is desirable that they establish sufficient support systems for such work.

Promote cooperation with forum activities

Forum activities and public SSOs must strengthen ties. Also, an appropriate category of corporate form needs to be defined for groups operating forum activities.

Develop clear definitions and flexible management of IPR policies in SSOs

SSOs should develop explicit IPR policies to avert conflicts concerning IPR. Meanwhile, IPR policy operation must be under a flexible system that would be least cumbersome for standardization participants and compatible with that of other organizations.

Establish systems to deal with ex post abuse of IPR concerning standards

Systems that respond to IPR issues after standardization should be developed. Possible suggestions include publicizing information to external organizations and notifying potential patent holders; and improving SSOs' measures to deal with ex post cases (e. g., adoption of alternative technologies in standards).

Support patent pool formation

Construction of a basis is essential to help facilitate the creation of patent pools, including the following:

- **Establish a system to determine the essentiality of patents.**

- Provide incentives for R&D oriented companies to participate in patent pools, such as allocating a greater share of royalties to companies according to the quality of their contribution; Determining this only by the number of contributed essential patents seems barely reasonable for those companies.

- Improve measures by SSOs, such as providing options concerning participation in a patent pool at the time of a standard's adoption. For example, request potential participants to make a commitment to participate in the pool in addition to complying with reasonable and nondiscriminatory (RAND) licensing terms.

- Make effective use of the Fair Trade Commission of Japan's preliminary consultation system concerning business activities.

- Develop a tax system that ensures elimination of double taxation.

- Construct systems to foster human resources versed in IPR strategies.

Nurture human resources with comprehensive expertise of IPR and standardization

It is essential to foster human resources with the ability to construct R&D strategies reflecting both aspects of IPR and standardization. Subjects may include identification of essential patents in patent pools. Training curricula can be incorporated in management of technology (MOT) programs.

Promote interaction among policymakers

Policymakers should construct a system to deal with patent conflicts, especially for ex post cases. Promotion of standardization by applying standards in government procurement should also be essential. In addition, in order to facilitate the measures mentioned in this section, the authorities should define the roles of different organizations in the management of intellectual properties after standards implementation.

Notes

[1] The members of the study group are Kenichi Hatori, National Institute of Advanced Industry Science and Technology; Hisashi Kato, Mitsubishi Electric Corporation; Souichirou Kozuka, Faculty of Law, Sophia University; Koichi Sumikura, National Graduate Institute for Policy Studies; Yoshinobu Tsuji, Ministry of Economy, Trade, and Industry; and Toshiya Watanabe, Research Center for Advanced Science and Technology, The University of Tokyo.

Section 4

Strategic Standardization

"*I not only use all of the brains I have, but all I can borrow.*" This sage advice from Woodrow Wilson, 28th President of the US, points to one of the greatest values of standardization: knowledge sharing. By participating in standards setting activities, organizations have the opportunity to exchange knowledge about technological innovations, best practices, user requirements, and industry dynamics, often in ways unparalleled during other business activities. There are few opportunities, other than in standards setting activities, where businesses can participate in this type of knowledge sharing—especially with their competition. Based on this exchange, businesses *can* decrease development time by building on existing technology, design more effective marketing strategies, and spur innovation by bringing new ideas back into their organizations. "*Can*" here is the operative word. The problem is that most companies don't have the strategies and processes in place to capture this information, act on it, and then reapply what they have learned back out to their standards setting activities. As a result, the valuable knowledge that can be gained by participating in the standards setting process remains locked within an individual or possibly their department, never achieving its full potential.

Why do corporations spend significant money on standardization each year and fail to take advantage of one of its key benefits? Most organizations simply do not have a comprehensive standardization strategy. And, the select few that have such a strategy often do not integrate it into their business processes. The reality is that many companies continue to remain oblivious to much of their standards activities, even to the point of their own participants opposing each other either within the same SSO or unknowingly creating conflicting results in separate standards setting organizations. To truly capitalize on standardization and all of its benefits, companies must have a comprehensive standards strategy that is integrated into their business processes. Regardless of whether the majority of standardization decisions fall to individual departments or to a centralized standards department, it is essential that standardization activities be driven by a comprehensive company strategy.

How should a company develop such a strategy and, once it is developed, what is the best way to implement it? To answer these questions, we go back to Woodrow Wilson's advice and begin by borrowing the brains, thoughts, and ideas of others. In this section, experts in the ICT industry share their advice on creating and implementing effective standardization strategies. While you may not agree with everything they say, their experiences provide a good starting point for developing and discussing your own standardization strategy and business process integration plan.

The section begins with Ray Alderman's market-level overview of where and how standardization fits into the two most prominent ICT markets: niche markets and commodity markets. Once you understand where your business competes most effectively and when standards come into play, the next step is to choose the right type of standardization tool depending on a company's situation and goals. Based on research conducted during the creation of Britain's National Standardization Strategic Framework, Stephen Munden of the British Standards Institution explains that "the right mix of innovation, cost, value, and standards...can change industry structure." In his article, Munden provides practical advice for selecting the right standardization tool for the right time. Along those same lines, Mike Smith of ISO discusses the standardization options available to organizations, with a particular emphasis on international standards.

Is a centralized standardization strategy appropriate for your organization or are standardization decisions best left to individual departments? For answers to this question, read Deepak Kamlani's article on "Innovation Strategy and Corporate Standards Management," which provides a view on centralized standards management from someone who works with numerous ICT companies to create and manage standards setting organizations. Don Deutsch, Oracle's Vice President of Standards Strategy and Architecture, shares his strategy for corporate standards management and provides advice for evaluating and selecting the most appropriate standardization venues in his articles.

Just how do the pros do it? Is Oracle's approach typical of other organizations? Andrew Updegrove of Lucash, Gesmer and Updegrove shares his survey on how standardization decisions are made by Hewlett Packard, Sun Microsystems, and a major non-technology company, along with the implications for standards setting organizations in his articles.

Regardless of what standardization decisions are made, the strategy itself must be integrated into business processes. By taking a look at geospatial standards, Dr. Carl Reed of the Open GIS Consortium examines how standardization strategies must not only be adopted into business practices to be successful, but must address the business context and the people involved as well.

No standards strategy today would be complete without addressing Open Source Software (OSS). John Terpstra discusses the role of standardization in making money from OSS and proposes that the law of diminishing returns, not open source, is the true enemy of proprietary software.

Finally, the debate over what constitutes an "open standard" continues to flourish. The decision to participate in open standards setting organizations or opt for those that limit participation will directly impact the speed and possibly the market perception of the resulting standard. Stephen Zilles provides a comprehensive definition of "open standards" and proposes a new strategy for standardization—"mostly open."

In a recent survey, IDC found that standardization increased the speed of innovation, enabled market entry by new companies, and expanded markets.[1] And a Delphi study concluded that, "Standards have shifted into high gear, not only garnering attention from business buyers but more important, they are being seen as a mandate for competitive stature, cost effective IT and operational excellence."[2] With the recognition of standardization as such a powerful management tool, will your company continue to ignore their presence, relying on pockets of disconnected standards activities within the organization to determine your ability to compete in the international marketplace? Or, will you take a close look at your corporate goals, develop a comprehensive standardization strategy, and integrate that strategy into your business processes? The choice a company makes today will directly impact its ability to compete tomorrow.

---

[1] IDC, 2001, "Standardization: The Secret to IT Leverage," p.2.

[2] Delphi Group, June 2003, "The Value of Standards," p.4.

21

Building a Business Case for Standards

RAY ALDERMAN
VITA

Abstract: *Standards are powerful mechanisms for rapid market development—from high volume component markets to low volume niche markets that capitalize on service and intellectual value-add. Companies who understand the dynamics of a product's specific market and then evaluate and integrate standards into their strategic plans accordingly are in the best position to create, recognize, and seize new market opportunities. This chapter discusses the dynamics and appropriate standardization strategy for specific types of markets.*

Strategic Planning

For technology companies, building a business case for participation in and adoption of industry standards is neither a purely analytical nor purely subjective exercise. In fact, such an analysis is mostly empirical and industry standards must be integrated as a cornerstone in a company's strategic plans to be successful.

About 40 years ago, Bert McCammon of Management Horizons defined the Strategic Plan as follows: "The task of strategic management is to develop a long-run, time-phased plan that will produce an attractive growth rate and a high rate of return on investment by achieving a market position so advantageous that

competitors can retaliate only over an extended time period at a prohibitive cost." Times have certainly changed. This strategy works when product and technology lifecycles are measured in years. It's not very useful when they are measured in months. You must remove "long-run" and "time-phased" from the definition to make sense today.

When technologies and their associated products have short lifecycles, you must drive volumes up rapidly, drive your costs down rapidly, and accomplish this over very short time

---

"When technologies and their associated products have short lifecycles, you must drive volumes up rapidly, drive your costs down rapidly, and accomplish this over very short time periods. "

---

periods. Few companies can do this alone. It takes catalysts, infrastructure, and an ecosystem to develop and exploit short-term market and product opportunities.

There are only two basic markets for OEM companies in technology: low volume/high margin markets (niches) and high volume/low margin markets (commodity markets). The two remaining markets, high volume/high margin (monopolies) or low volume/low margin (the Graveyard) segments are not viable markets. Larger technology companies are attracted to the high volume/low margin (commodity) markets, and their strategy is to trade margin for market share to drive their volumes up rapidly. The primary value-added in a commodity market is manufacturing value and that value is a function of volume, typically about 7-8% GPM in electronics manufacturing. This strategy comes from the work and empirical observations of the Boston Consulting Group documented in their work, "Perspectives on Experience" (BCG-1968).

BCG examined the "experience curve," and their conclusion is that every time industry volume of a product or technology doubles, all companies in that product segment see their costs decline by 20-30%. If a market for certain products and technologies promises large volumes, the strategy is to gain market share rapidly (i.e., trade margin for market share) and drive your costs down faster over higher volumes than your competitors. Such a market opportunity demands the creation of industry standards for the volumes to materialize. Standards are the catalysts.

Creation of an Ecosystem

High volume/low margin markets

An example can be seen in the connector industry. Volume OEM users of such technology products like connectors will not accept a single-source component supplier. They will demand multiple sources based on an industry standard that provides complete mechanical and electrical compatibility. This technology standard will also establish the basis of competition. Everett Rogers (University of Michigan) defined the lifecycle curves of technologies and products some years ago based on the adoption rates and consumer behavior of certain technologies and products. Those phases are: innovators, early adoptors, early majority, late majority (at the peak of the lifecycle curve and trending down), and laggards. According to Clayton Christensen (*The Innovator's Dilemma),* the basis of competi-

tion changes over time as a market and technology matures. His observations show the basis of competition on the lifecycle curves as: functionality, reliability, convenience, and price.

During the period when competition is based on functionality, the market becomes fragmented with all the competitive, but incompatible, implementations. Consequently, the mainstream volumes are delayed and the benefits of the experience curve cannot be recognized. If the volume can't materialize, then all the differentiated products define niches where volumes are low and margins/prices remain high until one of the implementations gains enough market share to drive out the other players. But, technology lifecycles are too short to

---

"The goal of a standards committee is to create a level playing field where the functionality-based competition phase is shortened, the different implementations are harmonized into compatible and conforming products, and the basis of competition is moved to reliability, convenience, and price more rapidly than would occur under normal market forces"

---

depend on this mechanism to gain market dominance.

The goal of a standards committee is to create a level playing field where the functionality-based competition phase is shortened, the different implementations are harmonized into compatible and conforming products, and the basis of competition is moved to reliability, convenience, and price more rapidly than would occur under normal market forces. OEM volume users get their required multiple sources for the connectors, and the basis of competition moves to reliability, convenience, and price. This process rapidly decreases industry time-to-volume for new products and technologies and engages the mechanisms of the experience curve.

The connector industry has known for many

years that standards are the catalysts for creating large volume markets. They know that prolonged competition, based on functionally different connector implementations, delays the market's time to volume. They know that delaying time to volume delays their cost reductions promised by the experience curve. They know that they must move their products and technologies into the early majority phase of the lifecy-

---

> *"...volume OEM users see standards as Mechanisms that remove risk from their component choices. "*

---

cle curve quickly because that's where volumes increase dramatically. And, they know that volume OEM users see standards as Mechanisms that remove risk from their component choices. Consequently, the market leaders in the connector industry embrace standards as a primary element in their business strategy. Technology standards mesh perfectly with the characteristics and behaviors of the connector market. The EIA (Electronics Industry Association) is the premier organization focused on the standardization of connectors.

Secondary markets

The benefits of a connector standard don't end with the connector market. The standardized connectors are placed on printed circuit boards (PCBs) containing many different semiconductors (as well as other components) that accomplish numerous different computing functions. Those PCBs are placed in metal racks holding those circuit boards. Many OEM manufacturers use those standardized connectors in many end product markets. If each of those OEMs designs a different form factor for the PCBs, the metal racks, and the cabinetry, time to volume is again delayed, and we lose the advantages of the experience curve in this secondary market. Consequently, the connector industry participates heavily in the development of electronic packaging standards constructed by numerous other standards bodies. Examples of

prolific electrical packaging standards are IEEE 1101 (19-inch rack standards and PCBs using the 3-row DIN connector), VITA 31 (19-inch rack standards for PCBs using the 2mm HM connector), VITA 34 (19-inch rack standards for PCBs using the RTGig NG connector), and PICMG-3 TCA (rack standards for PCBs using the 2mm ZD connectors).

These electronic PCB and rack standards not only define the PCB dimensions and metal rack mechanicals, they also define the shock, vibration, cooling, power distribution, and backplane requirements. Creating the connector standard and harmonizing all the competing implementations is simply a starting point. These PCB and packaging standards create an ecosystem that's imperative to market development for the standardized connector. Now, OEMs can adopt a packaging standard based on a connector standard and decrease their time to volume. This, in turn, decreases the time to volume for the connector products, and we have an effective positive feedback loop. Electronic racks and cabinet standards create another high volume/low margin commodity market, and all the major manufacturers in this segment use standards as a primary element in their business strategies.

Tertiary markets

Now that we have connector standards and electronic packaging standards, tertiary markets will develop that bring additional demand, increase volume, and drive costs down the experience curve. Using the IEEE 1101 mechanical standards, VITA created VITA-1.1 VMEbus Specification. VMEbus is a standardized set of bus protocols and silicon requirements that allow PCBs from multiple manufacturers to interoperate. VMEbus is one of the primary technologies used in most Military systems for weapons and other applications (Patriot Missile System, Abrams Tank, Apache Helicopters, signal processing SONAR and RADAR systems onboard ships, UAVs, etc.). PICMG used the VITA-31 mechanical specifications for their CompactPCI and 2.16 Switched Ethernet architectures targeted at the telecom equipment industry. These tertiary markets are niches, but they are quite large. VMEbus markets are near $800 million per year, while the cPCI and 2.16 markets are near $400 million. Comparatively, the connector and electronic packaging markets are multi-billion dollar markets. But, as you can see, they operate interactively and symbiotically. A single connector standard has a multiplier of somewhere around 100,000, according to my observations— for every $1 in connectors shipped, $100,000 dollars in equipment is shipped. A connector is a component. Without the component standard, the ecosystem of derivative standards couldn't be built. Without the ecosystem, the benefits of the experience curve couldn't be recognized.

Component standards are an absolute necessity in the technology industries. Component standards lead to implementation standards. Implementation standards lead to application standards. Application standards lead to subsystem standards. Subsystem standards lead to system standards. This progression shows that standards create an ecosystem. And, that ecosystem is a value-added chain. Different companies with different specific compentencies can participate at different levels in the value-added chain, as long as the infrastructure of derivative standards is healthy and stable.

Low volume/high margin markets

Smaller technology companies traditionally compete in low volume/high margin (niche) markets. Niche markets do not operate on the principles of the experience curve like the connector market since niche markets are low-volume markets. The primary value-added in a niche market is either service value (integration of components and subsystems into application-specific systems) or intellectual value (adding very unique and specific knowledge and capabilities to a system or subsystem). Service value-added produces about 25% GPM, while intellectual value-added can reap upwards of 60% GPM. Companies competing in niche markets trade volume for margin since the volumes in niche markets are low. Niche markets cannot leverage volume and there's little elasticity—

dropping your price by 50%, even if your costs are going down, will not result in a doubling of sales.

Just because the volumes in niche markets are low doesn't mean there's no need for standards. Many niche markets are quite large. Military, medical, transportation, test and measurement, traffic control, and partical physics (colliders) are some examples. Each of these market segments have specific methodologies in how systems are constructed and how they behave. These tertiary markets use the component, PCB, packaging, and interconnect standards created in the larger high volume/low margin (commodity) markets.

But, they implement them in different ways.

Smaller companies who compete in these niche markets use many of the standardized components that are travelling down the experience curve in the high-volume markets. This process invokes the "genetic inheritance" phenomenon: the components you use in your product will bring with them the price/margin characteristics of that components' primary market. So, if you are using very inexpensive standardized components in a unique way in a niche market, the pressure will be on you to continually reduce your costs, even though you don't have the volume or the experience curve to leverage.

Strategic standardization

Standards created for niche market technology implementations must define a minimum of interoperability and conformance requirements. Standards for a component, like a connector, must define every mechanical and electrical detail to insure compatibility between conforming products. Niche market standards are a framework for innovation and should standardize only the basic framework. Smaller companies must innovate behind the standard to differentiate their products. Larger companies who use component standards must compete on volume and drive the experience curve downward.

As an example, the VMEbus standard completely defines the PCB and rack mechanicals, the connector, and the complete bus protocol requirements. Smaller companies can decide to make high-performance processor cards, or I/O cards, or memory cards, or communications cards that conform to the standard. Niche market standards create many submarkets for smaller companies to exploit and differentiate

---

"Niche market standards are a framework for innovation and should standardize only the basic framework. Smaller companies must innovate behind the standard to differentiate their products. Larger companies who use component standards must compete on volume and drive the experience curve downward."

---

by focusing on certain technologies or functions. Component standards offer few market-segmentation possibilities. But, some commodity market standards do have segmentation options. Take the Personal Computer (PC) market for example. Smaller companies can take PC processors, I/O silicon, form factors (i.e., PCI slot-card board format), and software and implement those components in ruggedized chassis. Those smaller companies can market those systems as low-cost industrial control computers to the industrial manufacturers. They must differentiate with I/O interfaces not normally found in a PC, and they package the controllers differently for the industrial environment.

The success of a standard (and the companies who adopt that standard), whether aimed at the high volume/low margin (commodity) segment or the low-volume/high margin (niche) segment, is a function of the value-added chain, or ecosystem. Intel has been very effective at building ecosystems around their proprietary processor and chipset technologies. They have created defacto interconnect standards like PCI and PCI-Express and put those technologies under the control of the PCI-SIG, an independent consortium. Those specifications and technologies are freely available to all the players in the semicon-

ductor industry. The PC market promises high volumes for products that meet those interconnect standards, and multiple companies compete on volume and ride the experience curve down in cost as demand continues to double. Intel creates and feeds the ecosystem, and they benefit by increased demand and volume shipments of their processors and chipsets.

According to Shinichi Yano in "The New Lanchester Strategy," you are not a stable player in a market unless you have 26.1% market share. You cannot control and drive a market unless you have 41.7% market share. Never exceed 73.9% market share; you begin to lose the benefits of the experience curve above 74%, and the Justice Department takes an interest in your business practices at that point. That's why the high volume/high margin monopoly markets are unattainable.

The PC industry is a case in point. The supply-side structure of most high volume/low margin commodity markets is an oligopoly—there are four or five suppliers. In such a market, one or two of the suppliers are trying to achieve 40% market share to control the market. No one supplier has over 30% market share in PCs. Therefore, the PC market is very unstable and marginally profitable because one or more of the suppliers is always driving their price/cost curve down to attain 41.7% market share. Hewlett-Packard bought Compaq and raised their share above the others. But, further consolidation must occur before the PC market stabilizes. Similar situations existed in the steel, chemical, petroleum, automobile, and railroad industries.

None of the PC suppliers control the standards associated with PCs. All the hardware standards for the PC market are controlled by Intel, who holds more than 40% of the microprocessor market. All the software standards are controlled by Microsoft, who has more than 40% of the PC software market. The PC market is a pure example of a defacto standard working to drive the experience curve. And it's a perfect example of standards creating ecosystems. The standards used to create the PC market are component standards. The PC market and the PC software markets are secondary markets derived from the component standards created by Microsoft and Intel. Tertiary PC-derivative markets are numerous.

In low volume/high margin niche markets, the supply-side structure is a polyopoly (many suppliers). Niche market standards are typically derivative standards based on other components from larger high volume/low margin commodity markets. Typically, no one vendor has more than about 15-20% market share in the niches. No company has the market share to push the price/cost curve down, and niche markets are not elastic. No single company can control the technologies or product standards. Consequently, niche markets are stable and profitable. Companies who compete in these markets are more open to participating in standards committees and adopting those standards, since no large company can control the outcome.

The experience curve and technology standards interoperate well when large commodity markets sustain growth. When business conditions deteriorate and growth declines, volumes for the components go down. When these product volumes decline and costs are no longer riding the experience curve (i.e., the time to volume doubling increases), companies are pushed into the low volume/low margin Graveyard segment. There are only two methods to get out of the Graveyard: raise your margins (i.e., move into the low volume/high margin niche segments by adding service and intellectual value, and reducing costs through staff and plant reductions), or move back into the high volume/low margin commodity segment (i.e., taking business from competitors through aggressive pricing or mergers/acquisitions). Both solutions require a company to evaluate the standards associated with the products and technologies in their specific industries.

In prolonged downturns, we see the participants in standards efforts begin to exercise their intellectual property (IP) holdings. Patents grant a legal monopoly to the holder. Companies assert their IP at standards meetings in hopes of (1) receiving patent fees for any of their IP put into the standard, and (2) gaining a monopoly position with their IP in a standard. Both behaviors are targeted at increasing their margins and volumes to move the company into the high volume/high margin market segment.

All certified standards developers are bound by anti-trust law. Standards can only contain essential patents that are offered for license under RAND (Reasonable And Non-Discriminatory) terms to all companies who make products conformant to the standard. Certified standards developers cannot create monopolies or duopolies with their standards. If a standard is found to contain such essential patents, and the holders of the IP will not license under RAND terms, the patented technology is removed from the standard and another unpatented methodology is inserted. Companies who do not follow standards with their products are exposed to patent infringement assertions while those participating in standards development committees have collective protection and solutions against such claims.

Standards are mechanisms for the rapid development of markets. Some standards work cohesively with the experience curve to build high volume markets at the component level and those markets operate on Manufacturing value-added. Other derivative standards create secondary and tertiary markets that operate on service and intellectual value-added. Every technology standard creates market opportunities for large and small companies based on their specific competencies and capabilities.

It would serve every company in the technology business well if they evaluated and integrated standards into their strategic plans. Companies can find great opportunity in the ecosystems and value-added chains created by technology standards.

22

Strategic Standardization:
Right Tool, Right Time, Right Job

STEPHEN MUNDEN
British Standards Institution

Abstract: *There are many futile arguments about whether standards are good or bad, whether they inhibit innovation or promote it, whether they are barriers to trade or promote market access, and whether standards process/body A is better than B. Research conducted whilst preparing the United Kingdom (UK) National Standardization Strategic Framework suggests that more focus should be given to the understanding, selection, and implementation of a standard. This article is based on the author's conviction that it is not what standards say but what they do that is important. Selecting the right tool for the job is essential. Accordingly, the article concentrates on how to select the right standardization strategy and tool to get a specific job done in a timely manner. The views expressed are those of the author and not necessarily those of the British Standards Institution.*

Introduction

During the development of the UK's National Standardization Strategic Framework (NSSF),[1] the Steering Group, comprised of representatives from the British Standards Institution, the Department of Trade and Industry, and the CBI, spent a great deal of time trying to understand the scope and complexities of how standardization works.

To aid our understanding, we developed a roadmap of the standardization system.[2] We concluded that much of the discussion to date had concerned the processes and products of standards development but far less consideration had been given to the needs of stakeholders (business, society, and government, as well as the standardizers themselves) that should drive the system and the outcomes (as opposed to outputs) of the system. Thus, the scope of standardization includes requirements capture, development of the standard, promotion and acceptance, testing, attestation, and exploitation. It also became apparent that the system is not well understood, nor is it easily accessible to many. This has led to the under use and misapplication of standards and standardization solutions. Further, there appear to be no credible, practical economic models available at macro (i.e., national) or micro (i.e., organizational) levels to guide government officials and management into making the right strategic and tactical choices for their organizations *based on adequate return of investment.* Research work is currently underway in the UK and with other collaborators to develop such models. In the meantime, practical guidance on how to select appropriate routes through the standardization maze seems appropriate.

Why bother? To begin with, standards impact billions of dollars of exports along with an estimated $20-$40 billion of trade affected by non-tariff barriers. Couple that impact with

> "...standards impact billions of dollars of exports along with an estimated $20-$40 billion of trade affected by non-tariff barriers."

the millions of dollars made or saved last year by using standards and developing a strategic approach to standardization, and standardization becomes mission critical. Standards, whether they are formally called that or not, underpin almost everything we do or come in contact with. They literally define the rules of the game, whether that game is product creation and sales, buying and using products or services, or running your home affairs. Like it or not, all of these activities are subject to standards of some kind. The fundamental choice is to either understand and use standardization to your benefit or remain ignorant of it and suffer the consequences. Specific circumstances dictate the viewpoint held on standardization. For example, the producer—purchasing materials to standards and employing standard production methods—may permit the optimum selling price to be levied. The consumer, however, is looking for a price that provides the best value. In order to limit the scope of this article, the business viewpoint has been selected, although similar points also apply to the consumer, the politician, or any other perspective.

Given the apparent lack of understanding, it is not surprising that one of the key problems encountered is access to and navigation through the standardization system. In simple terms, it is important to select the right approach, based on need, for getting the job done in a timely manner. The lack of a sound business model for standardization makes an organization's management of it difficult. In many cases, it is clear that the inability to measure leads to fragmented efforts that are often not linked to business strategy. As a result, resources are wasted

and the objectives are never achieved. Two outcomes are commonly found: (1) either a company is engaged in standardization, notably standards development, in which case its participation efforts may be uncoordinated, leading to the creation of many disparate efforts—perhaps one of the reasons for the proliferation of consortia; (2) alternatively, the company withholds resources, has no way of obtaining leading business intelligence, and is subject to the rules of others.

When it comes to application, minimal knowledge of how standardization solutions

> "In many cases, it is clear that the inability to measure leads to fragmented efforts that are often not linked to business strategy."

may be applied often causes resources to be wasted and a negative view of standardization to form. For example, some companies "rubbish" ISO 9001 while others, who can demonstrate financial and other business benefits, praise the standard. Others disparage ISO 9000 because it does not define all aspects of a business and therefore is ineffective. Although it should be intuitively obvious that a business cannot be based on one limited standard, this misperception illustrates the danger of incorrect or minimal knowledge of standardization. Unless companies understand how to make a standard work for them, adoption will be minimal. Most importantly, companies must understand that it's not what the standard *says* but what it can *do* that is important. The course of action will be different, depending on whether you are trying to prevent competitive disadvantage, gain competitive advantage, or enlarge market space. In all cases, however, the objective should guide the selection of the appropriate standardization tool during each stage of the process.

What Are You Trying to Achieve?

A business faces many strategic choices. The right mix of innovation, cost, value, and standards—de facto or otherwise—can change industry structure. Where these factors converge, the rules of the game may be changed. Effectively participating in the definition of standards that will determine the rules for interna-

> *"The right mix of innovation, cost, value, and standards — de facto or otherwise — can change industry structure."*

tional competition is essential to any leading business seeking to maintain competitive advantage and, possibly, change these rules. The act of participating alone allows for the anticipation of new standards and helps determine their impact on technology and markets, thus allowing strategic positioning of an organization. The standardization system is also unique in that it brings industrial partners together. When industry collaborates, effective solutions to common problems are found, such as developing cost effective ways of meeting common regulations. The insights gained simply by reviewing the options with others can often justify participation.

Standardization is a key factor in determining marketing strategy. They are a primary route for demonstrating compliance with laws and regulations, which may impact market choice. Similarly, health, safety, and environmental risks may be reduced by measuring performance against standards and demonstrating improvements.

Using proven solutions recorded in standards may reduce technology risks. Acceptance is often greater and the market larger for products that conform to standards or have standard interfaces.

Operational strategies can also benefit from standardization considerations. Capital tied up in product, operating, and maintenance inventories may be minimized through variety reduction. In addition, using standard solutions permits new processes and plants to come online sooner. It also avoids duplication of efforts, reduces lead times, and increases purchasing power. There is also a marked shift to the standardization of business practices. Standardization is necessary when hardware and software from different companies must work together as a single operating system. It is also necessary when the operations of a business must work across the boundaries of collaborative firms. Standardization can therefore become of vital consideration in supply chain strategies. The skeptical might ask how many companies even realized that they were embarking on a standardization program when they were shoehorning their business processes into enterprise application systems.

Standardization is a horizontal strategic consideration impacting all aspects of the business. To achieve strategic effectiveness, a business has to understand the requirements of the marketplace, possess the organizational and technical capabilities to address perceived market requirements, define the economic requirements and probable results from various courses of action, and understand the major business opportunities and threats. The claim here is not that standardization will solve all of these issues, but that it forms a good platform for action and certainly needs to be taken into account to achieve success.

External business drivers

Although the sectors served by a business will contribute to shaping its external environment, at the macro level it is possible to generalize about the context in which a business operates. The main drivers that strategists need to consider are common. These include:

- **Globalization**: Reduced tariffs and other forms of protection, worldwide trend towards deregulation, and privatization of markets have all facilitated globalization.

- **Technological innovation:** This is especially relevant for information and communications technologies, which are a key to providing economic growth. By facilitating access to information across geographic boundaries, these technologies have increased the possibilities for individual relationships. In addition, the significance of individual country governments has been reduced while the influence of multinational enterprises and other organizations has increased.

- **Customer demands/quality imperative:** Customers are now able to compare prices easily, shop on a global basis, and better understand markets. This, in turn, is driving down prices and increasing demands for better quality products and services.

- **Unprecedented competition:** As a result of the above, companies are able to enter new markets, reconfigure supply chains, and offer innovative new products, all in shorter timescales.

- **Shrinking product life cycles:** Technology is being developed at faster rates and time to market is being reduced.

Strategic response

Drawing on research that I conducted in 2001,[3] I have concluded that, simply stated, a business is about four things:

- **Wealth creation:** the primary purpose of all business

- **Cost reduction:** the cost/price balance often being the basis for competitive advantage

- **Mandatory issues:** adherence to regulations and other "must do" things (such as ensuring that the plumbing works)

- **Renewal:** critical to either keep up with or ahead of others

During the course of this research, I also found that companies may innovate in three primary areas: customer experience, value delivery system, or strategic innovation. Each of these bears a little more explanation.

Customer experience

Nick Scheele, Chairman of Ford in Europe, said it well when he noted, "You have to be prepared to offer not just a product but a total service experience, through the whole life of the product."[4] Today's customers expect not only an explanation about product features and benefits, they need to be convinced of the entire consumption situation, which includes their expectations of what the value proposition will ultimately deliver.

Value delivery system

Building on Porter's introduction of the concept of value chains, Lanning (1998) claims to have taken the argument one step further by coining the concept of "value delivery system," which he defines as "business as an integrated system entirely oriented around the delivery of a chosen value proposition. That is, a business should be defined and managed as a value delivery system rather than by the conventional model of a product supply system."

Strategic innovation

Forces of change, such as digitization, the Internet, and the convergence of technologies, present new opportunities for business innovation. Hamel and Prahalad (1994) noted that "a company can control its own destiny only if it understands how to control the destiny of its own industry." However, as we have seen earlier, instead of positioning their companies in known industry structures by considering how to change the rules of engagement, managers may create new structures.[5]

Although a company may achieve sustainable competitive advantage that allows it to outperform its competitors by operating at lower costs, appropriate strategic positioning is required to command premium prices. This involves a complex mix of the right goal, a differentiated value proposition, a distinctive value chain, the right tradeoffs, and strategic fit. Choosing the right strategies can be a difficult task. Taking the above extended definitions of product, delivery, and strategy and mapping them against the four business imperatives listed previously, a useful grid is offered to help develop specific strategies based on the options available and the organization's motivations and capabilities.

Although the grid may be used to develop any type of strategy, the examples chosen represent choices associated with standardization strategies. Working left to right and top to bottom:

- **Value chain interoperability:** Which standards are needed to ensure that my value chains can interact with those of my suppliers, customers, and collaborators? How do I connect my business with others?

	Customer Experience	Value Delivery Systems	Strategic Innovation
Profit		e.g., Value Chain Interoperability	e.g., Market Creation
Cost	e.g., Product Standardization	e.g., Management Systems	
Mandatory	e.g., Cost Effective Compliance		
Renewal	e.g., Reduced Risk Innovation		

Source: Stephen Munden, 2001

- **Market creation:** How do I restructure the existing market or create a new one?

- **Product standardization:** How can I employ standardization's ability to provide supplier choice and drive down costs by using standard parts in my purchasing strategies?

- **Management systems:** How can the standardization of my business processes yield cost improvements? (Ignoring the misuse of consultants and poor implementation by others [!] but noting the savings of those that have shown cost reductions.)

- **Cost effective product compliance:** Can standards be used to meet European CE Marking regulations, for example?

- **Reduced risk innovation:** How do I employ new or existing standards to reduce the risk of invesment in new technologies or product lines?

Selecting the Right Tool

Ironically, one of the problems in the standardization system is that there is no standard classification of standards! Since the focus of this article is to use standardization to actually do something, a taxonomy based on function (Tassey, 1999) has been chosen. It comprises four categories:

1. *Quality/reliability*—"Standards developed to specify acceptable product or service performance along one or more dimensions such as functional levels, performance variation, service lifetime efficiency, safety, and environmental impact. Such standards specifying a minimum level of performance often provide the point of departure for competition in an industry."

2. *Information*—Standards providing evaluated scientific and engineering information in the form of test and measurement methods for describing, quantifying, and evaluating product attributes. Transaction costs between buyer and seller are reduced by virtue of their acceptance.

3. *Compatibility/interoperability*—"Standards that specify properties that a product must have to work (physically or functionally) with complementary products within a product or service system." Interface standards do not affect the design itself but allow multiple proprietary component options to coexist. They allow products to work together and support the growth of networks of complementary products.

4. *Variety reduction*—"Standards limiting a prod-

uct to a certain range or number of characteristics such as size or quality levels." Many standards reduce variety to attain economies of scale.

In practice, any one standard may embody aspects of all four. To make matters worse, anybody can (and often does) develop standards. Another issue then is what "authority" will the standard command and how will this impact promulgation and adoption? Further, have you the resources to pay for speed and control, or are your objectives such that time is on your side and collaboration is possible and desirable? In any case, you are faced with another four choices, this time about the route chosen to get the standard developed and established:

1. *Formal standards*—The "traditional" route using organizations such as International Organization for Standardization (ISO) and International Electrotechnical Commission (IEC) and national bodies such as the British Standards Institution. The authority conferred is high and the "promulgation factor" also high, due to the extensive international networks employed. However, the processes of transparency, integrity, inclusiveness, etc. come at a price. It takes time (and money) to achieve consensus.

2. *Consortia*—The other end of the spectrum, where speed and control are assured but the cost may be very high and market acceptance is not assured.

3. *Alliances*—Nice if you have the clout and are one of the partners, but again success may not be assured at the speed one might think. Consider Wireless Application Protocol (WAP) and Bluetooth.

4. *Open Source*—If your strategy is to spread your technology, rather than to protect and license it, open standards provide a possibility. Here costs and control are low, but if the standard catches on, it can be a powerful technology adoption accelerator. A prime example here is Linux.

One distinction to make, which is particularly applicable to ICT standardization, is that between Open Source—a method of creating a standard—and "open systems" standards. Open systems generally refer to three kinds of standardization:

1. The standardization of the interface between computers and their applications. This impacts portability (i.e., the ability to move an application from one computer to another).

2. Standardization of the communications interfaces, allowing data and messages to flow from one computer to another.

3. Standardization of the interface between computers and peripherals, allowing the physical mixing and matching of various kinds of hardware.

Standardization should be considered as systemic. One factor invariably links to another. Successful strategies are, therefore, likely to be a combination of aspects. For example, contrast the strategy of controlled migration, a combination of compatibility and control, used by "Wintel," to the discontinuity or paradigm shift created by CDs, a combination of openness and performance.

A simple way to begin developing appropriate strategies is to think in terms of control and stimulation. Options available to control costs or meet regulatory requirements point to the use of different tools from strategies concerned with market penetration by new product offerings. The first may concern the deployment of existing, formally established standards able to

> *"A simple way to begin developing appropriate strategies is to think in terms of control and stimulation."*

produce economies through variety reduction or lowering of supplier costs. The second requires more of a "battle mentality," where competition is likely between the dominant firm and the collective efforts of others, between open standards and proprietary, and between the different ways

Figure 2: Product life cycle model

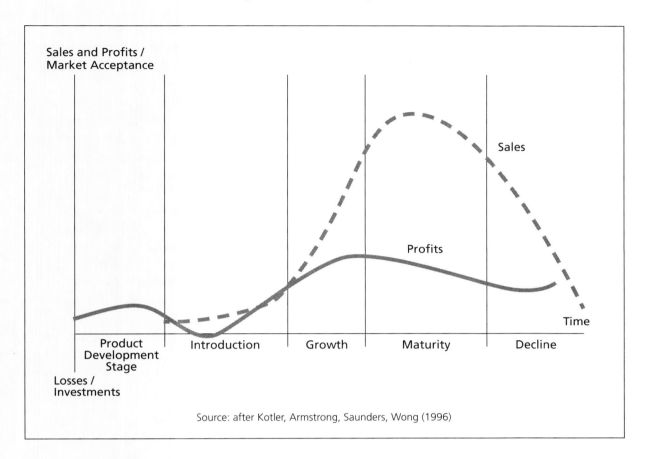

Source: after Kotler, Armstrong, Saunders, Wong (1996)

of setting standards (single company investment with associated patenting and licensing versus consensus agreement and open distribution).

Timing is Everything

The product life cycle model is useful when considering the timing of appropriate action. What a business is trying to achieve varies with time for any one technology, product, or process. The basic model is represented below, although in practice it is recognized that many of the activities will be concurrent, not sequential. There is not room in this article to go into the importance and details of the model here, but the basic stages are:

1. *Development*—investment in a new technology or product concept begins, costs grow but there are no sales

2. *Introduction*—sales growth is slow and profits are nonexistent due to development investments

3. *Growth*—a period of rapid market acceptance and increase in profits

4. *Maturity*—marked by a slowdown in sales growth because the product or technology has achieved acceptance by most potential buyers. Profits level off because of the marketing spend to defend against competitors or new innovations

5. *Decline*—when sales fall off and profits drop

Moore (1995, 2000) discusses the concept in terms of a technology adoption or market acceptance and relates this to strategic marketing decisions as they apply to the "high-tech" market in some detail. This helps to see the relationship between the firm's actions above and market place activity. For the same stages as above, Moore uses the following market profiles:

1. *Innovators*—technology enthusiasts, game for any new gadget

2. *Early adopters*—revolutionaries in business and government who want to use the innovation to break with the past and start something new

3. *Early majority*—the pragmatist who buys something, preferably proven to achieve a purpose

4. *Late majority*—the price-sensitive, skeptical, and demanding conservatives

5. *Laggards*—the real skeptics who really are never convinced of the merits of the new

Relative to standards, market acceptance can be viewed in terms of consensus achieved. This relates to both the degree of authority that a standard enjoys and also its promulgation. Generally, this also applies to the time axis. More consensus is possible over a longer period of time due to the greater practical inclusivity. Thus the tool selected must fit the circumstances. It is likely that early specification during the development and introduction stages will be required in a far shorter time than full standards at the mature stage in stable market conditions. The combinations resulting therefore provide the strategic choices to be made in terms of positioning, differentiation, and so forth.

The following table provides a summary of examples of some of the strategic combinations to be considered.

Standardization at the beginning of the life cycle clearly has a more anticipatory nature than at the mature stage, where actions are more likely to be responsive or concern adoption.

Conclusion

Although standardization methods, tools, and measures may be generic, their application must be specific to the organization. Corporate, operational, and functional strategies need to be defined before the assessment of the strategic potential of standardization can be assessed. Corporate objectives, such as cost leadership, differntiation, and dominance, can be achieved through the application of selected standardization strategies using the appropriate tools at the right time.

Table: Selection of standardization solutions at life cycle stages

Stage	Development	Introduction	Growth	Maturity	Decline
Technology Adoption	Innovators	Early Adopters	Early Majority	Late Majority	Laggards
Strategic Objectives	Risk Reduction / Modularization / Building Block Systems	Product Leadership	Customer Intimacy / Product Leadership/ Operational Excellence	Operational Excellence / Customer Intimacy	Operational Excellence
Typical Standards Questions	What technology meets the standard?	What standards should the process follow?	What tests / marks are required for the market?	Can standards reduce component costs?	
Standards Tools	Information	Compatibility	Quality / Reliability	Variety Reduction	Variety Reduction

Notes

1 Available at www.nssf.info.

2 A diagram and explanation of "How Standardization Works" is available at www.nssf.info.

3 For further information on these concepts, see the "How Standardization Works" map at www.nssf.info.

4 "Making Sense in a Topsy Turvy World" as reported at http://www.inspiringchange.co.uk (April 20, 2000).

5 *Platform Leadership*, Annabelle Gawer and Michael A. Cusumano, (Harvard Business School Press, 2002), provides examples of how Intel, Microsoft, and Cisco have used standardization to drive industry innovation.

Bibliography

Gawer, Annabelle & Cusumano, Michael A. *Platform Leadership*. Boston: Harvard Business School Press, 2002.

Hamel, Gary/ Prahalad P K. *Competing for the Future*. Boston: Harvard Business School Press, 1994.

Kotler, Philip/ Armstrong, Gary/ Saunders, John/ Wong, Veronica. *Principles of Marketing—The European Edition*. Europe: Prentice Hall, 1996.

Lanning, Michael. *Delivering Profitable Value*. Oxford UK: Capstone Publishing Limited, 1998.

Moore, Geoffrey A. *Inside the Tornado*. New York: Capstone Publishing Limited, 1998.

Moore, Geoffrey A. *Living on the Fault Line*. Oxford UK: Capstone Publishing Limited, 2000.

Tassey, Gregory. *Standardization in Technology-Based Markets*. National Institute of Standards and Technology, 1999.

23

Innovation Strategy and Corporate Standards Management

DEEPAK KAMLANI

Global Inventures, Inc.

Abstract: *Centralization is a dirty word. For many it conjures up images of bureaucracy, inertia, and socialism and all its perceived and attendant ills. Yet, corporations do centralize many critical functions, and they do direct functional policy and practice from this perspective— planning, hiring, and supply chain management are some examples. In this article I attempt to make the case for a Corporate Standards Practice, in the context of corporate objectives, innovation strategy, research and development investment, and the need to generate a return on investment from these programs.*

I'm Here from Corporate...

And I'm here to help. Anyone who has worked in a large organization will recognize the disbelief, smirks, and outright hostility that statement can provoke. After all, corporate people are those who look past the great collateral you just produced and point only to inappropriate use of the company logo; they make you travel on every airline but the one you have the most frequent flier miles on or the one that gets you there quickest; they make you sign up for the health plan your family doctor isn't on; and they make you use computers you hate. All of this because the organization must have standard ways of doing things to achieve some mysterious benefits they call scale and leverage. And along the way— they bounce your expense reports. Small wonder then, that for business unit and field personnel, the person from corporate is typically seen as someone to work around, not with.

While the relative merits of decision making in centralized corporate versus distributed business unit models have been and will be argued through time, the need for a commercial corporation to grow profitably—relative to public or private investor expectations and the competition— cannot be contested. Corporations essentially manage two curves: revenue and costs. Of the two, revenues are susceptible to competition, economic, and other environmental factors, while costs are more clearly in the corporation's control. Therefore, if centralization offers supply chain efficiencies—as demonstrated through volume procurement, headcount rationalization, or process streamlining—corporations will pursue that path.

Standards however present a whole new challenge. On one level, they are part of the supply chain. Corporations can mandate, for example, that all ICT purchases must be standards based solutions and leave it at that. In this scenario— which I will refer to as *ICT Consumption*—the purchase goals are interoperability, eliminating reliance on proprietary technology ("lock downs"), and the ability to pick and choose between multiple vendors for the best applications based on the relevant standard, the lowest price, and the best support. In these situations, ICT is a key enabler—it provides more, better, faster information and communication for decision making—but it is no more than that. The consuming entity provides non-ICT products and services, perhaps consumables like soap, hamburgers, and paper products or constants like books, paper clips, and picture frames. Other than ensuring that their offerings comply with any mandated national standards, for example Underwriter's Laboratories (UL) and its equivalents in specific markets, such entities have limited if any interest in the development of ICT standards. In these situations, centralization reduces to specifying purchase criteria, selecting the vendors, and negotiating the deal.

Conversely, private corporations backed by venture capital or those that appear on the many Tech 100 lists have acute interest in participating in the creation of ICT standards. In this scenario, which I will refer to as *ICT Production*, corporate

---

"...ICT Standards can, if staged properly in a category, be the key vehicle to monetize the upfront dollars invested in development..."

---

business models, market valuations, the ability to maximize shareholder value, and long-term survival are at stake. Such entities deal daily with what Sir Harold Wilson, an ex Prime Minister of Great Britain, called the "white-hot heat of technology." The onus here is to not burn. Rather it is to innovate and monetize upfront (often substantial, but usually speculative) investments in new technologies through increased sales in existing markets, the launch of new products and penetration of new markets, and incremental revenue streams and profit pools based on intellectual property licensing, for instance. Various authors and commenta-

tors have noted the core relevance of standards development to these objectives.[1]

At the base, while not all IP is created for industry standards, all ICT standards contain intellectual property and patents. Accordingly, ICT Standards can, if staged properly in a category, be the key vehicle to monetize the upfront dollars invested in development either through the disruption of competitor business models based on the licensing of intellectual property embedded in an existing standard or the creation of "end run" markets that bypass current product/market paradigms.

The numbers are gigantic. Independent studies indicate that:

- US firms spent about $194 billion in Research and Development in 2002—a year in which budgets were severely constrained due to the post-bubble meltdown.

- Patent filings globally are in excess of seven million annually (but 90% of these fillings are for protecting the same patent in multiple patent regions) and the US Patent Office receives more than 300,000 filings per year.

- US firms spent $45 billion in 2001 just to prosecute and maintain patents.

- By 1998, revenues attributable to licensing of intellectual property had reached $100 billion worldwide.

- IBM, the habitual US leader in annual patents granted, surpassed $1 billion in annual licensing revenues in the late 1990s and has, during the past ten years, generated in excess of $10 billion in *bottom line contributions* from IP licensing.

We should note that these numbers measure R&D and patents across all industries, not just in ICT alone. But the point is clear. Intellectual property is a big business, with real revenue and real profit streams—and in the long run, realization of return on investment (ROI).

The question, then, is how IP creation relates to corporate objectives. According to *Technology Review*, an MIT publication, IBM, for instance, spent $5.3 billion on R&D in 2002—the highest absolute number among IT firms—but at 6.2% of revenues, it came in lower than Sun Microsystems ($2.1 billion, 11.5%) or Microsoft ($4.4 billion, 17.3%). Either way, these huge numbers represent upfront, speculative investment with the *potential* for future monetization through the creation of intellectual property. These investments dictate a Hypothetical Imperative,[2] which, to paraphrase Kant, is a "conditional rule of action, concerned with means and ends rather than with duty for its own sake." Translated, this means that corporate executives must correlate their means (investments) to ends (returns). IP incorporated in a standard is such an end, as is IP in a proprietary play. In the next section, I explore the relationship of ICT intellectual property creation to corporate innovation strategy and standards leadership.

Innovation Strategy and Standards Leadership

Commercial corporations can pursue six alternatives with regard to innovation strategy. These six alternatives—Offensive, Defensive, Imitative, Dependent, Traditional, and Opportunist—are summarized in Figure 2. The extent to which each innovation strategy supports corporate goals and posture, and ICT

orientation and standards leadership are also indicated.[3] I have categorized ICT orientation as *Producer, Adopter, or Consumer, and ICT Standards Leadership on a Must Have to Not Relevant scale.*

Innovation strategy stems from corporate objectives and goals. For many ICT companies, these objectives and goals flow from the relative need to demonstrate market leadership, technology leadership, and to convert these positions to measurable ROI. If a company chooses to be a

---

"If a company chooses to be a leader, it is implicitly establishing R&D and the generation of IP as a mission critical program."

---

leader, it is implicitly establishing R&D and the generation of IP as a mission critical program. Once IP is generated, the corporation faces the option of maintaining that IP in a proprietary mode, or pursing formal or community driven standardization. As illustrated below in Figure 1, whatever the decision, the corporation must establish a high profile in the standards world, if only to understand the value of the IP relative to any options available and the means (licensing model) by which ROI will be generated.

Figure 1

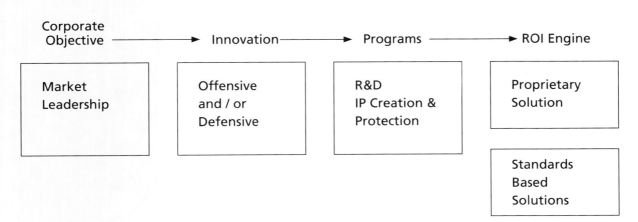

Returning to the Innovation Strategy options, given the typical mix of products, business segments, and customers most ICT producing corporations are involved in, a single innovation strategy is unlikely to apply universally. A more rational selection might involve a "portfolio of strategies," balancing Defensive, Offensive, Imitative, and Opportunist Innovations against perceived long term goals, opportunities, and threats. Companies not involved in ICT products and services can typically include each alternative in determining which path to pursue. The pressure is not so acute here to be in the top tier of companies offering solutions with differentiated technology or solutions incorporating proven technological advances.

Companies with ICT at the core of their offerings typically do not have all these options available. Whether the product category is semiconductors, routers, computers, consumer electronics, operating systems, or computing infrastructure, the companies involved win top tier positions at least partially (in some cases in large part) because of their technological prowess and their ability to create and harness IP in their solutions. The phrase "Innovate or Die" characterizes their orientation, assuming a top tier market position is required. And it typically is—many firms abandon markets unless they can capture and maintain the number one or two position.

Of the alternatives identified, neither the Dependent nor the Traditional innovation strategies offer any realistic choices for companies in the ICT space. As their description implies, such strategies are better suited to companies not involved in high-technology industries (i.e., businesses where products are static or custom/customer driven). The strategies are also incompatible with typical ICT company goals of technological leadership, marketing orientation, and commitment to offer products and services of excellent quality and value to customers. Companies pursuing these innovation strategies

either adopt or consume ICT, and standards leadership is either not desired or not relevant.

In relation again to ICT companies, both the Imitative and Opportunist strategies are also of limited applicability. While the Imitative Strategy is one that many companies have successfully followed, the reliance on acquired designs and licenses, which can be lost or revoked, may eventually force the corporation to concentrate more on its own, in-house innovations. In the baseline however, the company is choosing to adopt non-company IP and standards leadership is not necessary. Similarly, the Opportunist Strategy offers the option of following multiple niche market development strategies, but it is of potential only if a second or third tier position is acceptable, and it negates the possibility of an impact entry in evolving markets with attendant forfeit of early revenue and profit. Here the company straddles the adopter/producer border and so a standards leadership position may be necessary.

Fundamentally it follows that only the Offensive and Defensive innovation strategies are available as choices for the corporation that desires to produce ICT and bake this output into industry accepted standards *(de facto and/or de jour)*. Whereas Offensive innovation offers the ability to capture and hold markets as a first mover, it also carries inherent and sustained risk—the risks associated with this strategy again militate against its consistent selection. In this scenario, standards leadership is a "must have." As a natural and ongoing process, therefore, Defensive innovation may prove to be the most viable alternative. Although the risks associated with this strategy are also high, they are balanced by the fact that neither profitability of new ventures nor the company's overall technological position are sacrificed, *provided* it is able to react quickly and effectively to trends in the market. Here standards leadership is not as critical—participation is a must but leadership is "nice to have."

Figure 2
Corporate Innovation Strategy and ICT

Innovation Strategy	Goal	Posture/Capability	ICT Orientation	ICT Standards Leadership
Offensive	Achieve Market & Technology Leadership	Strong R&D Investment IP / Patent Monetization First Mover Market Benefits	Producer	Must Have
Defensive	Improve & Leapfrog Others' Innovations	Strong Development & Design Product Differentiation Fast Follow Market Entry	Producer	Nice To Have
Opportunistic	Deliver Solutions for Identified Gaps	Entrepreneurial Focus Exploit Opportunities Serve Rapid Change Markets	Adopter / Producer	May Need
Imitative	Emphasize Licensing & Acquiring Know-how	Strong Integration Engineering Compete on Lower Unit Costs Serve Captive Markets	Adopter	Not Necessary
Dependent	Follow Customer Input, React to Specified Needs	Strong Customer Interaction Low Overhead Serve Niche Markets	Adopter	Not Desired
Traditional	Deliver Static Products	Strong Process Focus Craft Skills Serve Volume	Consumer	Not Relevant

Note: The first three columns of this table are adapted from "The Economics of Industrial Innovation," Christopher Freeman (Penguin).

In relation again to ICT companies, both the Imitative and Opportunist strategies are also of limited applicability. While the Imitative strategy is one that many companies have successfully followed, the reliance on acquired designs and licenses, which can be lost or revoked, may eventually force the corporation to concentrate more on its own in-house innovations. In the baseline, however, the company is choosing to adopt non-company IP, and standards leadership is not necessary. Similarly, the Opportunist strategy offers the option of following multiple niche market development strategies. However, it is of potential only if a second or third tier position is acceptable, and it negates the possibility of an impact entry in evolving markets with attendant forfeit of early revenue and profit. Here the company straddles the adopter/producer border and so a standards leadership position may be necessary.

If this linkage proposed in this chapter between corporate objective, innovation strategy, IP creation and protection, and ROI generation is accepted, the question that must be resolved is the management model as related to the steps beyond objectives and strategy setting. As noted before, R&D spending— the engine for IP creation— is in the $200 billion range in the US alone. With spending at individual big companies in the mid-multibillion dollar range and expenditures representing between six and eight percent of sales on average, corporations have traditionally chosen to manage the R&D effort centrally as a corporate function. In some cases they have even centralized the conduct of R&D in a specific structure (e.g., Bell Labs in days gone by). This corporate direction is geared to linking the steps in the objectives-strategy-funding steps in Figure 1 as expected, given the large number of patents granted annually (IBM obtains more than 3,000 patents annually by itself). So the corporation is simply executing the right asset management model in centralizing the function in the corporate domain.

Traditionally, however, corporate management and direction has stopped at IP creation and protection. Where corporations have chosen to generate ROI through standardization programs, the actual participation and representation in standards bodies has been left to the individual Strategic Business Unit (SBU) responsible for a particular market. In the next section, I highlight the large internal fragmentation risk this approach leads to and present a case for corporate standards management.

Corporate Standards Management—A Model

To begin, it is necessary to provide some context. Until the early 1990s, ICT standards were created almost exclusively by national (ANSI, BSI), regional (ETSI), or international (ITU, ISO) Standards Setting Organizations (SSOs). Much of the activity focused on telecommunications, as the "I" in ICT was still evolving. In these early days, decentralized corporate divisions (Strategic Business Units, SBUs) drove participation in SSOs and customers required the support of standards in products and services. If a supplier supported a standard that a customer mandated and won sales as a result, the SBU went further in meeting or exceeding corporate performance expectations, the corporation delighted the market with better results than expected, and customers received greater assurance that their purchases would interoperate and not be subject to orphaned/proprietary/monopolistic behavior. While this translated to a win-win for all concerned, standards in this era were effectively a *sales tool*.

Telecommunications deregulation and the Internet changed everything. As sizable markets evolved around new technologies, many corporations began an earnest examination of their "dusty patent" portfolios and, in some notable cases, attempted to extract royalties from suppliers who had—often inadvertently—incorporated patented IP in their offerings. Thus, by way of example:

As Information Services markets expanded, a company attempted to assert patent claims to Dual Tone Multi Frequency (DTMF, Touch Tone to most of us), which enables such services to work.

- As Video Conferencing began to grow, various companies asserted claims to the IP in the Audio and Video Codecs embedded in standards approved even at the ITU-T level.

- As HTML and browsers unleashed the World Wide Web, a large European company asserted ownership of the patent for hyperlinks—the function at the core of the Web.

It is important to note that these actions were reactive (i.e., they occurred after the royalty/licensing revenue potential of IP in standards had become apparent). Something like this also happened in the Rambus/JEDEC case, where a proposed SDRAM standard was the subject of FTC antitrust action due to the alleged deliberate non-disclosure of key patent applications, and the attempt to extract licensing revenues by the patent holder after the standard had been approved.

With the parallel growth of de facto standards like Windows and fundamental technologies

---

"With the parallel growth of de facto standards like Windows and fundamental technologies like Java and LINUX/Open Source—each governed by different licensing schemes—standards completed the transition from sales tools to ROI Engines and Business Model Enablers."

---

like Java and LINUX/Open Source—each governed by different licensing schemes—standards completed the transition from *sales tools* to *ROI Engines* and *Business Model Enablers*. Consequently, the value of IP baked in community driven and SDO/SSO approved standards started to become apparent. Companies helped create standards by gaining community support for solutions incorporating their IP; they allowed extensions from third parties to fill voids; and they agreed to license their IP in standards approved by the community on pre-established terms (RAND, Royalty Free, Open Source, Public license, etc). Depending on the licensing

model, they either generated licensing revenue for dusty and fresh patents through this process, or they disrupted proprietary or alternative community based standards through it.

Consequently, today, the total number of independent, purpose built, standards creating organizations worldwide is in the many hundreds, if not thousands (note that this is anecdotal, not empirical data). This situation raises a new set of challenges. If participation in these independent organizations is driven at the division level, the corporation as a whole faces tangible risk. In my business, Global Inventures, we incubate and grow communities involved in the creation of standards and provide outsourced resources and management services to such organizations. During this process, we observe the following key issues, which are exacerbated in large Fortune 1000 companies, but not localized to them.

● **Opportunity loss.** This frequently occurs the moment a division signs a membership agreement and agrees to abide by the organization's IPR policy. Quite frequently such policies mandate royalty free licenses for IPR incorporated in adopted specifications. This provision triggers when a required disclosure of Necessary Claims in a submission to a proposed specification is not made. Therefore, if the appropriate participation and IPR checks and balances have not been performed at the corporate level, the corporation either loses an opportunity to submit its IP for a specification because the licensing terms are unacceptable, or it loses the ability to generate licensing revenue because the submission is competitively necessary but must be royalty free.

Opportunity loss also occurs in organizations with RAND licensing provisions, because the participating SBU is unaware of IP buried in the corporate patent portfolio that might apply to the organization's standards—in some cases we have seen a competitor's technology receive this benefit.

● **Strategy arbitrage.** This occurs when different SBUs participate in overlapping organizations in which the end standards are competitive. We have seen one SBU take positions on proposed technology solutions and IP licensing that inadvertently sabotage a winning

---

"We have seen one SBU take positions on proposed technology solutions and IP licensing that inadvertently sabotage a winning position for the other SBU. "

---

position for the other SBU. A variation of the "left hand not knowing what the right hand is doing" theme, the consequence here is sometimes redundancy but more typically unconscious arbitrage of corporate investment in innovation strategy.

🔹 **Participation failure.** This occurs because the SBU, managed and measured on a P&L (profit and loss) mandated by corporate financial plans, is either: (1) too focused on this primary mission to be aware of a standards initiative it should be part of; or (2) because it is aware but fails to establish the "mission critical" relevance of a new standards initiative to its future and passes on participation; or (3) because, although it correlates relevance to the future, it is unable to fund participation. All too often we hear—typically from a harried manager charged with delivering results *now*—responses like "we're too busy to participate" or "someone from my company should be involved, but I don't know who," or " we don't have the budget, so we'll pass for now." Participation failure also occurs when the assigned participant sees the effort as tedium and "a waste of my time" and/or because the assigned participant has, through behavior and personality, tarred the corporation and cornered its position to one of no hope in a submission selection process.

Earlier, I endeavored to establish the link between corporate objectives, innovation strategy, and corporate inventions as defined by corporate IP and patents. Opportunity Loss, Strategy Arbitrage, and Participation Failure represent breaks in this value chain and fatally injure the ability to monetize IP through the generation of incremental revenue and profit pools. For this

reason, we believe that standards management must be practiced at the corporate level.

What, then, is a best practices solution? I offer the following recipe for consideration.

✔ **Standards management must be owned by the CTO.** Given the positions at stake, C level ownership is a requirement. For the ICT Producer, this is where corporate objectives translate into innovation strategy, and this is where the resulting technology programs that might ultimately create defendable IP obtain funding support. For the ICT Consumer, this is where corporate objectives translate into

---

"...the monetization of corporate IP is subject to failure if participation in standards organizations is not properly planned and executed."

---

technology requirements and the make/buy decisions related to proprietary or standards based solutions are located. In both cases, CTO ownership provides for linkage and leverage from objectives to implementation.

✔ **The CTO should establish a standards management office.** As noted earlier, the monetization of corporate IP is subject to failure if participation in standards organizations is not properly planned and executed. Our experience suggests the following essential functions to prevent fragmentation and failure:

1. *Landscape analysis.* This is a necessary first step in evaluating the relative value of standardizing IP or maintaining a proprietary posture. Landscape analysis identifies relevant organizations, "who is doing what," and whether the corporation should participate in these efforts or create new initiatives to support monetization strategy. This step mitigates the opportunity loss behavior we observe frequently and provokes the make/buy analysis we think is essential.

2. *IP harvest plan.* Once standardization opportunities are identified, it is important

to establish the IP pool the corporation may already have available— or need to create if unavailable at all, or if the IP is available through competitors. Performed in conjunction with internal legal staff, the Harvest Plan specifies the corporate IP gaps and overlaps that affect the ability to disrupt existing markets and licensing models or create new schemes. This step provides a foundation for systematic competitive gain and a consolidated approach to IP creation and monetization.

3. *Participation definition/approval.* This step develops a "participation package" for the corporation and the SBUs. It includes, at minimum, a clear definition of IP licensing schemes acceptable to the corporation (RAND, Cross-Licensing, Royalty Free, Open Source, etc.) and the structural conditions and guidelines necessary to avoid allegations of antitrust and anti-competitive behavior (for example open membership policy, clearly specified and communicated technology selection process, inclusive participation, action on member proposals). Subject to these criteria, participation in a particular organization can be quickly approved at the corporate level for rapid engagement and traction.

4. *Budgets and resource allocation.* This activity, which should be integral to the annual planning cycle, involves proactive allocation of hard dollars for new and renewal membership fees, special needs based sponsorship of key programs, and to fund resources within the corporation at either the corporate or SBU level to participate in relevant standardization efforts. It ensures the corporation is in the right places with the right people at the right times, and mitigates the risk of participation failure.

5. *Coordination and communication.* This activity completes the corporate practice. It requires regular top-down, peer level communications and bottom-up informa-

tion exchange. Progress reporting and communication at the corporate and SBU levels are essential to ensure that efforts are synchronized, new opportunities or threats are identified, participation is maintained, intensified or terminated, and the right decisions are enacted in light of corporate objectives and innovation strategy. In the absence of this activity, internal fragmentation occurs and the opportunity loss (strategy arbitrage) participation failure cycle takes hold.

✔ **The commitment must be long term.** We observe that corporations tend to pendulum shift their commitment to standardization efforts. While not immune to cutbacks in hard times, quite often this is a result of a lack of understanding of the role standards play in achieving long term strategic goals at the very top levels in a corporation. Funding is seen as an expense versus an investment, and the adverse impact of short-term fluctuations in commitment is not factored into decisions. Absent a long-term commitment and view, one that is correlated to the corporate strategic plan and a key driver therein, such efforts are doomed to "run in place."

Trends in ICT and independent studies validate the value and continued adoption of this approach. In the first instance, as ICT becomes

---

"...those companies with centralized e-business units are not only more likely to have standards definition, but are also more likely to gain adoption of defined standards—smart companies are continuing to invest especially as protocols and standards are more adopted across the organization."

---

more and more complex and specialized, it will become increasingly necessary to establish leading technology positions in evolving or nascent markets to survive long term. This suggests increased investment in R&D and mandates measurable ROI. As indicated here, a coordinated standards management program can be an effective tool to generate and sustain the desired results.

The 2003 results of the annual Line56/A.T. Kearney benchmarking outlook on e-business confirm the potential gains at the buyer level and opportunities for vendors. The study found that e-business now represents 20.3% of all IT spending and that "management of e-business is now most commonly centralized within the corporate technology organization—consistent with the trend towards centralization revealed in the 2001 study." The study also noted that "those companies with centralized e-business units are not only more likely to have standards definition, but are also more likely to gain adoption of defined standards—smart companies are continuing to invest especially as protocols and standards are more adopted across the organization."

Summary

Richard Feynman, the Nobel Prize winner for Physics once observed, "For a successful technology, reality must take precedence over public relations, for Nature cannot be fooled." We also know from Aristotle that "Nature abhors a vacuum." While a decentralized, relatively autonomous organization structure may in fact be the right way to conduct business, and good public relations as well, the realities of innovation strategy, the substantial corporate investment required in offensive and defensive innovation, and the returns anticipated must take precedence. A centralized standards function provides the most likely success vector under these circumstances. If standards are not managed centrally, the corporation takes on the large risks identified here, which in essence create a vacuum addressable by rivals with alternative solutions and monetization trails.

Notes

[1] *The Standards Edge.* Sherrie Bolin, ed. (Ann Arbor Michigan: Sheridan Books. 2002).

[2] Kant also defined a Categorical Imperative, "the obligation to do one's duty for its own sake and not in pursuit of further ends." Kant's concern was ethics. . Adapted to business terminology and context a Hypothetical Imperative is Categorical. For example, ROI is categorical—and categorically not hypothetical.

[3] Innovation Strategy, Corporate Goal, Posture/Capability are my summaries from *The Economics of Industrial Innovation,* Christopher Freeman (Penguin Books, 1974), © Christopher Freeman. Interpretation errors and omissions are my responsibility. Christopher Freeman was Professor of Science Policy at the University of Sussex, England.

24

Best Practices and Standard Setting (How the "Pros" Do It)

ANDREW UPDEGROVE

Lucash, Gesmer & Updegrove

Abstract: *Three of the most active participants in standard setting today—Hewlett-Packard, Sun Microsystems, and a major non-technology vendor company—tell how they decide what organizations to join (and not join), and what standard setting organizations can do to better serve their members. The results of this small survey indicate that valuable information regarding standard setting participation strategies and best practices could be obtained by undertaking a wider sampling.*

Introduction

Participation by commercial entities in standard setting has steadily grown over the past 20 years, if for no other reason than as a response to the rapid proliferation of consortia and fora that has occurred during

> *"The largest corporations today participate in an astonishing number of such collaborative efforts—150 or more."*

the same time period. The largest corporations today participate in an astonishing number of such collaborative efforts—150 or more. The aggregate expenditure of financial and human resources on standard setting on an industry-wide basis is therefore enormous.

Given this investment, industry in general should benefit from developing consensus on the type of "best practices" that could aid vendors, end-users, and government in deciding which standards efforts merit their participation. Presumably, such best practices might be most likely to originate in those organizations that have made the greatest investment in standard setting, and therefore have had the greatest incentive and opportunity to refine their decisional process.

Questions and Answers

In order to determine what lessons may be learned from such companies, the *Consortium Standards Bulletin*[1] secured the cooperation of the Directors of Standards of three of the most active participants in all types of formal and informal, national and international standard setting organizations (SSOs). These Directors agreed to answer a lengthy questionnaire intended to determine how they evaluate which organizations to join and whether continued participation is worthwhile. We also asked a series of questions inquiring how SSOs could better serve their needs.

The detailed—and often blunt—answers that we received in response to our survey provide interesting insights for all that participate in the standard setting process, as well as for the organizations within which that process is conducted. While there were many commonalities in the approaches taken by all three survey participants, there were also intriguing differences in the philosophies that underlay their strategies. As a result, there were significant differences in those strategies as well.

The results of this initial sampling indicate that conducting a similar survey involving a larger and more diverse group of participants (e.g., including both large and small vendor and end-user companies, as well as academic and government entities) would be well worthwhile. With the results of such a richer data set in hand, a serious effort to develop valuable best practices could commence. Correlating the standard setting approaches taken by vendor respondents with their long term competitive success would provide results that would be even more intriguing.

Methodology

Process: The survey was conducted in June 2003. All questions were submitted and answered electronically, without consultation between the participants. The survey questions were intended to address several areas of inquiry, and were grouped accordingly. Each respondent was permitted to decline answering questions where confidentiality or other concerns arose, but all three respondents answered almost every applicable question. Precision in numerical data was not required where exact data was unavailable or unduly burdensome to access.

Survey Participants: Each company respondent has recognized the importance of standards and of coordinating its standard setting activities by appointing a Director of Standards, and each gave its Director of Standards permission to respond to the survey. The individual respondents are some of the most experienced standards experts in the IT industry; each has decades of experience in the world of technol-

ogy and standard setting and speaks from a depth of experience gained through participation in many of the industry's most important SSOs. They are:

Hewlett-Packard: *James Bell* is the *Director of Standards and Industry Initiatives* for Hewlett-Packard Company. In that capacity, he is responsible for leading the development and execution of a focused strategy for effective, coordinated participation by HP businesses in industry consortia and standards organizations. He also represents HP on the Governing Board of The Open Group and serves on the Advisory Council and Advisory Board of the World Wide Web Consortium. During 1995 and 1996, he served for fifteen months as President and CEO of X/Open, President and CEO of the Open Software Foundation, and after their merger, President and CEO of The Open Group.

Sun Microsystems: *Carl Cargill* is Sun's *Director of Standards*, and manages Sun's standardization strategies, activities, and portfolio. He has been directly involved in standardization for nearly twenty years, and has written widely (including two books) on standards topics. He has also testified before Congress on the topics of consortia in standardization and before joint hearings held by the Federal Trade Commission and the Department of Justice on the necessity for Royalty Free IPR rules for consortia. Among other standards organization positions, he serves on the W3C Advisory Board and the Board of Directors of the Open GIS Consortium, and is the Chairman of the Governing Body of The Open Group.

Company #3: *Director of Standards*, Major Non-Technical Company [Details not permitted to be disclosed]

Summary of Results

The notable results of the survey are below, grouped by topic and identified by letter in the same manner as the questions were presented in the survey.[2]

A. What is your level and manner of participation? While all three organizations are heavily invested in standard setting, both of the technology vendors participate far more heavily (by a factor of five) over the non-technology vendor (HP and Sun each being involved in 150 SSOs or more, while Company #3 is involved in only 25 to 30). This should not be surprising, since technology vendors need standards to create product opportunities, while non-technology vendors most often join SSOs in order to influence standards development for their particular businesses and learn how to deploy standards effectively. Such end-users of standards are also less likely to be interested in promoting the adoption of standards.

Both Sun and HP are frequently recruited by SSOs soliciting their financial and technical support, receiving as many as one serious solicitation per week (HP: approx. 40 per year; Sun: 1 per week average). These solicitations appear to be productive for both sides, since the likelihood of success in the recruiting effort is relatively high (HP gives serious consideration to about 20 SSOs a year, while Sun takes an active interest in about 12). In fact, HP is recruited by almost every organization that it joins (unless it is a founder). Sun, on the other hand, identifies about 50% of the organizations that it chooses to join before it is solicited, indicating a more proactive approach. Despite the size and prominence of Company #3, it joins SSOs as a result of solicitation only 15% of the time, indicating that SSOs may be neglecting recruitment opportunities in the end-user community

The likelihood of success in recruiting a given company, however, relies in part on its philosophical beliefs about how standard setting should be conducted. Both HP and Sun are responsive to newly formed SSOs, while Company #3 prefers to work with existing SSOs, in order to limit the proliferation of new, untested (and possibly redundant) organizations. This difference in opinion also surfaced when the questions turned to founding new SSOs. Both HP and Sun actively participate in founding new SSOs (HP: about 15 a year; Sun: about 3, with this number likely to rise in the future), and each is considering starting several new SSOs at this time. Company #3, on the other hand, is not

likely to help found a new organization.

What leads a company to tackle the cost, effort, and uncertainty of founding a new SSO, rather than look to an existing organization? Bell cites the need for "Focus, speed, and seeking members with shared objectives." Cargill offers three reasons: first is a bias against accredited SSOs (an opinion not expressed by the other two respondents), which he feels often compromise the integrity of results in order to achieve consensus. The second is the lack of an existing organization able, or willing, to undertake the project. He states the third reason candidly:

> You can start an SSO to counter another SSO—not a nice thing, but sometimes politically expedient. This leads to standards wars, which can be ugly, however, and therefore this is a last resort.

Finally, Cargill notes a fourth alternative, which has become increasingly popular: starting an open source project, with no formal consortium structure at all.

B. What types of organizations do you join? All three organizations join all types of SSOs. Each participates in both consortia as well as accredited organizations, and each is involved in national, regional, and global organizations. Sun, for example, participates in both European and Asian regional organizations, as well as in accredited national bodies in Britain, Canada, Norway, Sweden, and Ireland. Europe's strong efforts to create standards on a regional basis was clearly reflected in a question asking the respondent to give "notable examples" of regional bodies in which the respondent companies participate: Six European bodies were named, and three US organizations.

C. How do you make your decisions procedurally? While each company has centralized the process of participation approval to a degree, there are many variations in how the process is carried out. In the case of HP, business approval is needed before an application is considered by the standards office. At Sun, central clearance is required but Cargill indicates that it is difficult to enforce this rule. He estimates that 30% of the applications for new memberships escape central review. Like HP, the business decision to participate is made first (at the business unit level) before the approval of the central standards office is sought. At Company #3, new guidelines for evaluating SSO membership applications are now being reviewed. The guidelines "emphasize the need for a clear business case, management approval, legal review, and Standards Office coordination."

None of the three organizations have an overall policy over what types of organizations to join (e.g., by business area, type of organization, etc.), nor any formal checklist against which each organization is judged. At Sun, for example, the consideration of a new application by the standards office occurs on a case-by-case basis, with any identified concerns being resolved through discussion.

All three organizations indicate the need for an application for membership to be supported by a "champion" in order for it to be approved. At Sun, that champion usually needs to be a vice president or a Senior Technical Fellow, representing an informal, but nonetheless effective, internal filtering process as a precondition for central approval.

Consensus was clearest on the question of intellectual property rights (IPR) policies, with each company giving IPR policies a careful review. The responses to the IPR question are worth noting verbatim:

Do you formally review an organization's IPR policy before joining?

HP: Yes, very carefully

Sun: Always, and in excruciating detail

#3: Yes, this is critical and a potential showstopper

While the respondents uniformly require the central review and approval of new memberships, they are more relaxed on the subject of membership renewals. HP reviews renewals only if there have been major changes (e.g., to the organization's IPR policy), while Sun has no formal review policy for renewals. Company #3 notes that it is currently putting "an informal process in place" for vetting renewals on an annual basis.

D. How do you make your decisions qualitatively? Sun and HP responded to a question asking them to rank several specific reasons for joining (or, if necessary, founding) an SSO, but the priority that they placed on some criteria varied significantly: while each ranked the absence of a standard or the need to promote a new business method or market as a strong motivator, only HP ranked "ability to influence final standard" highly. Similarly, while HP found concerns over the "wrong" standard or the "wrong" companies setting a standard as a motivating concern, Sun ranked both of these factors as being less important.

In the open-ended questions, each organization reported a surprisingly varied set of criteria that may lead it to join—or pass on—a given organization. Again, some of the responses are worth reproducing verbatim:

What are the three most important things that you look for in any standard setting organization in deciding whether to join?

HP: Topic and goals; process and other members; cost effectiveness vis-à-vis alternatives

Sun: Is someone going to commit engineering resources (we ask it three times)

#3: Technical Relevance; IPR Policy; Political Viability (can it get the job done, or is it just a travel club?)

What are the three things that are most likely to make you decide not to join?

HP: Same things

Sun: Senior management approbation

#3: Perception it is not really open; lack of IPR policy; Doubts that the standards produced will be timely

E. How important is standard setting to you? On a scale of 1 to 10 (1= least important, 10=most important), both HP and Sun gave participating in standard setting a 10, and Company #3 gave it a 9. Similarly, the companies ranked participation in organizations that "promote the adoption of standards and business models" 8, 8, and 9, respectively. When asked to rank the importance of SSOs to their companies now, in comparison to two years ago, HP and Company

#3 both responded "greater," while Sun responded "much greater." The areas of their businesses to which they found standard setting to be most important, and the reasons why, were "Enterprise software business, because of complexity" (HP), and "Networking and remote computing—there currently are no standards" (Sun).

While the importance of standards and participation in standard setting was ranked as very high by all three organizations, only HP assigns a budget line item to this activity. However, both HP and Sun reported that amounts spent on standard setting participation had increased over the past several years (and by 10 - 15% per year, in the case of Sun). The recent economic downturn affected renewals and approvals of new memberships in the case of Company #3, but had only a "slight" impact on HP, and no reported effect on Sun's spending.

F. Which organizations do you view as being the best? Internet consortia were the clear winners in this category, with both Sun and Company #3 commending W3C, and Sun adding IETF as being "highly effective." When asked to name "notable failures," Cargill's well-known low opinion of SDOs shone through, while the thoughtful answer of Company #3's Director of Standards was interesting: "The list of organizations that I have been disappointed in is long. I'm not sure how many I would describe as 'failures'…they just didn't do what I thought they should do."

G. What should consortia and SDOs know about how to get you to become a member? The respondents were unified when asked "What do consortia and/or SDOs do wrong that you most wish they would focus on improving?" All found various aspects of communication and marketing to be deficient. When asked what SSO's don't do, but should, Bell would have existing organizations provide a structure and process that would allow more to be done through existing SSOs, while Cargill wished that SSOs would take up the task of educating people about the need for standards.

Each of the respondents also had some more direct advice to the SSOs of which they are a member. Turning again to a specific question and the responses:

What agendas, if any, do you suspect standard setting organizations may sometimes have that you do not feel are in the best interests of their members?

HP: Self preservation. Divergence of staff's and members' agendas

Sun: They want to continue living well past their "sell by" date

#3: *SDOs* - Too much focus on maintaining the status quo and protecting the "old boys" group privileges and bias

Consortia - Many only pretend to be open and industry-centric when they are actually very company-specific or cartel-specific

The last question of the survey was an open one, inviting the respondents to offer any other messages to SSOs that they chose. The Standards Director of Company #3, who is a true believer in the importance of standards but has seen his share of shenanigans over the years, responded as follows:

"If you're not open to all interested parties, you're not open…shame on you

If you're not in it for the common good… shame on you."

Carl Cargill echoed the same sentiments in a different way, providing a fitting epilogue to this survey. In his response, he made this simple request:

"Cooperate with one another."

Copyright © Andrew Updegrove

Notes

[1] Updegrove, Andrew, Survey: *Major Standards Players Tell How They Evaluate Standard Setting Organizations, Consortium Standards Bulletin (June, 2003), http://www.consortiuminfo.org/bulletins/jun03. php#featured.*

[2] For the full results of the survey, see Updegrove, Andrew *supra.*

25

Darwin, Standards, and Survival[1]

ANDREW UPDEGROVE

Lucash, Gesmer & Updegrove

Abstract: *Effectively adapting to change and leveraging new opportunities is essential to economic success. Companies skillful in this process secure advantages over their less adept competitors. Incorporating standards planning into corporate strategy provides just such an opportunity. Close observation of standards activity over the past few years reveals emerging trends among current standards participants. Analysis of those trends suggests specific best practices and predictions of future developments that IT companies can use to compete more successfully.*

Introduction

One of the cardinal frustrations of evolutionary scientists is the inability to speed up the evolutionary clock in order to observe species changes in process. In fact, the Holy Grail of anyone in this field is to stumble upon and document a new species in the process of branching off of an existing one. Such a quest is more realistic for those who actively observe the standards world, since the pace of change is infinitely more rapid. In fact, an example of "standards process speciation" has recently occurred with the development of the open source community solution for some types of interoperability issues.

Of course, the more pervasive manifestation of evolution in nature is gradual adaptive change—the less dramatic series of adjustments resulting from the fact that those individuals that are best equipped to play at the game of life are most successful in passing their genetic information along to their progeny.

Commercial entities are captive to the same dynamics, but with a difference: if they can figure out the course of the future better than their competitors, they will be more likely to thrive

> *"One of the few ways to glimpse—and even influence—some aspects of the future is through the exercise of an active, informed and coherent standards strategy."*

and pass increased value along to their shareholders. One of the few ways to glimpse—and even influence—some aspects of the future is through the exercise of an active, informed and coherent standards strategy. Given that reality, it is surprising that there has been comparatively little serious study of standard setting. Hence, there is little broad understanding of its dynamics, and a failure by many companies to fully exploit the competitive advantages that a carefully crafted standards strategy can secure.

The chapter entitled "Best Practices in

Standards Setting" contained in this book summarizes the results of a detailed survey completed by three companies that are heavily invested in the standard setting process. While the number of respondents to the survey is not statistically meaningful, the companies involved are major participants in the standard setting process and their influence is significant (both by their participation in many organizations at the Board level, as well as by example). As a result, a number of interesting and useful observations can be drawn from their responses to the survey.

And more intriguingly, a number of recommendations and predictions can be extrapolated from the same data, when conjoined with first-hand experience.[2] These recommendations can help IT companies to be more successful in the Darwinian struggle for success.

Observations and Predictions

If one rises above the operations of any individual SSO or participant and looks at the reality of standard setting today, some clear trends and their probable future courses begin to emerge. Some of the more significant are as follows:

The level of central control over standard setting participation is not great at many companies, but will increase. Despite the level of importance of standard setting to technology companies, and the risk that valuable intellectual property rights (IPR) may be compromised by participation, oversight of participation has not historically been strict at many companies. However, oversight today is much more centralized than just a few years ago, as a result of the great publicity given to a number of legal proceedings relating to IPR and questionable (or worse) conduct in standard setting. Once a centralized review process has been put in place for the purpose of safeguarding IPR, its capabilities can be extended in other ways to bring greater coherence and efficiency to a company-wide standards strategy. Companies would be wise to make use of such enhanced capabilities.

Corporate focus on IPR policies will become even greater. While the trend towards tighter supervision over IPR policies will certainly continue, achieving meaningful internal control over participation by company representatives in SSOs represents a significant challenge, especially for large corporations with operations in many countries. Due to the practical impossibility of each company conducting day-to-day legal supervision of its hundreds of engineering and other employee representatives participating in a myriad of SSOs, the only pragmatic way to avoid jeopardizing valuable IPR is to focus on an SSO's IPR policy—as well as its process mechanics—in order to lower the risk inherent in substantially unmonitored participation. Policies that are poorly articulated and do not require clearly documented assertions regarding IPR, for example, present a higher potential for errors and disputes.

Vendors disproportionately participate in—and therefore disproportionately control—many SSOs (and especially consortia). This may have a negative impact for all concerned. Not only do vendors tend to join more SSOs, but they often join at higher membership levels and consequently pay the lion's share of the budgets of such SSOs through their dues. In many organizations, they also take the lion's share of the board seats. Even if there is no actual intention to weight results in favor of vendors, there can be a negative impact due to lack of diversity of interest and experience in

---

"Vendors would therefore be well advised to welcome diversity of members and opinions rather than exploit their numeric and economic influence."

---

the high-level decision making that charts the SSO's course. Vendors would therefore be well advised to welcome diversity of members and opinions rather than exploit their numeric and economic influence. Otherwise, the standards offered to the market by the SSO may be unattractive to other vital constituencies and fail to become widely adopted.

Only a subset of companies actively starts new SSOs. As a result, these companies are likely to be more influential in standard setting and enjoy a competitive advantage. It is a simple truth that the founders of a new SSO will usually have a disproportionate impact on the initial work product than those that come afterwards. Hence, even if influencing the final work product is not a goal, that impact will likely nonetheless exist. This will not always be good.

Accredited SSOs and consortia can both be "gamed." It is necessary to thoroughly understand how an organization works prior to joining in order to judge how "open" it truly is. And after joining, it is even more necessary to understand how an SSO works in order to be aware of—and protest—actual abuse as and when it arises. Those

---

> *"Those companies that train their participating personnel most thoroughly will be able to defend their interests more effectively."*

---

companies that train their participating personnel most thoroughly will be able to defend their interests more effectively.

Even companies that make huge financial and human resource commitments to standard setting participation often do not follow a rigid process for vetting participation. This manifests itself not only at the application stage but throughout the period of membership. Through personnel changes, a company often "forgets" that it is a member of an organization, ceases participating, and yet may even pay up when it receives a membership renewal notice. The result is not only financial inefficiency, but also loss of opportunity.

Despite the proliferation of SSOs, IT companies still find that they need to start new ones. This is in some ways a commendable as well as a regrettable condition. One of the reasons that consortia became popular some 20 years ago was because a market that evolves as rapidly as the IT space requires rapid responses. By evolving

an alternative process in addition to the already established accredited organizations, industry was able to react more flexibly and quickly when nimbleness and speed were needed. However, forming a new organization has its own risks: starting up takes time and money, and the results are dependent on multiple variables, including the success of recruitment, the ability to set an effective process in place, and avoiding proprietary influences. There is much to be said for the existence of organizations such as W3C, OASIS, and Open GIS, which host (and welcome) many processes under one roof that are consistent with an over-arching and coherent strategic mission.

ICT standards are becoming more effective and important. With the advent of the Internet and technologies such as wireless, an increasing number of products are becoming dependent upon available, timely, and effective standards. Those companies that have an Office of Standards are more likely to be able to realize such realities, articulate them to decision makers, recommend effective actions, and supervise execution, thus conveying a competitive advantage over companies that are less standards-aware.

The importance of standard setting is not sufficiently recognized at the institutional level. The fact that most companies do not include standard setting as a budget line item may indicate that its value is insufficiently understood at the management level. This may be due to cultural factors, such as the separation between engineering and sales (and the fact that many peoples' eyes glaze over at the mere mention of the word "standards"). Institutional recognition of the importance of an effective standards strategy, however, is an essential first step towards mounting a coherent competitive plan.

Recommendations to Companies

The observations above suggest that those who most actively participate in standard setting do so to gain strategic advantages. If it is true that pursuing an effective standards strategy can secure strategic advantage (and the major commitments by leading IT vendors to standard setting indicates that they believe this to be so), then those of their competitors who are less active or skillful in this area may be expected to suffer. This should be reason enough for those companies that have not incorporated standards participation into their strategic plan to consider such a course of action. The following are some specific recommendations to consider when performing such an evaluation.

Recognize at the corporate level that effective standards participation is mission critical, and incorporate standards into overall strategy. In order to compete effectively, standards need to be integrated into central strategy, rather than relegated to the status of an engineering-level pastime. Once standards planning is included in strategy, it is highly advisable to create a centralized standards office to effectively coordinate and manage disparate standards efforts in order to reap maximum advantage.

If standards in a given area are mission critical, then allocate resources accordingly. While a small company cannot afford a Standards Office, a large one can. (A small company can still retain knowledgeable advisors to assist its standards efforts, however.) Participation in standard setting fulfills many functions: influencing outcomes, gaining advance knowledge of important standards, gaining access to training for key personnel, and so on. The proliferation of regional, as well as national, SSOs has made the game more complex, and experienced, dedicated staff is needed to understand how the many pieces fit together. Such individuals are in very short supply, but there is no substitute for hands-on experience.

The level of experience of standards participants is often not high. Hiring, training, and deploying skilled personnel to participate in SSOs therefore represents a competitive advantage. This opportunity exists at the macro level (in setting overall corporate standards strategy), as well at the

micro level (in technical committees and on SSO boards) by influencing outcomes.

Those companies that do not favor forming new SSOs should consider becoming early members of new SSOs that they believe are likely to succeed. This recommendation stems from the observations that those who do form SSOs have the advantage of setting its technical agenda and are likely to disproportionately control the SSO for some period of time. Once such a group of companies has forced the issue by starting a new SSO, it may be strategically prudent for the founding companies' competitors to join as quickly as possible in order to ensure the neutrality of the organization and its eventual output. Companies that do not normally favor starting new SSOs would therefore be wise to actively monitor the activities of companies that are known for forming new SSOs, and act promptly in technical areas where their strategic interests are at stake.

Companies should make it known that they are willing to be founding members of new SSOs. This is the logical extension of the same precept. Most new SSOs go through a pre-public planning phase. During that phase, they will commonly agree upon the governance structure and perhaps the IPR policy as well, of the new organization. There is therefore a strategic advantage in being invited to become a founder in order to influence these outcomes, even if forming the new SSO would not otherwise be deemed desirable. It is better to be invited to the table at the earliest stage and be able to make an early assessment of the likely success or failure of the organization, than to be forced into a reactive, less influential posture after the new organization is announced.

Approval of joining and renewing memberships should be subject to more strict central approval. At present, many companies err on the side of decentralized business (and even legal) approval for SSO participation. While this is sensible in that management of the business unit involved may be best able to understand the advantages of membership, it makes it more difficult to weigh alternatives when opportunities exceed budgets, and may result in an incoherent (and even internally competitive) overall standards program. While the common practice of combining central approval based upon the recommendation of a senior "champion" provides a partial solution to this problem, a more complete solution would include centrally created and distributed parameters and criteria for participation, conjoined with a standard evaluation schema against which opportunities can be measured. While too mechanical an application of such a schema would be unwise, using a checklist as a tool to effectively present and evaluate opportunities should improve overall results. A shorter form with a similar purpose should accompany renewal applications.

With the increasing importance of standards, the costs of non-participation are becoming higher. In order to be competitive, end-users as well as vendors need to be increasingly knowledgeable about new standards that affect their enabling technology, even if they are less interested in influencing outcomes. Participation in many SSOs can be useful in advance planning and effective training.

Markets can be not only created but accelerated through collaboration. Increasingly, new product and service opportunities are dependent on not only the development of standards, but on the rapid adoption of those standards. SSOs can be effective on both fronts. The cost to a founder of forming a new SSO—even as a significant sponsor—is often trivial in comparison to the opportunity.

Recommendations to SSOs

Recruitment pays. Many under-resourced consortia invest comparatively little effort in seeking members. However, the indications of this survey are that even the largest corporations can be recruited by effective efforts. Accordingly, allocating funds to recruitment (including using dedicated staff or third party service providers) may be highly cost effective.

IPR policies are crucial. An SSO today cannot afford to have an out-of-date IPR policy. Not only may a defective policy result in commercial disputes, but it will make recruiting and retention of the most active members difficult, or even impossible.

Neither SDOs nor Consortia are "better." Members care about results—not labels. SSOs of all types need to understand—and serve—their customers. Like any other commercial enterprise, they cannot do so unless they thoroughly understand the customer and its needs.

Remember that management members are employees and not owners. SSOs should be about service, not self-perpetuation. While there is nothing wrong with creativity, entrenchment is invariably a negative. An SSO needs to be able to dispassionately tell the difference between prudently adapting to meet evolving market and technical realities and a reluctance to merge or disband when its day in the sun has passed.

Conclusions

Socrates is said to have once famously observed that, "The unexamined life is not worth living." Given the importance of standard setting to the modern commercial world, it is curious that there has been so little examination of the process of standard setting. When one observes the degree of activity and commitment of the largest technology vendors to the standards process, it becomes evident that an IT player that does not examine (or worse, even have) a standards strategy may eventually find that it no longer has a commercial life to live.

While such a statement may seem to smack of hyperbole, consider this: the faster the pace of technological change, the narrower the margin for error, the greater the reward to those who guess right, and the more severe the economic punishment of those who guess wrong.

Corporate managers would do well to recall their Darwin. Devising and deploying a standards strategy is too important to survival to be left to the engineers alone.

Notes

[1] This chapter is adapted from an article of the same name which appeared in the Consortium Standards Bulletin (June, 2003), http://www.consortiuminfo. org/bulletins/jun03.php#trends.

[2] "The author's experience includes forming over 50 consortia over the last 15 years, and advising them on diverse legal, business, and strategic matters."

26

Coordinating Oracle Participation in External Standards Setting Organizations

Donald R. Deutsch

Oracle Corporation

Abstract: *Corporate support functions augment Oracle's business-unit driven approach to participating in standards setting organizations. Recent initiatives help better manage the mechanical details and improve the efficacy of Oracle's standardization activities. Leveraging existing staff and capabilities without adding additional standards professionals, these initiatives address four aspects of standards participation and coordination: developing standards strategies and positions, facilitating knowledgeable participation in SSOs, communicating inside, and communicating outside.*

Background

Oracle Corporation participates in a large and increasing number of national and international standards setting organizations (SSOs). These include ANSI [1] accredited Standards Development Organizations (SDOs) like INCITS[2] and related activities under the auspices of ISO [3] as well as consortia and pseudo-consortia forums. Company employees participate in these bodies as individual technical contributors, working-group leaders, and members of executive boards and other administrative oversight committees. It is a major challenge to maintain a standards and consortia posture consistent with our overall corporate strategy and to communicate our positions to corporate stakeholders, including development, marketing, public relations (PR), legal, and legislative affairs. Oracle employees need assistance and direction to understand the responsibilities and risks associated with SSO participation and to effectively represent overall Company interests.

Just tracking all standards efforts at all levels and across all standards bodies and Oracle business units is daunting. Oracle representatives contribute to over 350 activities in over 60 SSOs;

> *"Oracle representatives contribute to over 350 activities in over 60 SSOs; because individuals often participate in multiple activities, we estimate that at any point in time between 250 and 300 Oracle employees are directly participating in external standardization activities."*

because individuals often participate in multiple activities, we estimate that at any point in time between 250 and 300 Oracle employees are directly participating in external standardization activities. This represents a substantial cost to the Company in both dollars (for participation fees and travel and lodging expenses) and professional time.

The recent focus on Intellectual Property Rights (IPR) within W3C, [4] the JCP [5] and other forums has magnified the importance of advising, supporting, and controlling the hundreds of individuals representing the Company in external forums. The rights granted and responsibilities imposed on Oracle representatives are as varied as the myriad of SSOs in which they participate. Ignorance of the sometimes obtuse rules under which Oracle employees participate in SSOs and the specific risks associated with their participation therein can hamper their ability to successfully represent Company interests; in the worst case scenarios, they can expose Oracle as well as themselves to substantial legal liability.

Standards Approach

Bringing to market the first commercial implementation of a Relational Database Management System using the industry standard SQL language, [6] Oracle has been active in and committed to standardization from its inception. As the Company and product offerings expanded over the years, so did Oracle's participation in external standards and consortia forums. The following paragraphs describe Oracle's overall philosophy for participating in external SSOs.

Business units drive standards participation

The process for determining relevant SSO activities did not change as Oracle grew from a start-up to the second largest independent

---

"Individual business units drive standards participation based on their understanding of customer/product requirements."

---

software vendor in the world. Individual business units drive standards participation based on their understanding of customer/product requirements. This "bottom-up" approach to standardization means that business unit managers determine whether and how much to invest in specific standardization activities. They commit the financial and technical personnel resources necessary for representing their customers' and products' interests. Although line development managers never stop asking for one, there is no corporate bucket of money to fund standardization activities. If Oracle is represented in an external forum, a senior manager has determined that activities in that SSO are important to our products' ability to address real customer requirements.

Corporate functions support standards efforts

The approach described above, where individual business units drive standards participation based on their product centric perspectives, helps to ensure that the external activities in which Oracle participates are relevant to near-term market requirements. However, this approach does not recognize and respond to the increasingly complex legal differences among SSOs; nor does it resolve issues when standardization activities cut across Oracle business unit boundaries. Technical representatives to SSOs are not well equipped to handle situations where standards are intertwined with government policy or regulation, and they have no interest in or ability to address marketing/PR issues. To address issues like these, four functions with Company-wide charters support and coordinate Oracle's participation in external standards and consortia forums: legal, external affairs, marketing/PR, and standards strategy.

1. **Legal:** Oracle's patent attorneys review participation agreements, provide business unit management with analyses of risks and operational procedures associated with participation in specific SSOs, and advise participants and their managers on IPR and other issues associated with contributions from Oracle as well as those from other SSO member companies.

2. **External affairs**: As Oracle's representative to legislative and regulatory bodies in the US as

well as throughout the world, External Affairs supports standards activities that lead to or are the result of governmental action.

3. **Marketing/PR:** Marketing and PR professionals with product specific responsibilities and expertise support SSO marketing/PR initiatives for their client business units.

4. **Standards strategy:** Reporting to Oracle's Chief Architect with responsibility for technology strategy across all business units, Standards Strategy facilitates and orchestrates all Oracle participation in external standards and consortia forums.

Occasionally, representatives from these corporate support functions participate directly in external SSO activities that focus on administrative, policy, legal, and marketing issues. Nevertheless, the vast majority of Oracle's representatives to external standards and consortia forums are technical professionals from the directly impacted business units. Figure 1 is a graphical representation of Oracle's organization for standards, one that is increasingly the norm

in the information technology industry; even some companies that historically had strong corporate level, top-down standards functions have distributed standardization responsibilities to business units in recent years.

Standards Support Initiatives

While recognizing the benefits of the bottom-up, decentralized approach to standards participation, Oracle recently identified procedural and organizational initiatives to increase the efficacy and impact of Oracle's participation in SSOs. These initiatives will help Oracle to better manage the mechanical details of standards participation and more clearly define the roles of organizational functions with respect to standards activities. The following four aspects of standards participation and coordination are addressed:

- Developing standards strategies and positions
- Facilitating knowledgeable participation in SSOs

Figure 1: Oracle's organization for standards

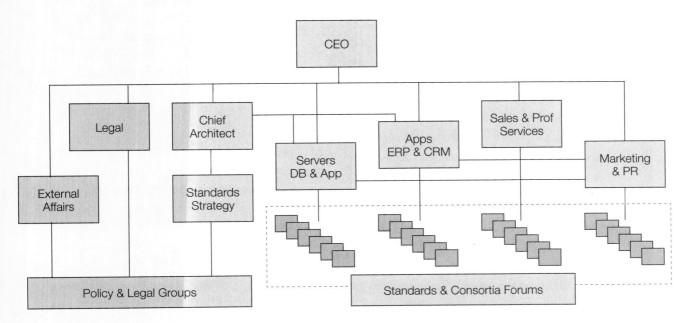

- Communicating inside
- Communicating outside

Consistent with Oracle culture and resource constraints, these initiatives were designed to leverage existing staff and capabilities without adding additional standards professionals. Individuals already working within Oracle business units (i.e., not incremental staff) are assigned additional responsibilities to support standards activities. Although many of these initiatives address more than one of the above objectives, they are described below under the aspects of standards participation and coordination that they most directly impact.

*Developing standards
strategies & positions*

A high-level standing committee advises executive management and Standards Strategy on strategies and policies concerning Oracle's participation in external SSOs. The Standards and Consortia Steering Committee augments Oracle's processes for guiding SSO participation decisions, oversees a periodic review for standards participation across all SSOs, and facilitates leveraging of Oracle's worldwide resources to better represent the company interests in standards and consortia forums. Steering Committee members represent all business functions impacted by and/or involved in Oracle's worldwide standards and consortia activities including (but not limited to): Standards Strategy, Legal, External Affairs, Marketing/PR, And Technology/Product Development.

The Steering Committee is responsible for the following:

- Advising Standards Strategy in defining and documenting the Company standards strategy

- Identifying characteristics for differentiating among forums that are preferred for achieving Oracle business objectives

- Recommending and reviewing Company standardization policies including those relating to intellectual property, royalties, and open participation

- Defining and reviewing processes for controlling and coordinating participation in SSOs

- Ensuring that standards and consortia activities are integrated and consistent with other Company activities, especially regulatory/policy initiatives

- Reviewing metrics of standards participation across all business units, SSOs, and technology areas and recommending changes in the focus and allocation of resources.

*Facilitating knowledgeable
participation in SSOs*

One objective of Oracle's standardization initiatives is to ensure that decisions about participation in SSOs are made with the necessary legal and executive approvals. These include decisions to create or participate in a new SSO, participate in an activity within an SSO that Oracle has previously joined, contribute technology to an SSO activity, and continue or withdraw from an SSO or a working group. The Company also wants to provide its representatives in external standards and consortia forums with the information they need to competently and safely represent Oracle's interests. To address these objectives Oracle maintains an SSO participants' database, assigns roles supporting standards activities to individuals already working on primary assignments in the Company, and provides templates to assist prospective and current participants in gaining appropriate approvals and documenting major decisions about their SSO activities.

1. **SSO participants database:** A definitive list of all authorized Oracle participants in external SSOs is maintained by Standards Strategy. The SSO Participants Database, which is readily accessible to everyone within the Company, includes ALL approved Company representatives to external SSO activities. The database serves as a controlling mechanism—until and unless a name appears in the database as a participant in a particular external standards or consortia activity, s/he is NOT authorized to represent Oracle in

that SSO effort. Reviews and approvals by executive management, legal, and standards strategy are necessary prerequisites to recording names in the database. In addition to employee names and specific SSO activities, the SSO Participants Database provides links to (and a repository for) information about the forum and related internal white papers and participation reports.

2. **Standards coordination roles:** Employees, usually engineers with other primary responsibilities, serve as two-way communication

---

"Employees, usually engineers with other primary responsibilities, serve as two-way communication conduits between corporate standards support functions and their respective organizations. "

---

conduits between corporate standards support functions and their respective organizations. Others are designated to lead Oracle's participation in specific SSOs.

- **Technical Standards Contacts:** As working technical professionals with a broad knowledge of activities within their respective organizations, Technical and Field Standards Contacts differ only in their organizational focus. Both cull standards information that is pertinent to their organizations from the information they receive; make visible standardization issues relevant to their products, customers, and markets; respond to inquiries and volunteer information about their standards requirements, and provide a contact point for others in their organizations on standards related issues.

  - *Technical Standards Contact (FSC):* TSCs are assigned for major technical/development units at headquarters as well as for remote technical/development geographies. They inform all interested parties in their organizations about standardization activities and solicit inputs

from them that are necessary to represent their interests in external standards and consortia activities. TSCs also assist engineers in their organizations in complying with Company policies pertaining to participation in SSOs and serve as contacts for questions about standardization; while they do not know the answers to most questions, they provide access to those who do.

  - *Field Standards Contact (FSC):* Representing vertical industries or field technical sales support functions including remote geographies (e.g., Japan), FSCs serve as two-way communications conduits and champions for their organizations in standardization activities.

- **Standards forum lead (SFL):** Individuals charged with being the lead Oracle representatives to and coordinators of all Oracle participation in particular SSOs, SFLs oversee Company participation in and make information about their SSOs visible to all stakeholders within Oracle. For SSOs with multiple activities that span Oracle business units, SSO Coordinating Committees are established to assist the SFL.

- **SSO Coordinating Committee (SCC):** This standing committee coordinates and controls participation in an SSO where Oracle's interests cross business unit boundaries. The SCC chair serves as SFL for and carries out his/her responsibility for overseeing Company participation in the SSO through the Coordinating Committee. SCCs are needed for multi-activity forums such as W3C, OASIS,[7] IETF,[8] and OMG.[9]

3. **Templates:** These predefined virtual document formats assist Oracle employees in documenting major decision points pertaining to participation in external SSOs. Electronic templates guide Company employees in providing the necessary information and gaining the appropriate approval(s) for significant stages in the participation life cycle, including

proposing to join a new SSO, requesting that Legal review a participation agreement, seeking executive management approval to join an SSO, and guidelines for participating in activities in a specific SSO.

Communicating inside Oracle

Making information about Oracle's participation in SSOs, including participation rules and procedures, easy to find and accessible is difficult in a Company as large and distributed as Oracle. Educating Oracle representatives about the risks and responsibilities associated

---

"Educating Oracle representatives about the risks and responsibilities associated with SSO participation and providing mechanisms for interaction among those active in standardization activities are also important objectives that drive our standards support initiatives."

---

with SSO participation and providing mechanisms for interaction among those active in standardization activities are also important objectives that drive our standards support initiatives. To address these inside communication objectives Oracle provides an internal web site, mailing lists, and related archives, SSO participant training, and periodic standards participants summit meetings.

1. **Internal web site:** As a single, widely visible, and easily accessible web site, it provides access to all SSO related information for employees, participants, and other Oracle stakeholders. This portal allows access to information previously found on several separate internal web sites, provides links to the SSO Participants Database, and includes information on joining, participating, and contributing to external SSOs.

2. **Mailing lists and archives:** Group aliases and mailing archives facilitate communication among SSO participants and other standards and consortia stakeholders, including a gen-

eral-interest standards mailing list and a related archive accessible from the internal web site, along with similar sub-lists and archives for more narrowly focused standards discussions.

3. **Training:** Online and face-to-face modules educate employees about their rights and responsibilities when representing Oracle in external standards and consortia forums. Training is both generic (i.e., applicable to any external forum) and specific to certain multi-activity SSOs such as JCP, W3C, and OASIS. Completion of generic and pertinent SSO specific training is a mandatory prerequisite for representing Oracle in an external SSO.

4. **Standards summit:** Periodic face-to-face and/or electronic meetings for participants and other stakeholders in standards and consortia activities are held to exchange information about ongoing standards and consortia activities, educate participants, solicit inputs on and coordinate actions with standardization strategies, identify conflicts, exploit synergies, and encourage and reward SSO participation.

Communicating outside

Making information about Oracle's participation in SSOs easy to find and accessible outside the Company is important for customers and analysts. Such communication provides opportunities to leverage interactions between standards and regulatory policy initiatives as well as to exploit Oracle's SSO activities for marketing and PR benefit. To address these objectives, Oracle is developing an External Web Site to serve customers and prospects as well as others interested in Oracle's participation in standards and consortia forums. This web site showcases our activities in SSOs and provides links to white papers and articles on Oracle's positions on key standardization issues.

Summary and Conclusions

Recognizing the increasing importance and burden of participation in standards and consortia forums, Oracle augments its business-unit driven approach with light-weight corporate support functions and initiatives to better manage and improve the efficacy of standardization activities. These initiatives include: a standards and consortia steering committee, an SSO participants database, technical and field standards contacts, standards forum leads, SSO coordinating committees, and decision templates. Corporate support functions and initiatives provide the desired coordination and control in a manner consistent with Oracle's culture and resource constraints by leveraging existing staff and capabilities without adding standards professionals.

Copyright © Donald R. Deutsch.

Notes

[1] ANSI: American National Standards Institute

[2] INCITS: International Committee for Information Technology Standards

[3] ISO: International Standards Organization

[4] W3C: World Wide Web Consortium

[5] JCP: Java Community Process

[6] SQL: Structured Query Language

[7] OASIS: Organization for the Advancement of Structured Information Standards

[8] IETF: Internet Engineering Task Force

[9] OMG: Object Management Group

27

Customer Participation in the IT Standards Process— Benefits and Challenges

ANN BASSETTI
CARL BUNJE
The Boeing Company

Abstract: *The major beneficiary of information technology (IT) standards is the customer or user of IT products and services. Logic suggests these information technology customers would be significant participants in the development of those standards. However, relatively few large customer companies are actively involved with establishing IT standards. Why not? This paper discusses some of the benefits and challenges associated with customer contribution to the development of IT standards. We issue a call-to-arms for broader customer participation in this arena.*

The Value Proposition for Users

Over the last couple of decades the world of Information Technology (IT) has become exceedingly complex, increasing exponentially with no sign of slowing. Businesses are now dependent upon IT for their day-to-day operations. As well, new capabilities bring hopes of a competitive edge in a wide array of business arenas.

Part of the necessary foundation for the successful business use of IT depends on interoperability between various heterogeneous components of an organization's:

- IT infrastructure
- Business and productivity applications
- Business information within the enterprise and among partners

Standards that ensure such interoperability, and products that adhere to such standards, are therefore crucial to users' success – whether in industry, education, finance, or government.

The standards that ensure interoperability must address the deep and wide array of IT domains:

- physical (connectors, voltages, etc.)
- communication protocols (IP, TCP, SMTP, HTTP, etc.)
- presentation formats (SGML, HTML, etc.)
- data formats (TXT, RTF, CSV, etc.)
- security formats (X.509, DSIG, etc.)
- semantics of information (XML, RDF, etc.)
- the behavior of key functionality (UNIX™ kernels, encryption algorithms, "plug-and-play," web services, etc.)

IT standards are especially critical in larger customer companies. Smaller companies are often able to make use of single-vendor, end-to-end solutions hosted in homogeneous computing environments for most of their enterprise. Deploying these solutions minimizes interface interoperability problems so long as care is exercised in selecting products with caution about product interdependencies.

This type of deployment is not usually viable for larger companies. Heterogeneity permeates big institutions. It is not possible, or even desirable, to completely eliminate all variation. New functionality sits alongside older legacy solutions. Other products are added with mergers and acquisitions. The cost of migration and conversion is often prohibitive. Subsets of users have special critical requirements, even if they are in the minority (e.g., engineers in an aerospace company). The breadth of larger businesses often implies significant variety of interfaces to partners, suppliers, and customers as well.

Without product interoperability, the customer company is forced to bear the burden of integrating the various components. Whether it is done in-house or contracted to suppliers or third-party integrators, this is an exception-

---

"Without product interoperability, the customer company is forced to bear the burden of integrating the various components."

---

ally onerous responsibility. The difficulty of integration increases with the complexity of the environment and is usually tied to particular versions of deployed products and the specific functionality required at the time of integration. Integration solutions must often be reworked whenever new elements are introduced, new functionality is required, or old elements are upgraded. Companies in this situation are hard pressed to keep up as the complexity of IT continues its accelerating pace.

Standards that ensure the interoperability of well-defined interfaces help to mitigate this

---

"Standards that ensure the interoperability of well-defined interfaces help to mitigate this burden by establishing the common ground for integration of complex systems."

---

burden by establishing the common ground for integration of complex systems. Such interfaces scale (to meet the needs of large numbers), are flexible, and are not locked in by one supplier.

Why Standards Organizations?

To meet this need, a number of standards organizations have emerged and evolved to define and establish IT standards. Some are non-aligned, neutral meeting places; some are vendor-sponsored; and some are mandated by a government. All draw their memberships from companies and institutions with vested interests in how standardization of information technologies progresses. Two of the primary constituancies are the IT *suppliers*, those who produce IT products, and IT *customers*, those who use IT products in their enterprises.

IT *suppliers* engage because their product strategies and business models can be impacted (beneficially or detrimentally) by which areas are standardized and what technologies the standards specify.

IT *customers* strive to influence the suppliers to meet their needs for interoperability in their business realm and within their infrastructure. In this paper, we address IT customer involvement. Although the benefits of customer participation appear clear, the challenges can be daunting—both within the standards development process and within the IT customer's own corporate environment.

Competing Goals

Consider the difference in objectives between suppliers and customers participating in the standards process. Both groups' objectives are oriented toward their bottom line, but it is a more direct connection for IT suppliers. Each supplier seeks competitive advantage by introducing and locking in important technical solutions.

Occasionally there is potential for synergy among several suppliers, if common ground can be found for opening a new market that an individual supplier might not be able start on its own. Partnering relationships must be balanced by sufficient caution to protect current or potential market share and ensure that intellectual property investments are preserved or leveraged. There is little room for altruism, unless it leads to new markets.

At the same time, each vendor wants to appear that they are collaborating with the rest of the industry for the good of all. Supplier participation in standards organizations may be more or less sincere, depending on the circumstances. In any case, if the vendors do not genuinely participate, there will be no true standards.

Conversely, there is little room for altruism on the customer side either, unless it also leads to strategic advantage in meeting IT and business requirements. Competition among customer companies is less dependent upon unique IT advantage than it is on efficient, skillful, and cost effective management of IT power for business objectives.

We, as customers, are looking to quickly and easily integrate critical capabilities into reliable and usable business tools, preferably at commodity pricing. We want flexibility for complex deployments and for quick changes in the future. We do not want to – indeed we cannot – be dependent on one or very few suppliers, because in most cases the functionality required by our business requirements cannot be supplied by a single or even small set of suppliers. Therefore we need to mix and match solutions.

"Customer objectives in standards participation focus on interoperability, functionality, and the longer-term hope that standardization will bring about commoditization that results in lower price points."

Customer objectives in standards participation focus on interoperability, functionality, and the longer-term hope that standardization will bring about commoditization that results in lower price points.

These opposing sets of objectives tend to balance each other, evolving towards common ground that supports both the suppliers' competitive needs and customer requirements. Usually there is an interchange in which suppliers suggest functionality or products based on their perceptions of users' requirements. Hearing proposals, users react. Sometimes the sup-

pliers respond, sometimes they don't. There is a constant tension between users wanting the sun, the moon, and the stars – all interchangeable and interoperable – and the suppliers offering specific countries, each with its own borders, language, and customs.

When the Process Goes Awry

As with any democratic community process, standards development works best when a range of voices are present and when all are approximately on an equal footing. Things go askew when:

- one or more vendors dominate, or tries to do so. In this scenario, the community spends more time trying to get back in balance, or fighting and fending off attacks, than in actually doing productive work.

- proponents of a technology idea "shop" their idea between standards groups, playing one against the other. This behavior, related to the first bullet, seeks to divide, manipulate, and conquer rather than collaborate. It wastes everyone's time, energy, and money.

- one or more key stakeholders – supplier or user -- does not participate. If a key supplier is not engaged, then the standard will probably not gain traction in the marketplace. If a key user is not involved, it is likely that important requirements will not be met.

- participants have different "skin" in the game, yet an equal voice. It is important to have a variety of perspectives when developing new technologies, including not only suppliers and users, but also leading-edge thinkers such as representatives from the academic and open source communities. Problems arise when any one person can hold up the process. Vendors, in particular, are frustrated by any delay, as they have significant investments and time-to-market pressures hanging in the balance. When any one group gets too frustrated they back out – to the detriment of all.

Similar problems arise in all communities, as they are rooted in fundamental aspects of human behavior and business competition. There are no easy solutions. Since these behaviors usually derive from strategic directions driven from high levelsin corporate management, executives in user companies can seek to impress upon their supplier counterparts that these tactics are actually damaging the users' businesses in the end. One hopes that the positive benefits of collaboration will outweigh the short-term gains of the behaviors described above.

While this paper focuses primarily on the benefits and challenges of participation, we might also mention another balancing act that is going on in parallel – that of the standards process itself.

- Each different standards organization has developed it own process for how work will proceed. It is important that this process seek the middle ground between speed and allowing enough time to do a thorough job.

- Since the whole point of a standard is to interoperate, it is crucial that the process also contain elements of architectural testing and overview for consistency with related technologies.

- There is often a need for liaison between standards groups working on related topics. Occasionally two groups will cosponsor one piece of work. At the very least, it is important to have good communication between standards organizations.

If any of these elements is missing, the system may also go out of kilter.

Customer Roles

Customers can play a number of critical roles in the IT standards development process, each with unique benefits.

Technical participation – The reality is that a) decisions are primarily made by those who are in the room; and b) technical details can make a big difference. Therefore, customers can exert the greatest influence by having a technical expert in the room who participates in devel-

oping the details of a specification. It has often been told that one customer representative has swayed a working session by being the only user in the room who can give a real-life perspective on a proposal. This is especially crucial

---

"...customers can exert the greatest influence by having a technical expert in the room who participates in developing the details of a specification."

---

if your company has unusual needs that more mainstream participants might not think of. (For instance, in working group discussions on how to take the Web technologies to alternative devices, Boeing seeks to ensure that such solutions will also work on factory devices – not only the more ubiquitous cell phones and PDAs.)

Critical observation – This activity is similar to direct participation, but with less involvement. In this case, a technically-savvy user representative might follow a mailing list or participate in early requirements gathering, but not be involved in day-to-day activities. This user representative is more involved than the general public, but less involved than a direct participant.

Governance and management – Because they have such a vested interest, suppliers tend to dominate standards organizations. They cannot afford to *not* be there. It is common for such companies to assign full-time, high-level employees as liaison to standards organizations. Their goal, of course, is to try to ensure the organization moves in a direction and is managed in a way that is compatible with the supplier's own goals. For balance, it is important that user companies are also represented in the general membership, boards, and management of standards organizations. Because suppliers are competing with each other, they have to be wary. The staff of the standards organization is beholden to their member companies and must be neutral to all. Users are free of those constraints, and therefore, can speak more frankly.

Funding – Of course none of this happens for free. If employees are assigned to participate, there must be budget to cover their salaries, travel expenses, telephone, and Internet connections. There must be internal agreement that this is time well spent. In addition, standards organizations often seek sponsorship for large meetings or funding for special projects. Funding by user companies lends an important air of neutrality to such events whereas funding from a vendor is often met with a suspicion that they are trying to co-opt the event.

Statements of support – When assessing the merits of an organization or a technology, one usually looks to see which companies are involved. By issuing public statements of support, a user company makes visible its technical alignments and provides an important boost to those it supports. Similarly, no supportive statement or membership can indicate that there are concerns or lack of commitment for an organization or a technology.

Challenges of Customer Participation

Although a user company may understand the benefits of standards participation, there are often internal challenges to achieving this goal:

- Will the company budget appropriately to support membership fee(s) and travel for their representative (especially if international)?

- Will the company commit adequate senior analyst time to be devoted to such work?

- Is there a senior analyst with appropriate technical knowledge, political skill, and motivation to participate and represent their corporation?

- In a vote or a technical session *who* actually determines the interest of the corporation? To truly validate a technical position internally would often take too much time. Therefore the representative must be trusted to carry the appropriate message or to know when it is vital to consult with colleagues "back home."

- Once standards are established, it is hard to reap the fruit of that work back inside a company. One must be diligent to educate his/her company about emerging standards and strive for practical implementations.

- Finally, user companies' commitments to buy, based on these types of standards, is mixed – and vendors know it. Too often, buying decisions are based on short-term demands with disregard for the long-term cost of integration or migration. This is a disincentive for everyone involved in the quest for interoperable solutions.

These challenges all reduce to a common issue—the perceived value of participation to the customer. The customer organization must recognize the value of standards participation at a level of management commensurate with the commitment needed.

Involvement at the level of Critical Observation is probably the most common level of customer involvement. It is the easiest to justify since it involves the least amount of commitment and can usually be sponsored at relatively low levels in the organization. The potential benefits of exposure to the issues involved in particular technical standards activities and

> *"The customer organization must recognize the value of standards participation at a level of management commensurate with the commitment needed."*

the directions being taken by those activities must be viewed as worth the commitment of a membership fee, nominal analyst time, minimal travel costs, and resources to disseminate the acquired information back into the organization. Additionally, some incentive might derive from the educational/professional experience such involvement may provide to individual analysts.

Active Technical Participation implies deeper involvement. Key technical personnel must be committed by the user company to bring customer requirements to the standards-development table and to ensure that the emerging standards adequately address those requirements. Sometimes a higher level of membership fee is required to participate technically. Travel to face-to-face meetings is often important and must be budgeted (and, these days, such travel is often international). Additionally, the user representative must be accorded enough time to consolidate a position from technical requirements across his/her enterprise, an often difficult and daunting task. Such a position is needed and expected to influence other participants in the process. Of course, Technical Participation can be driven by more localized requirements within the organization, but the leverage is much less significant that if it is the voice of the enterprise. The perceived value of this level of participation must therefore occur at a higher level of the organization and must be viewed as having more strategic alignment with organization objectives. Awareness of the value of standards participation at this level of management is crucial for gaining the necessary level of commitment and setting the appropriate expectations.

Governance, Management, and Funding are typically the most difficult to justify in the customer environment, since it usually involves a clear understanding at executive levels of how specific standards activities and organizations align with and support customer business strategies. Since IT is usually viewed as a supportive infrastructure and therefore tactical in nature, this is a hard case to make with sufficient imperative to warrant executive participation and sponsor-level membership. However, as the dependencies of businesses on IT continue to become more critical, in both strategic as well as tactical perspectives, this level of involvement may become more plausible. Today we see little participation at this level in standards organizations. Hopefully, as IT interoperability becomes more essential to the viability and competitiveness of customer organizations, we will see a shift to the point where customer participation is driving the direction of standards.

In Search of the Holy Grail

Customer participants can bring real interoperability and functionality requirements to the table. The experience of IT integration, driven by the need to meet specific business requirements, provides a sense of priority and urgency that is usually lacking among technology providers. If a sufficient number of valued customer companies that work with participating supplier companies can aggregate their requirements, the suppliers can gain some degree of confidence that the standards generated to meet these requirements will be on target.

This sense of legitimacy helps to change the "balance point," moving away from conflicting competitive interests to solving the real issues facing the users of IT. In this way, the customer voice brings an element of objectivity and neutrality to the standards process, somewhat akin to control rods in a nuclear reactor. It serves as a stabilizer factor that is often able to refocus attention on meeting market needs rather than on conflicting vested interests.

In the end, customers benefit because they get specifications that more closely align with their

---

" If a sufficient number of valued customer companies that work with participating supplier companies can aggregate their requirements, the suppliers can gain some degree of confidence that the standards generated to meet these requirements will be on target."

---

needs. Suppliers benefit by increased market opportunities. Standards organizations benefit by lively interchange and increased membership. Industry flourishes.

We appeal to our fellow users to join us in the fray. We need your voices!

28

Integrating Geospatial Standards and Standards Strategies into Business Processes

DR. CARL REED

Open GIS Consortium

Abstract: *This chapter explores the requirements and solutions for integration of geospatial standards and interoperability strategies into government and commercial business processes. It also looks in a general way at the necessity and difficulty of making a corporate commitment to interoperability. As the recent Delphi survey on standards emphasized, "Standards provide the ability to leverage IT investment in unforeseen ways. "Most business processes that could benefit from geospatial information don't yet benefit because spatial information has been locked in non-standard systems or "stove pipes."* [1] *A committent to interoperability and to standards unlocks this foundational information type, leveraging current IT investments in unforeseen ways. However, with geospatial data and processing as well as with other kinds of data and processing, it is clear that while technical interoperability is necessary, it is not sufficient. Therefore, the use of standards and interoperable architectures are secondary to an understanding of a given business process and how geospatial data and services and by extension standards can best be used.*

Introduction

As this chapter evolved, I quickly discovered that the requirements for integrating standards into business process are the same whether they are geospatial standards or finan-

cial standards. In all cases, the use of standards requires a commitment to interoperability. Therefore, much of this chapter has to do with achieving interoperability in an enterprise and the focus is as much on the use of standards in general as it is on geospatial standards in building the interoperable enterprise.

Enterprise Application Integration, Web Services, E-Government, Federated Architectures, Information Sharing—these are just a few of the catch phrases we hear everyday in the Information Technology (IT) community. Typically, as part of the business process—or workflow - in these application areas, a fundamental requirement is the access, use, and integration of distributed, often disparate, content and related processing services. This requirement cannot be met without an overarching reliance on standards and an enterprise wide commitment to the concepts of interoperability. By it very nature, such a commitment incorporates an open systems philosophy.

In the 2003 Delphi Survey,[2] portability of data and leveraging existing IT investments for the future were overwhelmingly the most significant benefits in using standards. In follow-up interviews, respondents were consistent in their observation that, although these benefits are not a new and sudden realization, the imperative to leverage standards in realizing these benefits is. While, in the past, vendor lock-in may have been considered a bitter pill that one had to swallow in order to deploy a solution rapidly, it is no longer acceptable. The increased value and liquidity of data and applications that result

---

"The climate of economic constraint and risk aversion along with the mandate to integrate systems on both sides of the firewall has created a shift in the sense of imperative to adopt software standards."

---

from standards has become much clearer to IT providers, buyers, and users. Within this context, there is a clear and sudden shift in attitudes towards software standards. The climate of economic constraint and risk aversion along with the mandate to integrate systems on both sides of the firewall has created a shift in the sense of imperative to adopt software standards.

Perhaps no other industry has such an enormous investment in legacy data as the traditional geospatial industry. Over the decades, governments and businesses have spent tens of billions of dollars collecting and maintaining geospatial information. Leveraging this investment is critical to meeting the requirements for many government and business enterprise applications. Integrating standards into solutions and integrating standards strategies into business processes provides the path forward to achieve this goal.

"The development of universal standards for geospatial data transmission would exponentially increase the use of the information worldwide for numerous functions including national security, environmental management and crime mapping," said Thomas Kalil, special assistant to the president for economic policy for the National Economic Council at the (Clinton) White House.

"The ability to manage and make sense of the information will be the challenge of the 21st century," Kalil said. "Open standards and interoperability are crucial to making a market take off...

and there's opportunity to integrate geospatial information and geospatial processing with the World Wide Web.

Government officials and organizations around the world are now stating the same requirement: *geospatial interoperability standards and interoperability need to be an integral part of their applications and business processes.*

What is the OGC?

The Open GIS Consortium (OGC) is a global industry consortium that envisions, "A world in which everyone benefits from geographic information and services made available across any network, application, or platform." Inherent in this vision is the requirement for geospatial standards and strategies to be an integral part of business process.

The OGC consists of 260+ members—geospatial technology software vendors, systems integrators, government agencies, and universities—participating in a consensus process to develop, test, and document publicly available interface specifications and encodings for the geospatial industry. Open interfaces and protocols defined by Open GIS® Specifications are designed to support interoperable solutions that "geo-enable" the Web, wireless and location-based services, and mainstream IT, and to empower technology developers to make complex spatial information and services accessible and useful to all kinds of applications.

Thus, OGC envisions the full integration of geospatial data and geoprocessing resources into mainstream computing and the widespread use of interoperable, commercial geoprocessing software throughout the information infrastructure.

What Does It Take to Integrate Geospatial Standards and a Standards Strategy into Your Organization?

So how can geospatial standards and a standards strategy become part of an organizations business process? Organizations will need:

1. An overarching commitment to interoperability and standards with the proper focus on geospatial standards

2. A commitment to collaboration

3. A commitment to define a geospatial interoperability and information framework that meets the business process requirements of the organization

4. A commitment to the collection and maintenance of geospatial metadata (data describing data sets)

5. A commitment to retraining and educating staff and management

These commitments may seem self-evident. However, if the organization does not fully embrace the tenets of interoperability and interoperable architectures, then long-term suc-

"A tactical-only solution is a waste of money—you need to adopt an Enterprise solution that addresses business context and people."

cess in integrating geospatial processes into an organization's overall business processes may be problematic. Typically what is required is a change in the corporate culture and this can be difficult: *A tactical-only solution is a waste of money—you need to adopt an Enterprise solution that addresses business context and people.*

What do we mean by interoperability?

Together with terms like "metadata" and "joined-up thinking," this word is increasingly being used in information management discourse across all of our information gathering institutions. The meaning of "interoperability," though, remains somewhat ambiguous, as do many of the benefits of "being interoperable." Therefore, the following definition of interoperability is suggested:

To be **interoperable,** one should actively be engaged in the ongoing process of ensuring that the systems, procedures, and culture of

an organization are managed in such a way as to maximize opportunities for exchange and re-use of information, whether internally or externally. [3]

Based upon this definition, it should be clear that there is far more to ensuring interoperability than using compatible software and hardware, although that is of course important. Rather, assurance of effective interoperability

"...effective interoperability will require often radical changes to the ways in which organizations work and, especially, in their attitudes to information."

will require often radical changes to the ways in which organizations work and, especially, in their attitudes to information. Within this context, the organization committed to interoperability needs to consider the following interoperability focus areas:

• **Technical:** This is the "nuts and bolts" of software and hardware interoperabity and where the work of the OGC and other standards organizations can be leveraged. Technical interoperability typically consists of selecting and implementing the appropriate software and/or internet interface specifications, common content encodings for transmission, and so forth. Quite often, within the enterprise, technical interoperability is the easiest to achieve in any given business process.

• **Semantic:** [6] More than any other type of digital content, geospatial content is an extremely rich content domain that requires special attention. The enormous variety of encodings of geospatial data and its semantics makes it particularly challenging to process requests for geospatial information. Work in the area of GIS interoperability and the work led by the OGC addresses some basic issues, primarily related to the geometry of geospatial features. Within an organization seeking to integrate geospatial data and standards into business process, it is vitally important that there is agreement on the proper use of metadata (see discussion on metadata). Proper metadata provides the foundation for semantic intoperability. The next level of semantic interoperability may require an organization to address issues related to differing data models, classification schemes, and so forth.

· **Institutional:** In order to share geospatial information within an organization or between organizations, institutional interoperability needs to be addressed. Institutional intoperability typically consists of defining the "rules of engagement" when two or more organizations need to share information. A typical example is in an emergency management services business application. When an emergency event occurs, the logistics staff will need immediate access to information from police, fire, cities, counties, state, and Federal agencies. During a crisis, there is no time to work out issues related to data sharing, such as privacy, confidentiality, accuracy, symbology, and so forth. These need to be worked out beforehand. Even within a single enterprise, institutional interoperability issues such as ownership of given data sets, common symbology, and cost sharing need to be discussed and resolved.

· **Political/Human:** The decision to make resources more widely available through interoperable business processes has implications for the organisations concerned (where this may be seen as a loss of control or ownership), their staff (who may not possess the skills required to support the new, interoperable enterprise and a potentially a newly dispersed user community), and the end users. Process change, and extensive staff and user training are rarely considered when deciding whether or not to release a given resource, but are crucial to ensuring the effective long-term use of any enhanced business process.

· **Legal:** Within the Geospatial domain, there are very definite legal implications to implementing the interoperable enterprise, espe-

cially if, as part of a given business process, geospatial information is going to be made available to a new set of constituents. In cases where organisations wish to disclose information, there are legal implications to such a decision. In most countries, the most obvious implication is adherence to privacy and confidentiality laws with potentially strict stipulations over use and publication of personal data. Additionally, the checks placed upon Government to protect civil liberties have the added effect of reducing Government's ability to exchange certain types of data in the most effective manner. Where resources have been compiled from different sources (county land use information plotted on a satellite image owned by a satellite processing company, for example), there may be Intellectual Property Rights (IPR) issues. A well-known example of copyright in the United Kingdom (UK) is allowable use of Ordnance Survey maps. For example, what is allowed within an organisation may not be permitted on the World Wide Web where anybody conceivably has access.

In all cases, the organization must provide a supportive infrastructure that allows the key constituents to collaborate in a non-adversarial environment.

Why commit to interoperability?

Without a corporate or enterprise commitment to interoperability and a concept of open systems, an organization cannot effectively integrate geospatial data, services, and pro-

---

"Without a corporate or enterprise commitment to interoperability and a concept of open systems, an organization cannot effectively integrate geospatial data, services, and processes into their overall business processes."

---

cesses into their overall business processes. Historically, spatial data and technology have been implemented as "stove-pipes" internal to a given department or an organization. As a result, over time the enterprise implements systems from multiple geospatial technology vendors, each system accessing mission specific repositories of spatial data—and none of these systems or content holdings are interoperable.

Today, these same enterprises are faced with the requirement to share data and resources between departments and also with out-of-enterprise partners. There are many drivers for this market force, including better customer service provision, improved revenue generation, cost sharing, better return on investment, and so forth. Traditionally, the knee-jerk reaction by many organizations to the requirement to share data and technology has been to standardize on a single vendor platform and a single content model. This is short sighted tactical thinking and does not address the longer term requirements of an enterprise—especially as one considers the requirement to collaborate more with external organizations, the availability of new spatial content sources, the pervasiveness of the Web, and the continued rapid evolution of hardware and software technology.

In today's IT and standards climate, it is no longer necessary to adopt a single vendor approach. Further, legacy investment in training, applications, content, and processes dictates a strategic commitment to interoperability. As Susan Cromwell[4] from the State of Arkansas points out, "The (State) GIS Forum members wouldn't 'buy into' standards that meant they'd have to change software or that would make data acquisition cumbersome. Data in the state's clearinghouse couldn't be locked up and available only to users of some products."

By implementing an interoperability philosophy (or policy) coupled with defining and implementing the appropriate interoperability architecture and framework for an organization, it is possible to implement enterprise wide sharing of geospatial content—independent of but sensitive to the content model, content location, and content ownership. It is also possible to leverage, protect, and even extend the value of legacy applications.

Build the interoperable enterprise through collaboration

Implementation of geospatial standards and interoperability cannot be done by decree. While an executive level statement or policy supporting a commitment to interoperability is required, implementation of any such policy rests with the employees of the organization. Therefore, a collaborative approach to defining and implementing geospatial standards and interoperability is required. The organization must build

---

"The organization must build an Interoperability Team and this Team must be enfranchised with the authority to make recommendations that result in organizational and technology change."

---

an Interoperability Team and this Team must be enfranchised with the authority to make recommendations that result in organizational and technology change. This interoperability Team must include users, IT professionals, technology providers, and key executive management (the champion for interoperability). The Team must adopt a consensus approach—much like a standards organization such as the OGC—to discussing and resolving issues, requirements, and recommendations. Above all, this interoperability Team must utilize a business centric methodology.

This Team would have a number of responsibilities, including:

• Defining the interoperability and standards vision for the enterprise

• Defining and documenting an information and interoperability framework for the enterprise

• Defining and documenting an approach to consistent metadata collection and maintenance

• Recommending procurement language that incorporates the organization's vision and mandate for the use of standards—specifically geospatial standards

By being very clear in defining the vision, information, and interoperability framework for the use of geospatial and other standards, the Team can communicate a very clear message not only to their technology providers but also to other staff in the organization.

A commitment to define an interoperability and information framework

The Interoperability Team should focus on defining an interoperability and information framework and an enterprise vision for standards and interoperability. For example, the US Government Federal Enterprise Architecture team defined a standards vision as:

Standards. *Establish Federal interoperability standards.* The Federal Government should adopt and use voluntary industry standards in which the interrelationships of components are fully defined by interface specifications available to the public and maintained by group consensus. The Federal Government should acquire and integrate preponderantly only those components conformant to these standards specifications. Non-proprietary system architectures and solutions are the goal; however, initially only partially and selectively compliant systems may be attainable. [5]

With a vision in place, the Team must then define, document, and present a methodology for enterprise agility and interoperability of both IT and geospatial standards into business process that uses the following business centric operational guidelines.[6] The team's approach:

- Addresses the root cause rather than just symptoms of integration problems by providing *semantic and pragmatic interoperability*

- *Is business-centric;* shifting power to the users and business experts; managing Enterprise artifacts and governance through Communities of Interests (CoI)

- Provides visibility, accessibility, understandability, using open *declarative mechanisms*

that allow for *mass customization* of diverse vocabularies and models within *heterogeneous environments*

- Insulates business from the high rate of technology change by dividing the problem into multiple levels and applying constraints properly to reduce complexity and promote reuse

- Provides for Enterprise agility and prepares the Enterprise for new opportunities in doing business

The Team should build a document that provides both a roadmap for going forward and traceability from vision to implementation. However, this document should not define the physical implementation.

An excellent example of such a document is the UK's E-Government Interoperability Framework [7] that begins by stating:

"Better public services tailored to the needs of the citizen and business, as envisaged in the UK online strategy, require the seamless flow of information across government. The e-Government Interoperability Framework (e-GIF) sets out the government's technical policies and specifications for achieving interoperability and ICT systems coherence across the public sector. The e-GIF defines the essential pre-requisites for joined-up and web enabled government. It is a cornerstone policy in the overall e-Government strategy."

A commitment to metadata

Perhaps more than any other data type, sharing of geospatial information within and between organizations requires a commitment to the collection and maintenance of metadata. The Team should work to define the core metadata elements that are required for any geospatial dataset. There is currently widespread global support to adopt the ISO Metadata (19115) standard to document and locate internal sources of geographic data. Any organization seeking to integrate geospatial standards into business process should consider adopting a profile of the ISO Metadata standard.

The ISO Metadata standard has an essential core of 21 data elements that have been agreed upon by member nations for consistent search and discovery of geographic information. However, the standard has the capacity to allow for more than 100 data elements that allow organizations to capture the level of detail they need to properly manage the characteristics of their geographic information holdings. The Team needs to reach consensus on accepting these 21 core data elements and/or define your organization's profile that identifies the additional data elements of the ISO Metadata Standard deemed necessary to support enterprise geospatial operations.

The work of the team should also include establishing an internal core capacity for instruction of metadata creation and maintenance for geographic information.

A commitment to retraining and educating staff

There will be resistance to change. There will be fear, uncertainty, and doubt resulting from a change in corporate culture brought on by a commitment to the interoperable enterprise and the integration of geospatial standards into business process. These are normal responses in the face of change—especially when the organization does not include staff in the process of

---

"...it is imperative that any organization committing themselves to interoperability and to using standards must also initiate staff training and communication programs."

---

change. It is human nature to fight to protect "turf." Edict does not ameliorate fear of change and staff uncertainty.

Therefore, it is imperative that any organization committing themselves to interoperability and to using standards must also initiate staff training and communication programs. The staff needs to know and understand the planned changes and approaches to implementing

technology for improved business processes. They must have a forum for not only expressing concerns but also for providing input to the RoadMap and vision.

Conclusion

A truly interoperable organisation is able to maximise the value and reuse potential of information under its control. This is true whether we are considering spatial data or financial data. An interoperable organization is also able to exchange this information effectively with other equally interoperable bodies, allowing new knowledge to be generated from the identification of relationships between previously unrelated sets of data.

Changing internal systems and practices to make them interoperable is a far from simple task. But the benefits for the organisation and for those who make use of information it publishes are incalculable.

Notes and Selected Bibliography

[1] A Delphi Survey, "The Value of Standards," ©2003 Delphi Group, Ten Post Office Square, Boston, MA 02109

[2] A Delphi Survey, "The Value of Standards," ©2003 Delphi Group, Ten Post Office Square, Boston, MA 02109

[3] Miller, Paul "Interoperability. What is it and Why should I want it?." 21-June-2000, Ariadne Issue 24 Originating URL: http://www.ariadne.ac.uk/issue24/interoperability/intro.html.

[4] Schutzberg, Adena, "Policy, Open Standards and GIS: The OPEN GIS Story in Arkansas." OGC User, August 2003.

[5] FEA Working Group, Federal CIO Council, E-Gov Enterprise Architecture Guidance (Common Reference Model), Version 2. July 2002

[6] Lubash, Mike, "Business-Centric Methodology for Enterprise Agility & Interoperability," DoD Financial and Accounting XML Community Working Group, September 2002.

[7] Office of the E-Envoy, "E-Government Interoperability Framework," http://www.e-envoy.gov.uk, April 2003

29

The Standardization Menu

MIKE SMITH

International Organization
for Standardization

Abstract: *Standards and regulations have always had a role in human societies and the relationship between them is currently receiving a lot of attention. At the same time, industry has developed new methods of reaching agreement on standards and formal standards bodies have reacted by creating new possibilities for participation and collaboration as well as new types of deliverables to respond to market needs. Market players conseqeuntly have a whole menu of options open to them when they need normative documents.*

From Caveman to Coalman

Although the public at large remains essentially unaware of the existence of standards, they are fundamental to the way that societies and communities operate. Most people would of course relate to behavioral "standards," the way that individuals are expected to act in social settings and in their day to day interactions with others. At a time when a lot of attention is being given to the relationship between voluntary standards and legislation/regulations, it is interesting to note that some behavioural standards are prescribed by law ("thou shalt not steal"), while others are voluntary (such as giving up one's seat for an elderly person on public transport).

Even in prehistoric times, it is hard to believe that human communities could function without some understanding of the behavioral standards that were expected in a community, although these would not of course be written. There were undoubtedly also other unwritten standards, such as for the materials to be used for making

> *"Although the public at large remains essentially unaware of the existence of standards, they are fundamental to the way that societies and communities operate."*

hunting implements, for the process of preparing furs for clothing, etc. In brief, even in those earliest times, "standards" served to codify human knowledge.

It is not too surprising therefore that standardization was also a fundamental component in many of the first civilizations when human activities diversified from the day-to-day preoccupation with subsistence to a whole range of activities including agriculture, animal husbandry, building construction, the arts, sports, etc., and commerce became the "glue" holding those civilizations together. In order to ensure a fair trading system, there inevitably had to be agreements on the value of traded goods and services and so were born the first written standards, usually for weights and measures. One of the earliest prescriptions of standards for weights and measures is included in the Code of Hammurabi, a king of Babylon in the 18th century BC, although, since this was a law, the standards should probably more correctly be considered regulations.

"Modern" standardization, or "industrial" standardization as it is sometimes called in recognition of the fact that it stemmed from the industrial revolution, started at the beginning of the twentieth century when most of the older standards bodies were established, although the origins of the International Telecommunication Union (ITU) go back even further. Of course, the world has changed significantly since then, as has the world of standardization.

A Short History of ISO

ISO is a relative newcomer to the world of standardization, having been established in 1947. This was the time of post-war national reconstruction in many countries and markets were essentially domestic. ISO's objective in those early years was to formulate agreements to help countries harmonize their national standards and, consistent with that aim, the technical agreements published by the organization were issued as "ISO Recommendations."

It was only in the early 1970s that the decision was taken that the organization should publish International Standards and, in view of what was to come, one can only admire the foresight of those who took that decision.

By the 1980s, international trade was starting to expand dramatically and the first signs appeared that the role of ISO was changing. Specifically, in a good few instances, ISO was asked to develop International standards in new fields rather than provide a forum for the harmonization of national standards. This is a trend that has continued until today. By the time we reached the 1990s, there was no doubt that we were seeing the creation of global markets and, despite the events that surround such occasions

as G8 and World Trade Organization meetings, there are few that would deny that globalization is upon us. And globalization has to be good for an international standards body, doesn't it?

ISO's development during the last two decades of the twentieth century was not however without challenges. Two particular challenges that need mention are the emergence of European standardization and what, in the IT sector, is often termed the "consortia phenomenon."

The European "New Approach"

One of the most significant recognitions of the role that voluntary standards can play in society occurred with the decision by the members of what was to become the European Union to create the Single European Market and bring it to reality by defining a new approach to European-wide legislation. This approach, which restricted regulations to the essential requirements needed to protect public health, safety and the environment, was supported by voluntary, consensus European standards. At the same time, ISO was concerned about the risk of Europeans diverting their focus and resources away from international standardization and into European standardization. Europe has always been a strong contributor to ISO and there were fears that international standardization in some sectors would become unsustainable without European participation. This effectively happened in a good number of cases but was ultimately solved through the establishment of the agreement (Vienna Agreement) on technical cooperation between ISO and CEN (the European Committee for Standardization).

Much has been written and debated about the Vienna Agreement, its advantages and disadvantages, but this is outside our present scope. It needs to be mentioned, however, because a good many ISO standards over the last decade were developed with the intention of also serving as European standards supporting European Directives.

In many countries there are long traditions of regulatory bodies making reference to standards in their regulations, comprising deemed-to-satisfy solutions, so the European "new approach" is in some respects not new. In terms of its scope however it is indeed an innovative new means of regulation.

To a large extent, this development and the references to international standards in the Technical Barriers to Trade (TBT) Agreement, amongst others, have brought the question of the relationship between technical regulation and voluntary standards to the surface. In the last few years, a number of inter-governmental bodies have undertaken studies related to the needs and possibilities for harmonization of technical regulations.

The Consortia Phenomenon

Starting in the late 1980s, there has been a trend, generally restricted to the information and communications technology (ICT) sectors, to establish consortia as a means of addressing particular technology issues within the ICT industry. Although initially it was often said that such groups were not set up to carry out standardization or that standards were a by-product of their activities, there can be no doubt that nowadays there are a large number of these bodies; that they vary considerably in scope, focus, and membership; and that a good number of them have output documents that are essentially used as standards within the industry.

Such groups often have closed memberships (restricted to a few companies) addressing very specific issues while others have very broad scopes and memberships. It is probably not coincidental that the growth of consortia has accompanied the decline, or even disappearance, in many companies of corporate standards groups.

The consortia phenomenon has essentially added an additional layer to the traditional hierarchy of company, national, regional, and international standardization. Where it would fit within that hierarchy is debatable. To some extent, it could be considered as company standardization jointly carried out between companies operating in a number of countries. But, there is also little doubt that in a good few cases

the work results of a consortium have enjoyed the status of a de facto international standard.

Not unnaturally, reflections were undertaken in ISO to try to understand what this phenomenon was telling the formal standards system. Speed of delivery was of course one of the first considerations that occurred to many. The formal standards system is often accused of being slow. However, there are many examples of ISO standards being produced rapidly, including in the ICT sector, and general experience indi-

---

" Another major factor is that standardization is not science—it is a negotiation process between market players until consensus is reached."

---

cates that the time taken to produce a standard depends on a number of factors not the least of which is the amount of resource that industry, in particular, is willing to make available for the work. Another major factor is that standardization is not science—it is a negotiation process between market players until consensus is reached. Reaching consensus can be a long process depending on the issues involved and the impact a particular standard might have in the market place.

A second consideration, however, was that while work is generally carried out through committee structures that seek to establish a balanced representation of all stakeholders within the formal standardization system, particularly at the national level, including suppliers, users, government, academia, consumers, etc., the operating methods of consortia basically limit participation in the work to the interested manufacturers/suppliers. In other words, in some cases, technical agreements that could be used in the marketplace do not always need to be elaborated through open processes involving all types of stakeholders.

It was these two considerations in particular that prompted ISO to review both its rules with regard to participation as well as its processes and the types of documents it produces.

ISO has long pursued a policy of "inclusiveness" based on the desire to collaborate, rather than compete, with other standards bodies. Its participation rules were accordingly amended to allow consortia and consortia-type bodies to participate in ISO work. The ISO/IEC joint committee for information technology (ISO/IEC JTC 1) also introduced a recognition process to allow such bodies to submit the results of their work into the formal standards system. In a number of instances, special agreements were concluded to allow joint development of standards between consortia and ISO.

In terms of deliverables, it was recognized that the ISO standards development process generates consensus at three successive levels, the broadest consensus being that of allowing the publication of an International Standard. At earlier stages in the process however, consensus is first achieved between experts in expert working groups and then again following the process of negotiating and reconciling national consensus positions. It was accordingly decided to allow committees to publish documents representing these lower levels of consensus, designated "Publicly Available Specifications" in the case of documents agreed between experts and "Technical Specifications" in the case of documents agreed between the national members of an ISO committee.

As a further development, ISO also introduced a workshop mechanism, completely separate from its committee processes, to allow interested market players to develop documents in workshops and publish them as International Workshop Agreements. ISO/IEC JTC 1 has similarly adopted the workshop mechanism as an option in its operating procedures.

The Standardization Menu

Globalization is making the world more complex, but one of the objectives of standardization is to rationalize complexity and those who need standards now have a whole menu of options to choose from.

Regulators need to consider whether the traditional, detailed technical regulations are needed in all cases or whether they can be replaced by "light" regulations supported by voluntary standards, using for the example the European model or possibly an intermediate model.

Market players essentially need to decide with whom they wish to reach agreement on

"Globalization is making the world more complex, but one of the objectives of standardization is to rationalize complexity and those who need standards now have a whole menu of options to choose from."

standards. If standards need to be developed as openly and as transparently as possible, then a formal standard is needed and the next decision is whether the geographical scope is national, regional, or international. There is also the question of how rapidly the standard is needed and whether, in the first instance, an intermediate deliverable such as a PAS, a Technical Specification, or possibly a workshop agreement would help to consolidate the market place.

In cases in which it is considered sufficient that a standard simply be agreed upon between a restricted number of market players, then a consortium-type approach is probably justified. This brings me however to another consideration, namely, cost.

It has been reported that there are some 400 consortia and consortia-type bodies in the ICT sector and most of the major ICT companies are members of many of them. The big multi-national

"Some reported figures indicate that companies can pay between 30 and 50 million USD annually to support these infrastructures."

companies are also often members of several national standards bodies. One cannot deny that supporting such a large number of parallel infrastructures is costly, and most of that cost is borne by the ICT companies themselves. Some reported figures indicate that companies can pay between 30 and 50 million USD annually to support these infrastructures.

Inevitably, one has to ask whether such expenditure is sustainable and whether there needs to be some rationalization of the structures producing standards for the ICT industry. That brings me to one more, and final, option offered by the standardization menu.

Most standards bodies have developed a long track record of excellence in such things as meetings management, including maintenance of membership lists, organization of meetings, logistics support for meetings, preparing meeting reports, carrying out follow up actions, general project management of standards projects, and publication of standards. These skills essentially need to be developed anew each time a new consortium is established.

There would seem to be a case, at least from the financial perspective, for using existing infrastructures to respond to standards needs. At least two ISO members have to date offered their services to external groups wishing to produce normative documents. These documents were not national standards but responded to specific needs of market players. I would maintain that this could well also be a low cost solution for the ICT industry in the future when it does not need formal standards.

Copyright © Mike Smith

30

Standards Making: Behind the Scenes
Evaluating Standardization Venues

DONALD R. DEUTSCH

Oracle Corporation

Abstract: *Considering five key characteristics can facilitate differentiating among the increasing number of standardization venues: initiation, access, consensus, encumbrances, and implementations. Each of these dimensions impacts how well a forum can serve the interests of individual participants as well as those of the industry and community-at-large. While seeking competitive advantage through standardization is rarely successful, we see in areas like Web Services this strategy being pursued today. When all is said and done, no standardization activity is worthwhile unless its outputs are widely adopted and embraced by the marketplace.*

Five Keys to Successful Evaluation

Today, everyone recognizes that software standards are necessary for interoperability; without standards the promise of the web world will never be realized. The hard part is determining which standards—and specifications that someday may become standards—are worthy of consideration. No one wants to back the wrong horse, and there are just too many horses in the race to make a safe bet. Press releases announcing yet another specification development effort with vague promises of future standardization flood the media, "consortia-of-the-week"

have become as common as ants at a picnic (or as Fergie on the cover of the Enquirer), and following the flurry of "standards" announcements in the web services space alone is enough to make your head spin.

It's very difficult to judge standardization activities as "good" (or likely to succeed) and others as "bad" (that is, a waste of time and resources). Evaluating standardization efforts is like looking at a shiny used car—you have to look below the surface to determine how well it will run. There is no sure-fast rule to follow, but substantial insight can be gained by considering five key characteristics:

- Initiation
- Access
- Consensus
- Encumbrances
- Implementations

Keys to gauging any standards development effort include the type of group developing the standard, the processes it uses, and the manner in which its results are made available.

Initiation

Standards and Consortia forums have dramatically different mechanisms for establishing new projects. Some, like the technical committees working under the auspices of ANSI (American National Standards Institute) and ISO (International Organization for Standardization), make proposals for new work widely available for review and comment prior to voting on whether to pursue the activity. The World Wide Web Consortium (W3C) has an extensive membership-review process to advise Tim Berners-Lee and the W3C Team in their architectural coordination role.

In contrast, the Organization for the Advancement of Structured Information Standards (OASIS) allows the proverbial three guys and a dog to propose a project—and you don't need the dog. Then, OASIS approves projects at the Board of Directors level without making the otherwise secret proposals visible even to their members.

Although greater visibility and better coordination should result in more successful projects, they can also slow down project initiation. On the other hand, rapidly initiated projects may fail because they do not address broad community concerns.

Access

When thinking about standards development organizations, most people have in mind something like the ANSI accredited committees of IEEE or INCITS. Standards, like wireless networking (IEEE 802) and ANSI/ISO SQL (INCITS H2), are developed in these formal or "de jure" Standards Development Organizations (SDOs) that are required to meet criteria for access and due process. Typically, these types of groups are open forums where all materially impacted parties are welcome and there are no substantial barriers to participation. While de jure forums tend to meet these criteria, many other so-called standards organizations fall far short—limiting participation through onerous fees or other barriers.

If de jure forums represent the epitome of openness, at the other extreme are single vendor specifications developed in the closed environment of one company. Only slightly more open are joint development agreements (JDAs) where two or three companies agree to work together to define a specification. Often JDAs are announced with substantial fanfare applauding the participating companies' contributions to industry standards and promising that the resulting specifications will be submitted to standards setting organizations. In reality, their objective is to define specifications in a substantially closed environment. Only when the technical details have been defined to favor the JDA participants are other interested parties invited to help anoint the work with the label of "a standard."

Access characteristics of consortia span a wide range—from JDAs masquerading as consortia (I call these psuedo-consortia) to forums like the W3C that are open to all—and every level of openness in between. Even the most open consortia sometimes have financial barriers to participation that may exclude prospective members.

Consensus

Some standards and consortia forums use very formal collaboration processes to gain consensus among their members. They have well defined procedures for developing specifications, making proposed specifications visible to (and soliciting input from) the impacted technical community, and traversing well-defined milestones to progress specifications from draft to standards status. Other groups are less formal, producing specifications and determining consensus using ad hoc mechanisms.

Whether the procedures are well defined and formal or minimally structured and informal

---

"Every member must participate as an equal and this equality should not be jeapordized by forum rules."

---

is less important than the way participants are treated vis-à-vis each other. Broad consensus is possible only when a standards setting body provides a level playing field. Every member must participate as an equal and this equality should not be jeapordized by forum rules (Note:

this does not preclude an organization from having more influence because its representatives contribute more to the technical effort).

De jure standards generally represent a broad consensus. Consortia produced specifications represent a range from broad to limited consensus, depending on the specific rules under which the consortia operate. Farther down the consensus scale are the pseudo-consortia and JDAs. By definition, because these groups limit those allowed at the table, pseudo-consortia and JDAs can produce results that represent only a limited consensus. Finally, single vendor specifications obviously represent a single company's perspective. Note that while there is a direct relationship between access and consensus (i.e., open forums tend to provide broad consensus and vice versa), groups of each type may have a range of access and consensus characteristics.

When evaluating a standard, determine where the standard's sponsoring group fits on the access/consensus range. Is the group one like the W3C that is open to all, has well defined collaboration methods, and all participants have an equal opportunity to influence the specifications? Or is the group actually a JDA or psuedo-consortia with a few participants who are more equal than others?

Sometimes it also is necessary to look at the participants in an activity and the discretion that they have in influencing the resulting specification. Increasingly, specifications produced under JDAs are submitted to forums under terms where they can gain the appearance of being open standards without risking changes that might cause the specifications to vary from products their authors soon intend to release or are already shipping.

Encumbrances

Regardless of other standards developing characteristics—except in the case of a single vendor specification (which by definition will be implemented and available ONLY from that vendor)—to be successful a standard must be widely implemented. Both the difficulty and expense associated with acquiring the specifica-

tion can determine the breadth of implementation.

The de jure world is saddled with a business model that uses the revenues from the sales of standards to support its standards bureaucracies. Although this type of encumbrance is annoying, it may not substantially limit implementation (because acquiring a standard is a one-time expense). However, because many consortia offer their specifications at no or nominal cost, formal standards bodies are under pressure

---

"The de jure world is saddled with a business model that uses the revenues from the sales of standards to support its standards bureaucracies."

---

to eliminate or reduce the fees they charge for acquiring specifications. Also, virtually all standards and consortia organizations now provide a mechanism to download standards using the web.

More serious encumbrances include the terms and conditions associated with implementing standards. A great deal of recent attention has been given to licensing terms in general and to royalties in particular. In some technical areas like consumer electronics, standards often incorporate proprietary technology for which royalty payments are expected and willingly paid by implementers. However, software standards have usually been royalty free. Recently, the ease of aquiring software patents has led some companies to charge royalties for the technology they contribute to software standards.

An important differentiator among standards development activities is the terms upon which the results are made available—royalty free or requiring some payment for use of the intellectual property therein. Oracle prefers that technical contributions to standards forums be made by default on a royalty free basis. If contributors are not willing to provide technology without charge, then we request up front notification of the terms under which the contribution is being offered—including what it will cost. Only then can we make a rational business decision about whether to help anoint their IPR in a standard. This approach has been incorporated into the W3C Proposed Patent Policy. We believe it gives W3C a substantial competitive advantage over other forums where results may be encumbered by royalty claims.

Implementations

As stated earlier, the best specification in the world is a failure as a standard if it is not widely implemented. Technically brilliant specifications representing thousands of hours of professional effort have resulted in standards that had little or no impact on the marketplace; that is, few if any implementations were ever released. The

> *"...the best specification in the world is a failure as a standard if it is not widely implemented."*

de jure standards process is often accused of producing academically interesting but commercially irrelevant standards such as the OSI (Open Systems Internconnect) communication protocols that never achieved the market share of IETF's (Internet Engineering Task Force) TCP/IP.

By no means do ANSI and ISO have a monopoly on this kind of failure, however. Specifications produced by JDAs, pseudo-consortia, and consortia must sink or swim in the marketplace as well. Many specifications from these alternative organizations have had little or no marketplace acceptance. Therefore, regardless of what kind of organization produces the specification, the real proof of commercial viability is whether the standard achieves dominance by becoming a de facto (or marketplace) standard.

Seeking Competitive Advantage

As the producer of the first commercial Relational DBMS, Oracle has been involved in standards making since the Company's inception. Today we have approximately 300 people working in more than 350 of working groups in over 60 standards and consortia forums. As our

participation has increased and become more diverse, one observation has remained constant: those who attempt to gain sustainable competitive advantage through the standards process rarely, if ever, succeed. Whenever it appears that one faction is gaining an advantage in the

> *"...those who attempt to gain sustainable competitive advantage through the standards process rarely, if ever, succeed."*

standards process, other participants start up competitive activities. The resulting multiple specifications in a single technical area inevitably confuse potential adopters/customers and slow or even kill marketplace acceptance.

Look at the area of Web Services today. Potential implementers and adopters must shift through the muddle among W3C, OASIS and many others forums to weigh claims and counter-claims in areas of web services such as Policy, Security, Choreography, Context, Coordination, and Transaction Management. Too many JDAs, pseudo-consortia, and consortia have been created in the web services arena solely in an attempt to gain competitive advantage. Unfortunately, history tells us the likely outcome—confused customers and adopters are likely to be paralyzed with indecision, products won't be

> *" If we continue on our current path, there will be no winners— we will all lose."*

built, customers won't buy, and web services will never achieve its potential. If we continue on our current path, there will be no winners— we will all lose.

Bottom Line

To smartly evaluate standards, it's vital to look behind the press releases and pass judgment based on the type of standardization group, whether it strives for consensus, its methods for building consensus, and whether it operates openly and fairly or suffers under dominance by a favored few trying to gain a competitive advantage. Oracle's position is that good standards making processes serve the industry and the community-at-large, are open and affordable to any interested party, are built upon a level playing field, and produce specifications that are likely to be widely implemented.

Open and fair standards are good for business—everyone's business—but especially Oracle's business. At Oracle, we don't seek to manipulate the standards process for competitive advantage. We work for standard interfaces that can be widely adopted and then we compete on our ability to produce better products using those interfaces. That's the bottom line.

31

Open Source Software, Standardization, Consumerism, and Making Money

JOHN H. TERPSTRA

PrimaStasys, Inc.

Abstract: *This chapter deals with the question, "What is the role of standardization in the process of making money from Open Source Software (OSS) in the Information Technology (IT) market." Arguments are presented to demonstrate that OSS and consumerism are key factors in establishing a successful model that benefits from the standardization process. Particular reference is made to the impact of standardization and OSS on innovation. It is concluded that the economics of the law of diminishing returns is the real enemy of fully proprietary, closed source software—one that threatens its very survival in a competitive and increasingly demanding computer software marketplace. Further, the article finds that standardization is a necessary and critical aspect of software consumerism and is key to sustained innovation in the IT industry.*

Discussion

The rise of Open Source Software (OSS) has been hailed by some as destructive of the Information Technology (IT) market at large. At the heart of the debate over free software lies the GNU General Public License (GPL), a license under which many significant OSS applications have been made available. The GPL is a popular OSS license mandating that derivative works of source code released under the GPL fall under the control of the same license. It further requires all source code of the derivative work to be made available to anyone who may ask for it.

Recently the press reported comments from a highly visible industry executive who claimed that the GNU General Public License (GPL) is about destroying value.[1] In May 2001, Mr. Craig Mundie of Microsoft said, "This viral aspect of the GPL ... effectively makes it impossible to distribute software on a basis where recipients pay for the product rather than just the cost of distribution."[2]

It is clear to all that much emotional venom is being spent and a passionate conflict is emerging.[3] Before delving into a discussion on the subject of standardization, it is beneficial to first consider a conceptual framework for understanding the relationship of standards to the life cycle of IT industry products and services.

A glossary of terms is provided at the end of the chapter to minimize confusion and for reference to how various terms are used in this chapter.

Products and Life Cycles

The Boston Consulting Group (BCG) has followed the practices of Fortune 1000 companies for several decades. Since the late 1970s, BCG's product portfolio matrix model has become a main-stay of marketing and market management practice. BCG found that successful companies maintain a profile of different products, each at different points in the BCG matrix. The theory is that *Cash Cows* generate profits that are needed to develop *Wild Cats* and *Stars.* Star products are ones that will be future *Cash Cows. Dogs* should be converted into *Wild Cats* or disposed of. BCG's emphasis has been on

develop and manage products and services in the market place.

A core factor in product portfolio management is the centrality of the Product Life Cycle (PLC) concept. Mature products are those that have declining sales as they move towards obsolescence. The product manager must make a decision: should research and development expenditure be increased and the product re-

BCG Product Portfolio Matrix

the processes of innovation and creativity as key instruments that may feed new products into a company's portfolio. Successful companies innovate and exercise creativity in the way they

marketed, or should developmental expenditure be reduced to permit profits to be plowed into other products?

In the event that a decision is made to inject

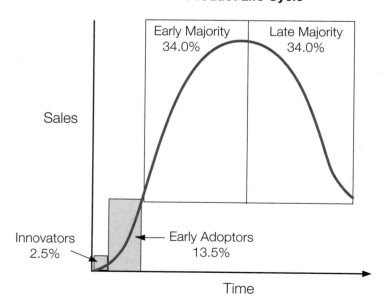

Product Life Cycle

further development funds into a product, it is possible that the overall market can be further expanded as product sales grow again. This type of positive effect is known as a *recycle*. Product recycle growth is usually not as profound as in the early stages of market development. Marketing research has shown that the cost of creating recycle growth will decline as the product reaches the end of its economic life. Thus, eventually it will make no sense to invest in additional product and/or market development. Those interested in further information on this particular aspect of product and market management are encouraged to refer to the following article: "Extending Product life Cycle Stages," Steinhardt, 2002. See: http://www.productmarketing.com/topics/2002/08gs.pdf.

The investment a company makes in the product/market mix may include:

- Product feature enhancement for existing market customers
- Feature addition so that the product can be introduced to new markets/customers
- Research to find new customer needs/wants
- Development of the distribution and resale channels to reach new customers
- Bundling of multiple products and services to broaden market reach

Competitive Reactions and Market Maturation

A most basic premise of modern marketing theory is that we live in a freely competitive world. All businesses are faced with competition and since, as BCG confirmed, market share is a key factor in profitability, there will of necessity be a scramble among competitors for market dominance. It is therefore understandable that as the IT market matures the competition increases. The entrance into the market of a competitive force that threatens the equilibrium of established players has predictable consequences. Established competitors feel threatened as the new entrant begins to exert a behavior that radically differs from accepted practices. This is clearly what has happened with the emergence of OSS and Linux based competition.

Established market players can respond to the threat in many more ways than we can cover here. For example, they can try to ignore the threat, change tactics (very difficult if a company has a lot of inertia in its established ways) to out maneuver the new competitor, or innovate to move ahead of the new market entrant. Each tactic has its own risks and potential rewards.

The producer has a financial interest in maximizing the value proposition of products and services so that the optimal consumer demand can be met. This means that if a consumer wants feature X, and Producer A can gain leverage over Producer B by delivering this feature, than there is a high probability that feature X may be added to the product offering. The producer employs a rich blend of people skills that enables the production of goods and services that consumers want. Consumers may buy these goods and services directly or through the agency of middlemen.

The traditional model has held to a belief that middlemen add value. Part of the value that they add is to make the distribution of goods and services to even difficult to reach consumers economically viable. The dawning of the Internet age has challenged this old paradigm, although it has not completely displaced it. Not all consumers use Internet services to locate a supplier. Additionally, not all suppliers can economically ship product to all potential consumers. The Internet age has materially challenged, but not invalidated, the old model.

True to the learning curve model proposed by classical marketing, information technology solution costs have fallen significantly, as have profit margins. This has eroded the IT reseller market. The clever reseller finds ways to provide services that customers want and learns to price them so as to maximize the perceived value to the customer while ensuring that they will receive the margins necessary to remain in business.

Inherent Market Risk Factors

The market presents a number of challenges. How a company responds to these challenges determines success or failure. The challenge of arriving at the optimal position serves equally as a means of protection for the incumbent producer and as a hindrance for new market entrants. In both cases, the following must be accomplished:

- Consumer needs must be accurately measured
- Software must be developed to meet these needs
- Delivery must be timely and accurate
- The software must be economically affordable
- The producer must find consumers
- The consumers' need for support must be satisfied

The high failure rate of software companies is testament to the risks involved in meeting these demands. The profit motive is a significant incentive to succeed. Those producers who get the recipe right may enjoy the rewards that can be harvested. This market model has variously been called the *free market* or the *capitalist model*.

Departments specialize in certain aspects of meeting each need. Each department represents a food-chain link, with each link being equally important. A weak link can put the whole business at risk. Software developers are just one facet of the needs satisfaction delivery process. If the business (producer) cannot operate with integrity and harmony, or if one department (or link) attempts to claim greater importance than another, then the business is placed at potential jeopardy.

It seems that the spirit of enterprise and risk taking that marked the beginnings of the software industry have been subdued over the past decade. It may be argued that this is the result of the learning curve effect by which discrete business transaction values decline as the market matures. This decline in discrete business value is a consequence of competition and standardization. It has been observed that as goods and services are standardized and the cost of discrete needs satisfaction declines, more potential consumers may enter the market. The net effect of this is that overall market value will increase.

In addition to learning curve effects one must also take into account the impact of competition over time. Entrepreneurial competitors are always on the look-out for successful ventures and new markets. Every new market that is successfully developed will attract new competitors. Consumers welcome the choice that

---

"It has been observed that as goods and services are standardized and the cost of discrete needs satisfaction declines, more potential consumers may enter the market. The net effect of this is that overall market value will increase."

---

competition provides. The combined effects of increased competition and growing efficiency of production means that suppliers can reduce prices well below the original market entry level.

When a product is first conceived of, knowledge of real market needs and potentials or technology requirements are poorly understood. The rate of learning increases rapidly as new obstacles are overcome. A great deal of innovation, experimentation, and creative opportunity handling will take place. First release products frequently provide incomplete, clumsy, or inefficient solutions. Eventually, after a product has been brought to market and becomes established in a company's portfolio, a more predictable path of development takes place as the product and the way it is delivered to consumers changes, matures, and planned updates and releases are made.

Immediately following product release, marketing activities center on finding new (innovator) customers to reach profitability as quickly as possible. As early adopters start buying into the product, functionality will develop at a furious pace. This growth slows late in the life cycle as identifying and adding new features becomes decreasingly cost effective.

Innovation and Standardization

While a product is gaining market acceptance it is not uncommon for there to be significant discontinuities in the compatibility of

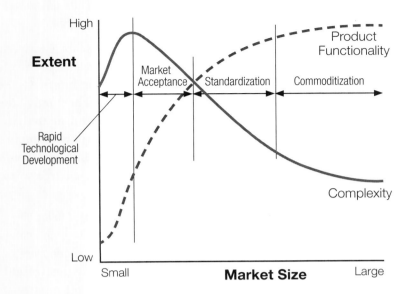

older releases with newer releases. Eventually other companies begin to see the market opportunity and start offering a competing solution. Customers who wish to migrate may demand the ability to take their data with them to the competing solution. At this point, interoperability becomes an important determinant of consumer appeasement and customers begin to react against incompatibilities.

It may be argued that before a market reaches maturity the technology of its products is still developing. If the rate of development outpaces the ability of the market to define and adopt

---

"...standardization fuels the move from specialist product marketing to consumer led marketing."

---

standards, then a great deal of specialist knowledge is necessary in the sale and application of new and emerging goods and services. One of the inescapable consequences of market maturation is the increasing prevalence of standardization. As a market matures and standardization takes hold, there is less demand for specialist intervention in facilitation of business transactions. Standardization is also a key factor in the achievement of higher product quality, which

ultimately helps to win greater consumer commitment and confidence. Thus, standardization fuels the move from specialist product marketing to consumer led marketing.

As a market matures, its goods and services approach commodity levels. Commodities are standardized to the point that the technological or physical attribute differentiation of a product becomes increasingly more difficult and counter productive. As a result, the market leader will win consumers through soft factors such as services offered, delivery mechanisms, and other intangibles.

Software consumers demand interoperability. They demand the ability to migrate their data across software applications. They demand lower costs, higher functionality, faster response to emerging new needs, and so on. Technology accelerates and intensifies cultural and economic trends, requiring increased standardization. Standardization is essential to reducing the cost of production, delivery, and to gaining mass-market presence.

Standardization permits a product to acquire predictable characteristics and behavior. It precedes the establishment of mass operation, low cost product sales, and support infrastructure and is essential to public confidence and widespread adoption. Standardization ultimately takes hold of core product functionality, user interfaces, interoperability, deployment mechanisms, and eventually pervades every aspect of the consumption process.

Products that are in the late stages of the life cycle typically gain few new features as updates are released. The cost benefit equation mitigates against it, particularly if the product is not the market leader.

As a market matures, one of the more subtle factors is the role played by middlemen such as resellers, service companies, public relations providers, advertising, and other means of gaining consumer acceptance and product/service dependency. It is thus fascinating that during the period 1998 through 2002 so many IT reseller businesses failed. Even the Value Added Reseller (VAR) support organizations fell victim to market distress as a result of the emergence of software consumerism.

VAR business reports suggest that the shakeout is turning a corner with positive market growth being reported for 2003. During the late 1980s and early 1990s, reseller margins on software were typically 30-40% of gross sales. By 2000, the average reseller margin had fallen below 15%. A software application like Microsoft Office today sells for less than one-third of the price at which it was first brought to market.

One might argue that the number of desktop computers has increased ten-fold since 1993 and thus the size of the market has grown. But most software today is sold either directly through corporate licensing deals or through high volume retail stores. The traditional reseller had to find ways to replace lost income. Many could not make the transition and fell away.

OSS Perceptions of Market Dynamics

There is within the OSS community a prevalent opinion that commercial software products built by proprietary for-profit businesses are deficient in quality and inadequately meet consumer demands. This perception is a fundamental dogma of the OSS concept.

In 1998 Salon.com[4] interviewed Eric Raymond,

author of *The Cathedral and the Bazaar* and a well known ambassador for OSS:

In some respects, Netscape's move seems to represent the resurgence of the old "gift economy" ideals of the Internet—the idea that the Internet could best move forward if everybody gave according to their ability, without necessarily expecting financial return. Has the gift economy influenced your own desire to play a role in the free software movement?

It's what I always wanted to do. The reason is really simple. Like most hackers, I don't really care about money very much. I do what I do primarily for artistic satisfaction, and what I want is to know that other people consider it good art. I mean, it's nice if I consider it good art, I generally know the difference and I can usually tell whether what I have done is beautiful or ugly. But you don't really know that you are evolving in the right direction unless reality and other people confirm that. So, like most other hackers, my most fundamental motivation is that I want other hackers to think that I'm doing good work. And I want them to believe I'm effective and fruitful and a good designer and so forth.

But what about intellectual property rights?

This is 180 degrees removed from any ideology about whether intellectual property rights are good or not. I don't care about that. I'm not interested in having that argument anymore. If your source is open, you get peer review, you get reliability. If your source is not open, you don't get peer review and you don't get reliability, end of story.

You have some harsh words to say about the way business people have traditionally looked at the software marketplace.

The thing I realized when I sat down and thought about business models is that nobody thinks about the economics of software. Nobody thinks real hard.

The OSS world is not concerned with matching consumer needs, it is principally focused on solving problems that are primarily of interest to the developer. In response to a consumer's request for a particular feature, the OSS developer is inclined to reply that the source code is open—so fix it yourself. This attitude is clearly

> *"The OSS world is not concerned with matching consumer needs, it is principally focused on solving problems that are primarily of interest to the developer."*

not conducive to mass consumer market appeal.

This situation is not necessarily incompatible in the long run with the need to satisfy consumer needs. We must not lose sight of the fact that, with OSS, the law of diminishing returns has a much less profound effect upon the slowdown in the rate of innovation and product feature growth. Since the source code is publicly available, anyone can make code, quality, and functionality improvements and many OSS developers who work on the code are not remunerated for the contributions they make. Thus the financial aspects of the law of diminishing returns are simply not applicable—the work continues and companies that integrate and market OSS products will spend far less than a company with the same goals for a product based on a closed, proprietary source.

There can be no denying the fact that much progress has been made and that OSS products such as Lindows, SuSE, and Red Hat Linux products have made great strides towards suitability for mass consumer markets. In each case, the commercial profit motive of each company developing the OSS products has resulted in closer approximation to consumer needs.

The emergence of OpenOffice, Mozilla, Evolution, KDE, Gnome, Samba, Apache, SQUID, PostgreSQL, MySQL, CUPS, Java, and other popular OSS packages are clear evidence of increased standardization, process maturation, and a developing consumer orientation. The Linux platform now has a standard specification (the Linux Standards Base) [5] that will facilitate interoperability and help sustain the growth of a commercial software market for third party applications.

Threats to OSS Continuity

There is however a latent threat that may affect key OSS packages. For example, OpenOffice implements file format interoperability with Microsoft Office products. It is likely that Microsoft may change the core file format for MS Office products and then seek the enforcement of recent legislation to protect the new file format from being copied. In another example, Samba implements the CIFS/SMB (Common Internet File System/Server Message Block) protocols to provide a high degree of interoperability with Microsoft Windows platforms. If for any reason Microsoft were to abandon the use of CIFS/SMB in favor of a new proprietary file and print sharing protocol, this could seriously impede the progress of the use of OSS based file and print interoperability tools like Samba. If, at the same time, Microsoft were to release new products that no longer function with tools like Samba, then they would essentially force their customers to lock in to their products and services.

Monopolies and Standardization

Many people believe that a company that dominates the market may not wish to be limited by standardization. Companies that dominate a market may seek protection of the monopoly they hold. Such protection may itself be considered a form of standardization.

A proprietary market leader (or dominator) does not share the priorities of the OSS movement. They may pursue standardization in the form of uniform government enforcement of

> *"Global uniformity of measures designed to protect intellectual property are essential to the survival of monopolies."*

protective measures that guarantee freedom to lock consumers into products and services through a combination of applied technological secrets, protocols, business relationships, and exclusive deals that limit consumer choices. In other words, monopolies seek legislative protection that will allow them to continue to dominate the market while escaping the consequences of both the learning curve and increased competition that typically comes with this position or market leadership. Global uniformity of measures designed to protect intellectual property are essential to the survival of monopolies. Countries which do not enforce uniform protective measures will permit the potential emergence of new competitors that may threaten the market hold of the competitor. For example, the rise of the Japanese automobile industry in the 1980s sorely undermined the USA auto market.

The OSS movement wants standardization in technology implementation, particularly in the areas of protocols, file formats, and ready access to source code that may be freely changed. They want a world in which there are no technological secrets. The OSS world demands barrier-free interoperability, full technical disclosure, and the ability to build software that can completely substitute or replace more costly proprietary software.

Market leaders may cast a mantle of fear, uncertainty, and doubt (FUD) to thwart competition. Witness the words of Mr. Craig Mundie (Microsoft) in 2001: "The OSS development model leads to a strong possibility of unhealthy "forking" of a code base, resulting in the development of multiple incompatible versions of programs, weakened interoperability, product instability, and hindering businesses' ability to strategically plan for the future. Furthermore, it has inherent security risks and can force intellectual property into the public domain."[6] Whatever the intent was, it did not work.

The emergence of the Linux Standards Base (LSB) standards for Linux distributions has wide commitment among OSS competitors and is explicitly designed to protect the commercial developer and the consumer alike from the very threat that Mr. Mundie was so concerned about. In addition, IP kept from the public domain not only suffers from higher innovation costs, but incurs a greater risk of obsolescence than any OSS application.

Market leaders are well aware that consumers expect software to meet their needs, including their constant demand for innovation. Innovation and product fluidity that can meet fickle consumer tastes and preferences can be costly to maintain. It is logical that market leaders should seek to protect their market and to hedge it against the growing assault from OSS solutions.

The Stock Market and Competitive Reactions

Investors in companies like Microsoft, SCO, IBM, Computer Associates, et al., are encouraged to invest when businesses are making positive attempts to close the door on competition, particularly when those businesses seek legal means to protect their property. This has been reflected in the way that share prices have rallied upwards after recent SCO announcements regarding pursuit of its Intellectual Property (IP).

In the real world, change is often met with extreme reaction. When a new paradigm is introduced, initial progress is typically rapid. When those threatened by change wake up and begin to react, there can be an impression of rapid regression. The market then evolves as rules of engagement catch up with the technological and emotional environment changes. Eventually, old ways die and new ones become normalized. To many, it seems as if for every market reaction there is a counter reaction that almost equals the force of the initial change. Eventually, the new dynamic overcomes the negative inertia of the counter reaction and a new equilibrium is established.

Two glaring examples of this are the way that Novell reacted to the introduction of Microsoft Windows NT and the way that Microsoft has reacted to the emergence of OSS.

Novell was the dominant personal computer network technology company in 1994 and ignored MS Windows NT and the networking technology it presented. Then as it started to realize the extent of the threat, Novell embarked on a program to discredit Microsoft's ability to deliver real mission critical network services. When Novell realized that their FUD campaign was not working, they intensified a campaign to demonstrate the benefits of the Netware Directory

Service as well as Microsoft's deficiency in not having this. At one point in the FUD campaign, it appeared as if Microsoft had been dealt a deadly blow. However, Microsoft responded by releasing Microsoft Active Directory and today has the dominant networking technology and the leading directory service.

In 2001, Microsoft began to realize the threat of OSS. Its initial reaction was to smear and belittle OSS. When they realized that this tactic was driving customers to evaluate OSS, they started a campaign to demonstrate that MS Windows 2000 could out-perform Linux—a campaign which ultimately failed. The threat to Microsoft is far from over and Microsoft now acknowledges the need to co-exist with OSS. Denial can last only so long before the new equilibrium must be approximated.

The key question for the OSS movement today is: What forces will control the new equilibrium? How will it arrive and who will be the key beneficiaries as the market shifts from one stage of tension towards another?

The Future of OSS

Prediction of future events is a risky business; there is no more than 50% probability that a prediction may be correct. Even so, we may prognosticate based on past experience. Kris Kristofferson gave rise to the immortal words, "Freedom's just another word for nothin' left to lose, nothin's worth nothin' but its' free."

Could it be that OSS is free because it has nothing left to lose? Hardly! OSS abounds in concepts of freedom to copy and use software without liability or right to use costs (license fees). However, the astute reader will recognize that the development of OSS can take place only at great cost. That cost is made up of corporate investments, the time and opportunity costs of OSS developers, and the time spent learning how to use and improve OSS by people like you and me.

If we want OSS to survive, then we had best hope that investments in development will continue. OSS development will continue so long as the software has somewhere to go, and that is the silver question: Where is it going? While I

am personally convinced that OSS will continue to move forward through a dedicated community that will see to the rise of free software regardless of the barriers, legal, political, sociological, economic, or otherwise, we must ask some core questions from a mass market acceptance perspective:

- What economic model will OSS find to sustain investment and development interest?

- Will OSS become technologically isolated by means of legislative prohibitions against interoperability?

- Will it be possible to gain widespread government support for OSS development and deployment?

Above all, can standardization help to secure a better future for OSS? Consider for a moment what would happen if certain OSS protocols (file formats, if you like) were to be adopted as a government and industry standard. Would legislative forces help to secure OSS interoperability?

Standardization of OSS applications as reference implementations of particular protocols can help to ensure that all players in the marketplace must continue to support them. Standardization levels the playing field of competition. It helps to establish new bounds for competition as it will shift the focus from technology lock-in to business process based competition. Consumerism is the inevitable result of product standardization. It results in more people being able to afford to enter the market. It makes competitors work harder and faster to satisfy consumer wants and desires and, consequently, results in reduced time to market. The reason so few companies like to play to those rules is that it demands innovation and creativity in meeting consumer needs.

Conclusions

This chapter has considered the IT market from a broad spectrum of issues. It demonstrates that the real forces that are shaping the IT industry are complex and varied. It does however make a clear case in favor of standardization as a precursor to a more open, innovative, and competitive consumer market. When consumers are given greater freedom and choice, competitors will experience the greatest success by the drive for standardization and innovation.

Notes

[1] "At the end of the day, the GPL [the GNU General Public License software license that governs Linux] is about making software free; it's about destroying value." http://www.computerweekly.co.uk/Article124260.htm

[2] "Some of the most successful OSS technology is licensed under the GNU General Public License or GPL. The GPL mandates that any software that incorporates source code already licensed under the GPL will itself become subject to the GPL. When the resulting software product is distributed, its creator must make the entire source code base freely available to everyone, at no additional charge. This viral aspect of the GPL poses a threat to the intellectual property of any organization making use of it. It also fundamentally undermines the independent commercial software sector because it effectively makes it impossible to distribute software on a basis where recipients pay for the product rather than just the cost of distribution.", http://www.microsoft.com/presspass/exec/craig/05-03sharedsource.asp

[3] "We're fighting for the right in the industry to be able to make a living selling software," McBride told the audience. He compared this right to the ability "to send your children to college" and "to buy a second home.", http://www.businessweek.com/technology/cnet/stories/5065286.htm

[4] See http://archive.salon.com/21st/feature/1998/04/cov_14feature.html

http://archive.salon.com/21st/feature/1998/04/cov_14feature2.html

[5] See http://www.linuxbase.org and http://www.freestandards.org

[6] See http://www.microsoft.com/presspass/exec/craig/05-03sharedsource.asp

Glossary

Open Source Software – Software for which source code is available. It is typically understood to mean without restriction from modification. There is an expectation in the OSS community that all changes made will be contributed back to the code maintainers. OSS is generally seen by vendors of proprietary software as anti-intellectual property (IP). By some, OSS is seen as anti-commercial also.

Standardization – The process by which protocols, application binary interfaces, libraries, binaries, and architectural implementations are ratified and brought into compliance with publicly arbitrated specifications and standards. Standards are designed to maximize interoperability and to minimize (eliminate) incompatibilities between equivalent products from competing vendors.

Consumerism – Understood by some as the mechanics of coercing people to buy and consume goods and services that they do not need. In fact, consumerism is the theory that an increasing consumption of goods is economically beneficial. I propose that consumerism and specialization are at opposite ends of a continuum that has innovation and early adoption at one end, and product maturity and mass market consumption at the other end. Mature products by definition have progressed beyond need for specialist modification and implementation, through a process of standardization, to the point where implementation has become an almost nontechnical matter. An example of a mature product is plug-and-play printing with complex printers that are supported by Microsoft Windows XP. Such printers are automatically recognized and are configured without human intervention and, from the user's perspective, they *just work*. Such devices contrast radically with printers sold 10 years ago, each of which required specialist installation. Clearly, consumerism results in improved economics of ownership.

32

Open Specifications: Mostly Open Standards

STEPHEN ZILLES

Zilles.net

Abstract: *There are times when an open standards process may not be the most effective route to a workable file format interchange standard. This can occur in newly emerging areas when there is insufficient agreement on the standardization approach. In this environment, Open Specifications provide a way to resolve disagreements on the preferred approach to standardization in the marketplace and allow rapid adaptation to true market requirements. The article presents a definition of an Open Specification and illustrates its use in several real world cases.*

Openness in File Format Standards

There is often great debate over what makes a standard and what makes the standard open. If you look at five or six definitions of "open standard" you will find a variety of views ranging from multiple criteria to just a few. The purpose of this article is not to extend the debate on openness, but to argue that there are times when mostly open may be more effective for the user community then fully open.

While standards are applied to many areas of our lives, this article will focus on Information Technology standards and, in particular, the subcategory of file format standards. File formats are used for interchanging information between systems whether the file is transmitted over a communications network or simply put on a storage system and retrieved at a later time. The specification for a file format describes the

> *"...there are times when mostly open may be more effective for the user community then fully open."*

contents of the file (stream) in sufficient detail so that a "writer" of the file format may construct a legal file instance and a "reader" of the file format may successfully construct a correct internal representation of the material that was conveyed using the file format.

Open standards

This article focuses on "mostly open" standards for file formats. To define what "mostly open" means, it is necessary for me to say what I believe an "open standard" to be. I believe that there are a relatively small number of key criteria for the openness of a standard and a greater number of additional recommendations that can be applied. I leave these additions to others [Krechmer 1998] and, here, list the key criteria:

1. For a specification to be at all open, it must be publicly available. That is, it must be easily accessible and available at a reasonable (preferably zero) cost.

2. The publicly available specification must be complete enough for one reasonably skilled in the relevant art to be able to implement both a reader and a writer for the specified file format.

3. The publicly available specification must be free of encumbrances, either from Intellectual Property Rights (IPR) or from licensing requirements that inhibit implementation of the specification. Some level of reasonable IPR fees may be acceptable as long as the terms are applied without discrimination among licensees.

4. The process by which the specification is developed is open; that is, (a) the process allows participation by anyone (who may have to join the sponsoring organization), (b) the rules of the process are fair (allowing all participants to be heard), and (c) the process uses consensus to develop the resulting specification.

The first three of the criteria allow any person or organization to implement to the standard. The last is intended to ensure that as many of the relevant inputs as possible are considered in the development of the standard. Some authors also want to ensure that the standard is designed to be extensible, but this, although a very good idea, does not seem to be a part of the openness of the standard.

"Mostly Open" Standards

If openness is defined above, then a "mostly open" standard is one in which the first three criteria hold, but not necessarily the last criteria. Since the first three criteria refer to the access and use of the specification, I will call any specification that satisfies these criteria an "**Open Specification**." This makes a distinction between the specification, which is what people use, and the process that produces the specification as a standard.

Why not a fully open process?

Why might an organization or group not want an open process? The simplest reason is that there is a cost to having an open process, especially where there is some level of polarization among the participants in that process.

Consider what happened with the development of PostScript [Adobe 1985], Interpress [Xerox 1984], and the ISO (International Organization for Standardization) Standard Page Description Language (SPDL) [ISO95]. These three specifications share a common heritage that began with work that was done at Evans and Sutherland [Gaffney 1976] and led in 1978 to the development of JaM at Xerox Parc.

Interpress

In 1981, JaM, a procedural language, was combined with other Xerox work on Press [Newman 1983], a declarative language, to produce Interpress, a specification for a language that describes pages to be printed. The combination provided the structure of Press with the graphic flexibility of JaM. Xerox considered this to be an important technical innovation and wanted to keep it a trade secret. At the same time, they were delaying putting Interpress into Xerox printers.

PostScript

The delay in putting Interpress into products led John Warnock and Chuck Geschke to leave Xerox and start their own company, Adobe Systems Incorporated. Although originally planned as a business to build typesetting systems, one of the key components was a device independent language for describing pages to be printed. This language, called PostScript, was an even more direct descendent of JaM than was Interpress. It was fully procedural, lacking the structuring that Interpress has.

What was more important for this article, however, was the strategy taken by the founders of Adobe Systems. In September 1984, well before the first PostScript product was released (the first PostScript product, the Apple Laserwriter, was introduced in January 1985), Adobe

Systems openly published the PostScript specification. This was a conscious effort on the part of the creators to enable early adopters to begin writing applications that generated PostScript. Within a year, more than 65 software companies had announced applications that used PostScript. Because the specification was both open and available, it allowed other companies to produce non-Adobe Systems implementations as well.

The early excitement generated by the Apple Laserwriter caused Xerox to rethink their strategy. By mid-year 1985, Xerox made the specification for Interpress publicly available [Xerox 1984] and opened a debate on what the standardized page description language should be [Seybold 1985].

The standard page description language

About this time, Xerox also began contacting formal standards development organizations. ECMA, the European Computer Manufacturers Association, began work on a standard page description language based on a Xerox contribution. Adobe Systems joined this effort shortly afterwards.

In 1987, the ECMA work was forwarded to ISO as input to the JTC1 SC18 WG8 project on a Text Presentation Metafile. JTC1 SC18 WG8 was, at the time, the ISO Working Group for Document Description and Processing Languages within the Information Technology area of ISO. The ECMA work became the foundation for ISO 10180 Standard Page Description Language (SPDL) [ISO95]. However, progress on this work was rather slow. There were basic disagreements on whether to build the standard on Interpress or PostScript and there were other requirements added by related ISO working groups.

During this time, choice of a standard page description language was played out in the public arena in terms of competition between the products implementing Interpress and PostScript. Because of its openness and availability, PostScript won the hearts and minds of a large portion of the non-Xerox printer manufacturers.

This led, in the early 1990s, to a compromise between Adobe Systems and Xerox. SPDL would have a structural model that was based on the Interpress structural model. This model structurally separated pages. But, the content of each page would be represented in the PostScript content language. To comply with other ISO requirements, SPDL would have both a textual encoding using SGML markup and a binary encoding using ASN.1. SGML is the Standard Generalized Markup Language (ISO/IEC 8879:1986), which is the precursor eXtensible Markup Language (XML) that is used to markup web pages as well as many other text and data sources. ASN.1 stands for Abstract Syntax Notation One and it is a method for compactly encoding finite collections of keywords and operators.

Working out the details of this compromise and documenting them in adequate detail took until the end of 1994. ISO 10180 was published in January 1995—ten years after the introduction of the first PostScript printer and the publication of Interpress.

Clearly, by the time the "standard" (from an official standards development organization) had been published, the public had already chosen a "standard." PostScript had become the "de facto" standard for page description and even Xerox began selling PostScript printers.

"Standards do not need to be ideal, but they do need to be timely and workable."

The slowness of the process is not a comment on standards development, but on the difficulties introduced when there are strongly held competing positions on the standard being developed. In this kind of climate, work may proceed too slowly to yield a workable result. Standards do not need to be ideal, but they do need to be timely and workable.

The process followed by Adobe Systems, that of making PostScript an Open Specification and (in the second edition of the Postscript Language Reference Manual) of including an explicit royalty free license to implement to that specification, was a strong contributing factor in the acceptance of PostScript as a "standard."

The key lesson is that when there is no agreement on how to proceed to a standard in a given

> *"...when there is no agreement on how to proceed to a standard in a given area then either no standard will arise or the marketplace will determine the 'standard.'"*

area then either no standard will arise or the marketplace will determine the "standard." The community clearly benefits when there are Open Specifications that allow multiple participants in the marketplace; this allows a choice of implementations and provides protection against any or all implementers ceasing to deliver relevant products. It also provides a strong level of achievability because data in the specified format can be recovered and reinterpreted at any point in the future, using the Open Specification.

The Portable Document Format

Adobe Systems soon began the development of the Acrobat product line and the Portable Document Format (PDF) [Adobe 1993]. With the experience of PostScript under its belt, it developed its strategy for introducing PDF. First, Adobe made the name of the product line, Acrobat, and the name of the file format, PDF, distinct so that users could refer to PDF without any trademark issues arising. Secondly, the file format was published as an Open Specification at the time the first product was delivered. From the beginning, the specification included a royalty free license for implementation. This led, quite quickly, to several competitive implementations of PDF.

At the same time the Acrobat products appeared, there were other similar products in the displayable presentation product space. These products had very different file formats that, at least initially, were not published as Open Specifications. There are many factors that contribute to success in the marketplace. However, the view that an Open Specification

was less proprietary than a private or closely licensed specification certainly contributed to the pervasiveness of PDF and the disappearance of the other formats.

Since a displayable presentation format was relatively new, requirements for this area were not easily predicted. It was only by delivering products and gaining experience with those products that the true requirements began to emerge. As a consequence, rapid development of versions during the early years of PDF occurred, similar to the trend we see today in some Web standards. These new versions, developed within Adobe Systems with input from outside sources, were published with the same royalty free license that accompanied the original version.

The development and evolution of PDF would have been more difficult with a fully open consensus process. Achieving consensus is a slow, difficult task unless there is only one clear path to begin with. That was not the case with PDF. As stated previously, standards must be workable, but they do not have to be ideal. In the case of PDF, the ability of one company to make executive decisions that resolved issues made the process go much more rapidly. (Having to document decisions in a form suitable for an Open Specification tended to slow the process down, but was also necessary.)

Lessons learned

When a specification is going through a high rate of evolution, it is often more efficient to have a relative small group control the evolution. However, this requires a high level of responsibility on the part of the control group. They need to preserve compatibility with previous versions and deprecate features only with due deliberation. They need to be aware of the requirements of the community being served by the Open Specification and include the features that have a high need. When done responsibly, this can lead to, and has led to, a useful community standard that has a range of implementations with different strengths. As these community standards mature, the rate of evolution drops and they become candidates for a fully open development process.

CGATS, ISO, and PDF/X

The ANSI accredited Committee on Graphics Arts Technology Standards (CGATS) recognized the need for a standard for transmitting digital pages composed of vector (as well as raster) graphics in the mid1990s. This was driven, in part, by the need to be able to digitally distribute advertisements to multiple publications in diverse locations. The prepress community, which provided most of the membership of CGATS, was already using PostScript Level 2 to exchange digital pages. Since this specification was capable of representing the kinds of advertising pages to be distributed, the first attempt at defining the prepress digital data exchange standard was based on PostScript. However, there were too many unresolved issues for that attempt to succeed.

PDF had been a possible first candidate but, when the work began, the first version of PDF lacked some of the functionality of Post-Script. With the release of PDF Version 1.2, PDF attained the functionality of PostScript Level 2—making PDF a prime candidate for a new attempt at defining a prepress digital data exchange standard. In fact, the relevant subcommittee of CGATS found that most of the functionality they required was already present, with only a small set of additional functionality needed for the prepress digital data exchange standard. The four features were: (1) a new entry in the PDF Info dictionary that indicates whether the objects in the PDF file have been trapped; (2) a new color space, ICCBased; (3) a method for embedding the data of external files as streams within the PDF file; and (4) a set of boxes that specify the extent of the content of a page, the trim size of a page, and the bleed size of a page.

The Adobe Systems representative to CGATS developed proposals to satisfy these requests and, after several rounds of negotiations, were accepted for the next version of PDF. The inclusion of these features in PDF 1.3 allowed the CGATS subcommittee to complete its work and publish a profile standard [ANSI 1999] that described how to use PDF for prepress digital data exchange.

The equivalent ISO organization to CGATS is ISO TC130 Graphic Technology. CGATS proposed that TC130 adopt PDF/X as an international standard. Although favorably inclined to this proposal, the ISO committee had additional requirements that they felt were appropriate in an international context. This led to another round of negotiations with Adobe Systems that resulted in further additions to PDF, including recording output intentions for color critical workflows. Furthermore, the ISO committee developed PDF/X as a three-part standard [ISO 2001] that supports three different workflows all using PDF.

Lessons learned

A formal standards development organization, such as ANSI or ISO, working together with the publisher of an Open Specification can effectively cooperate to the benefit of both organizations. In particular, it is both efficient and effective to develop profile standards for the use of Open Specifications. When a profile standard is developed using a fully open process, it establishes that particular version as the basis for the open standard. This provides protection to the standards developers because future changes to the Open Specification will not change the profile standard or the version of the Open Specification on which it is based. Of course, the open profile standard developers may issue a new version of the profile that is based on a future version of the Open Specification. Finally, this kind of cooperation depends on the willingness of the Open Standard publisher to work with the open standards committee developing the profile so that required features may be added.

Conclusions

Publishing an Open Specification enables wide adoption of a file format both by creators and readers of the file format. It is a strong commitment by the organization publishing the file format since it requires licensing the relevant intellectual property to implement and use the format.

The publishing organization also takes on the responsibility for maintaining and updating the specification. This implies maintaining, to the extent possible, compatibility with previous versions of the specification and adding relevant requested features within the scope of the specification. When this is done responsibly, the Open Specification creates an open marketplace that benefits the user community as well as the publisher. This article has shown three cases (PostScript, PDF, and PDF/X) in which the existence of an Open Specification has led to such community benefiting standards.

While these standards (with the exception of PDF/X) are not developed by a standard developing organization, the benefit to their users is just as great. This suggests that the use of Open Specification may be an effective way to jumpstart a standards process; a process that may or may not lead to a more traditional standards development organization. One way an Open Specification may be used by a traditional standards development organization is to write a profile standard for the use of the Open Specification in some particular workflow or domain.

Selected Bibliography

Adobe Systems, 1984. Incorporated. *PostScript Language Manual*, First Edition, Palo Alto CA, August 1984.

Adobe Systems Incorporated, 1985. *PostScript Language Reference Manual*. Reading, MA: Addison-Wesley.

Adobe Systems Incorporated, 1993. *Portable Document Format Reference Manual*. Reading, MA: Addison-Wesley.

Gaffney, John, 1976. *Design System Language*, Salt Lake City, UT: Evans & Sutherland. (Mentioned in the PostScript Language Reference Manual; see above [Adobe 1985]).

ANSI, CGATS.12/1-1999 1999. *Graphic technology – Prepress digital data exchange-Use of PDF for composite data- Part 1: Complete exchange* (PDF/X-1). New York, NY.

International Standards Organization, 1995. *ISO 10180 Standard Page Description Language*. Geneva, Switzerland.

International Standards Organization, 2001. *ISO 15930-1:2001 Graphic technology -- Prepress digital data exchange -- Use of PDF -- Part 1: Complete exchange using CMYK data (PDF/X-1 and PDF/X-1a*. Geneva, Switzerland.

Krechmer, Ken, 1998. "The Principles of Open Standards." Standards Engineering Society World Standards Day Paper Competition 1998, second place, (http://www.ses-standards.org/library/krechment.pdf).

Newman, William, 1983. "Press: A flexible file format for the representation of printed images." In *Actes des journees sur la Manipulation de Documents*. Rennes, France, 5 May 1983.

Seybold Publications, 1985. "Interpress vs. PostScript." Seybold Report on Publishing Systems, Vol 15, No 1, Media, PA: Seybold Publications. 9 September 1985, pp 22-23.

Xerox Corporation, 1984. *Interpress Electronic Printing Standard*, Version 2.1, Document XSIS 048404. Stamford, CN, April 1984.

Section 5

Cross-Industry Impact

"However beautiful the strategy, you should occasionally look at the results." While Winston Churchill probably didn't have standardization strategies in mind when he uttered these words, they certainly apply to the situation and to this book. A comprehensive standardization strategy includes processes for measurement. To date, few people can cite their return on investment (ROI) in hard numbers, although anecdotes are widely available. Perhaps this is because the impact of standardization is not directly measurable, at least in terms of increased sales, cost savings, or profits. Still, standards are creating a return on their investments as evidenced by the articles in this section.

Although it may not be possible to directly measure the ROI of a standardization strategy, regular assessment and refinement of that strategy should occur. As with any strategy, it is important to evaluate whether its implementation has produced the changes and results desired. Equally, a feedback mechanism and communications channel is essential so that those individuals implementing the strategy can help to fine tune its evolution.

This section heeds the words of Winston Churchill and looks not only at the results of individual standardization strategies, but at the results of standardization as a whole. While the system may need strengthening and stakeholders are truly involved in a dynamic tug-of-war, one thing remains true: ICT standardization is impacting industries across most business lines on a global scale. For prominent examples of this impact, you only have to look as far as the articles in this section.

Tony Scott and Ramasamy Uthurusamy of General Motors Corporation explain why "Standards are a way of life at GM" and share some of their standardization efforts and results. Standardization has long been known to have an impact on the automotive industry, but people are less likely to think of other industries as being as heavily impacted by standardization. After reading the article by Robert Noth, Manager of Engineering Standards for Deere & Company, it will become evident just how much thought progressive companies are putting into their standards activities. But standards don't always bring the benefits they promise, especially if the industry changes during the process. For a first hand account and honest assessment of a standardization strategy and its implications, read the article by Scott Markel and Michael Dickson on Life Sciences standards.

Of course, government relies heavily on standards and New York City (NYC) is no exception. Thanks to their foresight in using industry standards, NYC was able to respond rapidly to the emergencies caused by 9/11. The article by Richard Goodden, Pete Croswell, and Alan Leidner tell how spatial systems standards enabled these incredible results.

Standards not only impact individual businesses, but entire industries. As one can glean from the contributors to this section, the articles discuss standardization strategies for changing industries, including telecommunications, search engines, the mortgage industry, the geospatial industry, and the health industry. Although the industries differ in their products and markets, the need for cooperation and a healthy management of the dynamic tension that exists between its participants is prominent in each of these articles.

In ending this section and this book, it seems fitting to include once again an observation by Churchill: "Man will occasionally stumble over the truth, but most of the time he will pick himself up and continue on." This book has presented evidence of standards as a powerful management tool, one that can be used to strategically manage the dynamic tension that is inherent and essential in the marketplace today. Armed with the knowledge and advice from leading experts in government, industry, and academia, will you simply continue with "business as usual" to produce the usual business? Or will you act on your new found knowledge and capitalize on *The Standards Edge*?

33

Standardization and Market Creation

ANTHONY E. (TONY) SCOTT

RAMASAMY UTHURUSAMY

General Motors Corporation

Abstract: *Standards are a way of life at General Motors Corporation. This article outlines some of GM's standardization and market creation efforts that have already provided significant benefits. Examples of GM's participation in industry leading standards initiatives and GM's active participation in standards organizations and alliances evidence its commitment to the standards process and the implementation of standards. This article outlines some of the trends and challenges facing not just the automotive industry but also the software and technology related industries and standardization efforts in general. The challenges of software quality and technology sustainability are real and warrant significant attention.*

Introduction

Standards are a way of life at General Motors Corporation (GM). The very nature of its business demands it. GM is the world's largest manufacturer operating in 190 countries and delivering about 8.5 million vehicles through 14,000 dealers. It receives 180 million

> *"Standards are a way of life at General Motors Corporation (GM). The very nature of its business demands it."*

pounds of materials *daily.* It purchases 90 billion dollars worth of materials and services annually from 12,000 sources. Each of its vehicles is composed of 5,000 parts on average. In addition to being the world's largest automaker, GM is also a leading provider in the finance (GMAC) arena and in the telematics (OnStar) industry. Cars could not be economically designed, manufactured, sold, or driven in the absence of stan-

> *"Cars could not be economically designed, manufactured, sold, or driven in the absence of standards."*

dards. For example, can you imagine the chaos that would occur in the service and repair industry if every vehicle manufacturer arbitrarily decided on a different system of measurement for the nuts, bolts, and screws that are used to build a car? Or, alternatively the issues that would arise if vehicle manufacturers decided on different fuel standards for their vehicles? Even the driver interface to vehicles has been standardized in a de facto way. No vehicle manufacturer has decided to move away from the concept of a steering wheel, and acceleration and brake pedals for the user interface, even though there are plenty of alternatives available.

The automotive supply chain relies on established standards in EDI (electronic data interchange) to procure and deliver parts to the factories that produce vehicles, among other things. Designing cars has dramatically changed from a world where a small number of elite design engineers produced paper drawings of design concepts, which were then brought to life in the form of hand made clay models. Today's design engineers work in a highly collaborative environment where concepts for vehicles are produced and rendered in a virtually seamless digital world – made possible in part by the standardization that has taken place in the technology industry around design tools, file formats, and digital information exchange.

The automotive industry pioneered the idea of "Concept Vehicles." These vehicles have historically served the purpose of providing a glimpse into the future from both a style and technology perspective. Over the past century, GM has been a leader in not just style and technology, but also from a standards perspective. As well-received concept vehicles were put into production, the need to implement new technologies and utilize products from a variety of suppliers continued to fuel the demand for standardization. Historic examples include standardizing on 12-volt electrical systems and more trivial things like tubeless tires. More recent automotive examples include government driven standards around driver safety (seat belts, crash resistant bumpers, air bags, etc.) that have improved the automobile significantly. In the future, the design of a vehicle is likely to become more of a systems integration effort and less of a one-off "invent everything from scratch" effort, in part due to increasing standardization in the automotive industry.

Outside the automotive space, standards like TCP/IP and Ethernet are prime examples of the importance and power of standards, as well as their potential for extraordinary economic impact spanning decades. The SQL standard has created multibillion dollar markets and has enabled Oracle to become the second largest

infrastructure software vendor in the world. As some of the examples below illustrate, standards, especially in the automotive industry, not only enable savings in the billions but also serve as an imperative to survive and thrive successfully in the intensely competitive global marketplace.

As has been dramatically demonstrated in the technology sector in particular, standards enable vendors to compete on a level playing field. They allow competitors to compete based on performance, features, and value-added capabilities that benefit the customer while providing compatibility, reusability, interoperability, and

---

"Businesses and customers buy into the standard—not a specific vendor..."

---

portability. Businesses and customers buy into the standard—not a specific vendor— thereby leveraging their investment in new technologies and selecting best-of-breed solutions that interoperate. The explosion of the Personal Computer based on an original IBM design is an oft-cited example of this phenomenon.

General Motors Initiatives in Standardization and Market Creation

This section looks at some recent examples of GM's standards efforts, its leadership, its participation in standards organizations, committees, alliances, etc., and its role in standards education. It then outlines some standardization trends and challenges.

Since 1996, GM has cut its annual IT spending by almost a billion dollars due to standardization, commonization of solutions, and the reduction of its overall number of IT systems. Standardization in this area lets GM better leverage its size and buying power. For example, standardizing on desktop hardware allowed GM to gain a favorable contract with its desktop hardware vendor and significantly lower its per-unit costs. Similarly, choosing a single database vendor has allowed GM to lower its support costs vs. what it was costing to support multiple technologies. These are dividends that keep on paying back over time as more legacy environments migrate to the standard.

> *"Since 1996, GM has cut its annual IT spending by almost a billion dollars due to standardization, commonization of solutions, and the reduction of its overall number of IT systems."*

In the IT arena, GM has been actively using standard web services tools to leverage existing applications. A recent example of such a web services application is the GM Smart Auction system for selling vehicles that come off-lease. The application exploits the value of web services for integration by connecting software systems and applications internally and externally. As a result, GM saves several hundred dollars per vehicle and dealers gain more fine-grained control over their inventory.

Internally, GM's Information Systems and Services organization standardization efforts include the development of an ebXML Reference Implementation that has been endorsed by the AIAG (Automotive Industries Action Group) and STAR (Standards for Technology in Automotive Retail) organizations. It has also developed a GM Service Oriented Architecture (SOA), which is an open, Internet-based application development style with self described service providers (COTS, mainframe or Web), service requestors, and a registry to "discover" services. SOA at GM has two complementary layers, ebXML and Web Services and builds upon the existing, underlying components of standardized technologies and architectures.

STAR (Standards for Technology in Automotive Retail)

STAR (Standards for Technology in Automotive Retail) is a nonprofit, auto industry-wide initiative to create voluntary IT standards for how manufacturers, dealers, and customers communicate with each other. This will result in lower costs, more accurate and timely data, and increased levels of customer satisfaction. STAR will identify an Internet-based "blueprint" for connecting dealer and OEM systems, replacing today's proprietary data exchange networks with a common IT link in the dealership and to all OEMs.

RouteOne

Most automobile dealers have been using multiple methods of credit application submission including fax, Internet, and phone. GMAC (a wholly owned subsidiary of GM) became one of the founders of RouteOne to standardize this currently inefficient, time consuming, and costly business process. RouteOne will provide dealers and their customers with a single common credit application that simplifies and speeds the financing process using the latest Internet technologies. RouteOne's open credit aggregation system provides finance sources with access to more than 22,000 dealerships nationwide. At the same time, RouteOne maintains the value of the relationship between captive finance sources and their franchised dealers.

The Liberty Alliance

GM is a founding member of The Liberty Alliance, a global consortium formed to develop open standards for federated network identity. Active participation in this alliance allows GM to play a major role in the development of standards that meet its objective of leveraging the most effective Internet-based solutions for secure information management and interoperability in its interactions with its customers, business partners, and employees. The alliance recently released its Phase 2 specifications—an important step in creating a commonly accepted and more trusted way of building and managing identity-based Web services.

Internet Home Alliance

GM is a founding member of the Internet Home Alliance (IHA), which is a cross-industry network of leading companies advancing the home technology market. A nonprofit organization, the Alliance offers members breakthrough research for the emerging home technology market and provides established and nascent companies with the collaboration and real-world testing opportunities they need to launch their home technology products and services more quickly, successfully, and cost effectively.

Establishing standards for residential systems integrators is a critical factor in accelerating the adoption of home technology products and services. IHA and Computing Technology Industry Association (CompTIA) recently launched a nationwide certification program, Home Technology Integrator (HTI+), for technicians who install and network digitally based security, audio and video, computer, heating and air conditioning, cable and satellite, and telecommunications systems.

Global common shipping label

GM has been a leader in developing new logistics and supply chain innovations. Many of these involve standards developed internally at GM first. GM staff then proactively worked with global standards bodies and led the efforts to establish them as industry standards.

A good example of this is GM's initiative to develop an internal shipping label standard, which also served as a model for a global standard, that will eventually save a billion dollars for the OEMs and their global suppliers. The effort to develop a common label grew out of a global analysis of GM's labeling and information-gathering practices. The study showed that many of GM's plants had idiosyncratic shipping label requirements and labels had too little space for human-readable information. This slowed down the handling process and invited errors. By reducing shipping and receiving costs along with training for personnel, the label should benefit the industry. The internal standard (GM 1724) was based on ANSI, ISO, and AIAG open standards. The label combines human-readable data with a two-dimensional (2D), PDF417 symbology bar code and a one-dimensional (1D) linear bar code. The incorporation of a 2D bar code reduced the cost of scanning individual contain-

ers by $0.40 per occurrence. GM North America realized a cost savings of $100 million. GM proactively worked with AIAG and global standards organizations to establish a global common Global Transport Label (GTL) for use by all the suppliers and customers [AIAG B-16]. [1]

Real Time Locating Systems (RTLS) - INCITS 371 series

This leading effort focuses on the problem of real time location of assets. Monitoring of vehicles through a multi-station assembly line and especially within a delivery yard has been very time consuming and costly. GM's initiative to define and establish a standard for real time location of assets has resulted in rapid response and support from the standards organizations and corporations. The InterNational Committee for Information Technology Standards (INCITS) approved three new standards that define two Airwave Interface Protocols and a single Application Programming Interface (API) for Real Time Locating Systems (RTLS) for use in asset management. INCITS Technical T20 developed the INCITS 371 series of standards over a two-year period; the American National Standards Institute (ANSI) approved all three in the series as American National Standards within one week of approval by INCITS' Executive Board.

INCITS standards establish a technical standard for radio frequency beacon systems that operate at an internationally available 2.4-GHz Band frequency and are intended to provide approximate location (3m) on a regular basis (several times a minute). The standard is generally appropriate for applications in which assets need to be tracked throughout extensive areas that are within range of a permanent reader infrastructure.

GM expects that this standard will encourage widespread adoption of wireless location systems as the technology has already been proven to deliver tremendous bottom line cost savings for automotive and non-automotive enterprises around the world.

Tire and Wheel Label and Radio Frequency Identification (RFID) standard [AIAG B-11]

Technologies for item-level traceability during a vehicle's lifecycle are key to minimizing assembly costs, enabling accurate recalls, safety, etc. Tires have recently been the focus of safety and government regulations. GM with its RFID tags and standardization experience was a major contributor to the development of a standard for "Tire and Wheel Label and Radio Frequency Identification." The standard provides guidelines for the printing and placement of two-dimensional bar code labels and passive read/write RFID tags on tires and wheels for product identification. It will enable error-proofing the tire assembly process and automating the collection of tire information and traceability. At assembly time, the vehicle's identification number (VIN) can be added to the tag's memory whose content can be downloaded into an external database. The relevant history of the vehicle can be tracked allowing for accurate recall if needed.

SSM (Strategic Standardization Management) training

The importance of standards mandates the need for education and training in understanding and using standards as well as training in the standards development process and participation. ANSI[2] (American National Standards Institute) delivers a number of training courses. GM works with ANSI on these and, along with nine other large corporations, helped ANSI develop the "SSM Briefing for Corporate Executives" course.[3] SSM is a management discipline that investigates all aspects of standardization across a business or industry. This course focuses on training participants to:

- examine standardization as a business, political, and technical issue
- discover ways to ensure that their business is competing on a level playing field
- make standards policy an integral part of their business strategy that will reduce costs

and time to market, open new markets and increase sales, reduce trade barriers and enhance competitiveness

TMX [Translation Memory eXchange]

Since GM sells products and services in 190 countries, it has the responsibility to respect each nation's culture and local language. Localization provides the means by which any global company like GM can enter multiple markets with sensitivity and respect. A major requirement is the translation of manuals and documents from one language to another. In Europe for example, a service manual for each vehicle needs to be provided in 20 different languages. Manual translation was the general practice until about a decade ago but it cost millions of dollars, required a lead-time of at least six months, and more importantly did not allow reusability.

GM initiated efforts in machine translation (MT) of documents and played a significant role in the development of controlled-language technologies for MT. This reduced the manual translation cost to verification time level. It also created the potential for time and cost savings and reusability by capturing the translations into a memory. Sections of various sizes from words to phrases to sentences to paragraphs can be stored in the original and target language pairs and can be reused by MT systems as well as humans. This, of course, immediately raised the need for standards to ensure interoperability when different systems and people create and use the translation memories. The standards would also ensure that the creators of the original data retained ownership of the translations and reuse. This need led to the creation of TMX and significant savings in cost and time for GM and others who operate in a multilingual environment.

TMX [Translation Memory eXchange] is a vendor-neutral, open standard for storing and exchanging translation memories created by Computer Aided Translation (CAT) and localization tools. The purpose of TMX is to allow easier exchange of translation memory data between tools and/or translation vendors with little or no loss of critical data during the process.

TMX is the result of an initiative undertaken by the OSCAR (Open Standards for Container/ Content Allowing Re-use) committee, a LISA Special Interest Group. LISA (Localization Industry Standards Association) is the premier organization for the GILT (Globalization, Internationalization, Localization, and Translation) business communities. Over 400 international IT manufacturers and solutions providers with industry professionals have helped establish LISA best practice guidelines and language-technology standards for enterprise globalization.

TMX allows any tool using translation memories to import and export databases between their own native formats and a common format. This prevents tool users from being locked-in to using a specific tool and ensures that their TM databases can go through the rise and fall of different generations of translation tools.[4]

Standard for the Exchange of Product Model Data (STEP)

A supplier for multiple OEM's traditionally had to buy, maintain, and learn to use multiple CAD systems in order to work with the various OEMs. Because this situation was expensive, error prone, and inefficient, it was costly to the supplier and the automakers. It is increasingly necessary for the automotive supply chain to have the ability to exchange product data in an accurate, timely, and cost-effective manner. Concurrent engineering must be supported by enabling greater collaboration and coordination between the various vehicle development and redesign activities. This shortens both development time and time to market at a reduced cost.

Recognizing this need for a standardized process, GM joined the Product Data Exchange Specification, Inc. (PDES) in 1988. PDES, NIST (National Institute of Standards and Technology), GM, and others created the STEP (STandard for the Exchange of Product Model Data). GM was the earliest to implement STEP pilot programs and realized considerable cost reduction.

Automotive Multimedia Interface Collaboration (AMI-C)

Designing and implementing electrical architectures for telematics systems are expensive since every vehicle is different and have some design specific electrical systems. GM initiated and founded the Automotive Multimedia Interface Collaboration (AMI-C) with a few other automakers and suppliers to define a new architecture that is generic and simple enough to apply to all vehicles. When fully implemented, it will also reduce product development time and cost. AMI-C publishes the standards and specifications. AMI-C's architecture decouples automotive cycle times (3 to 4 years) from that of consumer electronics (about 18 months) with the potential to use the latest electronics as the vehicle comes to market. Up to 10 devices can be connected through standardized ports onto AMI-C's high-speed, fiber-optic network gateway. Vehicle Services Interface is another component of AMI-C that would enable vehicle independent connectivity of controllers like those used by OnStar, GM's Telematics subsidiary.

Trends and Challenges

The automotive industry will undergo five significant technology transitions in the next five to ten years. It will transition from:

- the current gasoline engine to a hybrid engine to fuel-cell powered vehicles

- its mechanically connected control systems to a drive-by-wire system

- its unique product specific electrical, hardware, and software systems to more standardized "architectures"

- proprietary vehicle technology to the adoption and implementation of IT standards like XML, Web Services, etc.

- "on-demand" to " almost always-on" vehicle connectivity to the Internet

The impact of these transitions on the automobile software support infrastructure is significant since automobiles are long-lived products requiring ten or more years of distribution, maintenance, and support. Almost no software company is currently capable of supporting ten-year-old releases of software. This is an important challenge facing the auto industry and the software industry that supports the automotive space.

Software quality and standards

Software quality and complexity reduction in the software environment is of major concern. The lack of standardized measurement of software quality is a major obstacle. Currently, widely accepted quality metrics do not exist for automotive or non-automotive software. Forrester estimates the cost of software bugs to be around $60 billion per year. InformationWeek Research revealed that 76% of the respondents

---

"Software quality and complexity reduction in the software environment is of major concern."

---

consider software quality a significant concern when choosing a software vendor. CIO Research indicated that 88% of respondents think the software industry needs more standards governing how they develop software. This lack of standards is costly as evidenced by virus attacks alone. These attacks cost companies billions of dollars and disrupt business continuity.

The complexity of software and its development introduce many quality issues. The Standish Group's 2003 Chaos Study identified that 51% of software projects will be challenged on time and cost, with an average cost over run of 43%. More importantly it pointed out that 45% of developed application functionality is never used. Gartner reported that 90% of failed projects do not have certified project managers. InformationWeek Research identified complexity of systems among the top 10 barriers to improving quality.

The significant challenge of software quality standards needs to be addressed. In the interim, General Motors, among others, are uti-

lizing ITIL, CMM, CobiT, Six Sigma, ISO 9000, Balanced Scorecards, and other technologies and methodologies to cope with this important issue. ITIL (Information Technology Infrastructure Library) is a well-established model for IT service management that is better known for operational process definitions than application management processes. CMM (Capability Maturity Model) is the de facto standard for application development and maintenance. CobiT (Control Objectives for Information and Related Technology) is a set of guidelines establishing which formal IS processes, practices, and controls should be in place. It is useful for understanding the universe of IS processes and setting initial goals. In addition, it provides support for continuous improvement or IS service optimization. Six Sigma is a philosophy and method adopted from manufacturing for setting acceptable defect levels and modifying processes until defect level is achieved. Its relevance to service and IT organizations is an ongoing debate. ISO 9000 is a standard for achieving predictability and repeatability in processes. It introduces discipline into an environment, but does not support continuous improvement or guarantee acceptable levels of performance. Balanced Scorecards are reporting and monitoring tools designed to provide a focused and balanced insight into performance

Software sustainability

Software sustainability over time is another major related concern. It focuses on the issues of quality in technology and on the issues around the ease of upgrade, replacement, maintenance, and integration of software in particular. GM, as a founding member, is working with the Sustainable Computing Consortium at Carnegie Mellon to identify relevant standards and sustainability solutions.

Software reliability

Software Reliability is critical for safe operation of vehicles as we transition to drive-by-wire technologies in our next generation vehicles. SAE (Society for Automotive Engineers)[5] and MISRA (Motor Industry Software Reliability

Association)[6] are defining standards and recommendations to develop reliable automotive software.

Conclusions

Standards are vital in any business environment but their development and implementation is usually a long journey. Automotive standards have taken decades to mature. TCP/IP, ITIL and RFID have taken more than a decade for significant practical use within the technology sector. Similarly, 802.11, USB 1 and 2, and XML standards have taken more than five years to become widely accepted. Despite all of this, the many benefits of standardization are worth the effort and the time.

Finally, it is important to have well defined company policies and procedures for both internal standards activities and the many external standards process opportunities. GM has benefited by its ability to interact with the auto industry, other related industries, government agencies, standards organizations, consortia, alliances, and academia. We recognize that there are some important challenges posed by software quality and sustainability and the need to find solutions for support of software over ten or more years. These are real world problems that need to be solved with collective effort. The right solutions will certainly create very large markets.

Notes

[1] Global Transport Label: http://www.aiag.org/.

[2] An ANSI event of note is the *World Standards Day* held during th*e World Standards Week* conference. The goal of World Standards Day is to raise awareness of the importance of global standardization to the world economy and to promote its role in helping to meet the needs of business, industry, government, and consumers worldwide.

[3] "SSM Briefing for Corporate Executives:" Please see http://www.ansi.org for more information.

[4] TMX: http://www.lisa.org/tmx.

[5] Society for Automotive Engineers: http://www.sae.org.

[6] Motor Industry Software Reliability Association: http://www.misra.org.uk.

34

A Standards Strategy

ROBERT NOTH

Deere & Company

Abstract: *Because the nature of John Deere's business makes standards a critical strategic matter, the multidivisional company created a council of internal experts to coordinate its approach worldwide. In this article, Robert Noth, manager of engineering standards for the company, traces the rise of standards as a strategic issue within John Deere and the company's response.*

Global Businesses Have Always Required Standards

John Deere is a worldwide corporation that conducts business in more than 160 countries and employs approximately 40,000 people worldwide. It is the world's leading manufacturer of agricultural and forestry equipment; a leading supplier of equipment used in lawn, grounds, and turf care; and a major manufacturer of construction equipment. Additionally, John Deere is a top producer of off-highway diesel engines in the 50 horsepower to 600 horsepower range, supplying heavy-duty engines and drive train systems for John Deere equipment operations and other manufacturers. The company also provides financial services and related activities that support the core businesses. John Deere factories are located in Argentina, Brazil, Canada, China, Finland,

France, Germany, India, Mexico, New Zealand, The Netherlands, South Africa, Spain, Sweden, and the United States. Affiliated companies produce John Deere products in the United States and Japan.

Building product to exacting design and performance standards has always been an element of John Deere's success. From the beginning, company specifications used by John Deere engineers included detailed instructions for applying and meeting them. Many of these procedures were repeated throughout a number of the company's specifications, and engineers adopted the practice of codifying and referencing them. The company also used local standards in the various markets it served.

As the company began expanding globally in the 1950s, it developed company handbooks to cross-reference national standards with internal standards for materials. This allowed our engineers to use local standards and suppliers at a time when each John Deere factory made most of the parts it used.

Today, as is true for many manufacturers, most of the content of John Deere products is purchased from a global supply base. Purchasing is more efficient when several factories can pool their requirements, so John Deere employees began working together as an enterprise, using more external specifications and standards. By the mid-1970s, John Deere engineers were specifying components and materials that met standards from organizations such as the Society of Automotive Engineers (SAE), the American Society of Agricultural Engineers(ASAE), ASTM International, the American Society of Mechanical Engineers (ASME), the Institute of Electrical and Electronics Engineers (IEEE), and the American Gear

---

"The policy now is to use external standards before developing John Deere standards, with a focus on using international standards whenever possible."

Manufacturers Association (AGMA) in US markets; the German National Standards Body (DIN) or the French National Standards Body (AFNOR) in their local markets; or the International Organization for Standards (ISO) when available for products with a more global market presence.

The policy now is to use external standards before developing John Deere standards, with a focus on using international standards whenever possible. This enables the use of more off-the-shelf components instead of customized parts.

Role of Standards

Standards, though, are far more pervasive in their effects than just as a way to simplify manufacturing and reduce costs. As our Chairman and CEO, Bob Lane, said when John Deere was awarded the Ronald H. Brown Standards Leadership Award at the US celebration of World Standards Day in 2001, "Standards play a critical role in the success of all new John Deere products, as well as our environmental and safety management processes. They provide measurement systems to support risk assessment. Standards reduce injury and environmental pollution. They support the innovative application of knowledge in the development of new products and management systems to help

our customers be more productive. Standards aid us greatly as they establish what is state-of-the-art for a given technology at a given period of time. They allow the sharing of knowledge

---

"Clearly, when countries or regional economic blocks impose their own standards, testing practices, and certification requirements, they are creating de facto non-tariff trade barriers."

---

across companies worldwide. And, standards set expectations that become the basis for improvement for the next quantum leap."

In fact, any company that aspires to serve customers well must have access to those customers and must innovate and improve constantly. All three of these requirements are dependent upon an environment in which standards are likewise user-focused and do not create barriers to trade, innovation, or improvement. Clearly, when countries or regional economic blocks impose their own standards, testing practices, and certification requirements, they are creating de facto non-tariff trade barriers. John Deere has always made it a priority to support industry and governmental efforts to reduce non-tariff barriers to trade in global markets.

Impetus for a Strategic Standardization Approach

Volume

Standards setting is an especially important subject for companies like John Deere. We sell high-value products in relatively low volumes

---

"By standardizing its processes and materials, John Deere is able to control costs and pass these savings on to its customers."

---

compared to other industries such as consumer electronics or automobiles. The expense of retooling for different requirements not only adds cost, but also lowers volume even further for various configurations, making it nearly impossible to recover the higher costs. By standardizing its processes and materials, John Deere is able to control costs and pass these savings on to its customers. And, as the pace of technology development increases, standards become important to John Deere and other manufacturers for another reason: minimizing the risk of investing in technology that becomes unusable.

Market demands

When it comes to meeting market demands, standards have an enormous impact. They can facilitate or retard development and innovation, depending on the degree of cooperation and support among standardization participants. Standards can also speed or hinder the delivery of market-appropriate technology, whether that technology is best-in-class or more simplified. For example, a farmer in China may want simple drawbar horsepower and be unable – or unwilling – to pay for anything beyond that, let alone the safety interlocks with electronics that top-end machines have. Providing the safest, most environmentally friendly machines possible consistent with the technologies the customer can afford in any given market is an ongoing challenge. Focusing on the most important environmental and safety concerns for the user and standardizing on certain technologies and design practices that address those concerns helps John Deere meet that challenge with a range of affordable product offerings in any given market segment.

Divisional thinking

Along with the move to global operations and external suppliers, the rapid changes in technology, and the arising differences in demand, has come the realization that standards are a strategic issue that calls for a strategic approach. Specifically, by the mid-1990s, we realized our various divisions were participating in standards making organizations as separate entities in both the national and international standards arenas. In addition, divisions were sometimes taking conflicting positions on public proposals.

Also, a growing number of issues transcended divisions, and we wanted to harmonize the thinking internally. For one thing, the lines between markets – agricultural, construction, and turf care— were, and are, blurring.

Regulatory issues

The growing importance of environmental regulation and the increasing concern about the impact of machines on the environment also became apparent. As a result, attention broadened from facilities like power plants and factories to products, users, and the public at large. And as customers are held responsible for their impact on the environment, they, in turn, hold John Deere responsible for providing products that enhance their ability to minimize those environmental impacts.

Government involvement: EC92

But the main impetus for this long-term reassessment of our approach to standards was EC92 — the formation and rapid expansion of the European Union and its quasi-regulatory approach to standards. As a result, John Deere's divisions began to communicate concerns over the impact this change would have on the business. For example, all of John Deere's divisions voiced concerns about machinery compliance with the market access requirements. The change in Europe called for a new level of attention to standards and compliance as a strategic matter that affects John Deere's core businesses.

Creating a Strategic Standardization Approach

Moving to a strategic approach is not as easy as it sounds. John Deere is a multi-division company. Our divisions – Agricultural equipment, Construction and Forestry Equipment, Engines, Consumer and Commercial Equipment, and Parts – all have strong leaders and high expertise in the markets they serve. This structure provides one of John Deere's abiding strengths in the marketplace, but it also calls for extraordinary efforts to coordinate and align strategic efforts.

The council approach

One of John Deere's methods for creating such alignment in strategic areas is through forums that allow division experts to work through differences in a manner that is consistent with the company's culture of shared respect, overarching concern for customers, doing the right things, and doing things right. In the standards arena, we created a forum called the Strategic Standards, Regulations, and Conformity Assessment Enterprise Council (SSRC). This council reports to, and takes direction from, John Deere's top manufacturing and marketing leadership. It serves at the behest of the Enterprise Product Development Process Council (EPDP), which in turn serves at the behest of the Management Council. The SSRC council updates the EPDP council biannually and the corporate social responsibility council regularly.

*Operation of the the Strategic
Standards, Regulations, and Conformity
Assessment Enterprise Council*

The SSRC's role includes the following:

- coordinate responses to standards setting organizations
- better manage the company's commitments to the voluntary standards process
- focus our participation in standards settings organizations on a single vision – one standard, one test, one certification accepted globally

Experts familiar with the products and people, along with the standards and regulations that affect their products, represent their divisions. The council also ensures that it has the approrpiate geographical representation from Europe, South America, North America, and Asia.

Although the council holds approximately six in-person meetings a year, most of its collaboration is conducted electronically using our knowledge sharing system, John Deere Mindshare. We use this system as a sort of virtual organization to gather intelligence on standards-making issues, or issues that might lead to standards-making, and to evaluate and assess the potential impact of proposed standards. We assess the potential impact by asking a simple question: Can we modify or improve the standard, or will we have to change our machines? We then assess the costs and benefits of each of those approaches. Then we make recommendations as to the urgency and the issue to the senior management of the businesses involved.

Through all of that, we try to stay focused on cross-divisional issues. That is, if an issue is likely to affect only agricultural equipment, the council doesn't get involved. Of course, at some point, the council may be called on to determine if the issue is an agriculture-only issue. The council also maintains liaisons with our public affairs organization because the links between voluntary standards, legislation, and regulation are becoming more important. In addition, it closely aligns its activities with corporate governance, which has ultimate responsibility for the product safety and environmental compliance areas. It's process is very pragmatic focusing on what might or should be changed in specific standards, legislation or regulatory rules that might provide a more cost effective solution without compromising the ultimate social objective.

The principles behind the structure

The council operates under a couple of basic principles relating to standards and business. First, standards have to be user-focused and performance-based to be effective. This is why one of our strategies is to maintain a vertical approach (based on machine type) for providing customer choices. That is, we try to make sure standards in any region take into account the actual use of the machine. As a simple example, in densely populated areas it is higly likely that

---

"...standards have to be user-focused and performance-based to be effective."

---

agricultural machines will be operated amid other traffic. Therefore, it makes sense to include extensive lighting and signage packages that are computer controlled. However, in Australia, South America, and the western United States, agricultural machines rarely mingle with traffic. Consequently, customers in those regions don't want the added cost of, say, lighting designed for densely populated areas.

In addition, we work hard to help those who propose standards understand that our customers are business people, many of them international players themselves, who are very sophisticated in conducting cost-benefit analyses. First and foremost, they want performance, reliability, and serviceability; then they want features that address safety and the environment.

Because most of the people who propose standards have never had to create a living from a few hectares of land or generate a return on a fleet of machines, we feel that we have to help represent the user – our customer – in the standards setting process. We take that role very seriously. As in most deliberative undertakings, many of the costs get piled on the empty chair, and we feel some responsibility to be there for our customers when they cannot contribute.

The internal arrangements for addressing standards setting is merely academic, however, if your engineers are not out there participating in the industry, coordinating with government affairs to brief government ministers, and reviewing the work on standards.

Participation is essential

There are only a few ways to influence standards—and participation is the most crucial. You have to participate in standards-setting bodies where you can, participate in industry organizations, and educate law-making bodies about the requirements of the market and business; all of these activities require the use of highly qualified technical experts and experienced business leaders. The challenge is to figure out how each standards-making and legislative process works in each country and simply take the time to participate in the right way.

John Deere is fortunate that its long history of participation in standards-setting organizations has led to a tradition of contributing, along with the institutional knowledge and memory to effectively carry on that tradition. Its employees participate in a number of standards developing organizations such as SAE, ASAE, and ISO, and the company is also active in the American

National Standards Institute (ANSI). Consequently, John Deere considers itself among the leaders of the global movement to promote one standard and one test for each product line. The goal is to reduce redundant requirements worldwide and ensure that Self-Declaration of Compliance (SDoC) to those standards remains an acceptable option in the marketplace.

The company also takes advantage of the opportunity for dialog with decision makers in such government agencies as the National Institute of Standards and Technology (NIST) and industry bodies like the Trans-Atlantic Business

---

"Just as we develop and coordinate a strategy for marketing, sales, product design, and finance, among others, we have found it crucial—and extremely beneficial—to create and coordinate a global standardization strategy that maximizes our business potential and our ability to meet customer needs."

Dialogue (TABD) and the International Cooperation on Standards and Conformity Assessment (ICSCA) to ensure that its voice is heard. John Deere annually reviews its participation in these organizations to determine the activities that help the company meet its strategic objectives.

The Secret of Our Success

Market conditions, international government involvement, and the regulatory environment will continue to change—offering challenges and opportunities to those who are not only aware, but proactively address those changes. Standardization is a strategic management tool that has helped John Deere capitalize on those changes for decades. Just as we develop and coordinate a strategy for marketing, sales, product design, and finance, among others, we have found it crucial—and extremely beneficial—to create and coordinate a global standardization strategy that maximizes our business potential and our ability to meet customer needs.

35

Case Study: The Impact of Spatial Systems Standards on the GIS Response to 9/11 in New York City

RICHARD GOODDEN
PETER CROSWELL
PlanGraphics, Inc.

ALAN LEIDNER
NYC DEPARTMENT OF INFORMATION
TECHNOLOGY & TELECOMMUNICATIONS

Abstract: *Standards enable efficient resource sharing by facilitating interoperability, portability, and maintainability. While these abilities are beneficial to the bottom line of all businesses, they become essential when lives and property are impacted. This chapter examines how a framework of standardization helped to ensure the speedy response of New York City to 9/11 and will continue to facilitate effective responses to potential emergencies.*

Introduction

The hype and confusion that has surrounded the issue of standards in spatial information technology and information systems in general can lead one to lose sight of the reasons behind the development and adoption of standards. Standards are not an end in themselves but the foundation to make information systems and databases easier to use, more flexible, and less costly. Figure 1 illustrates the

> *"Standards are not an end in themselves but the foundation to make information systems and databases easier to use, more flexible, and less costly."*

point that standards are the basis for resource sharing allowing more flexible access to and use of computing hardware, software, and data

through common user interfaces.

Standards can facilitate the sharing of information and computer resources within an organization and between organizations. The value of wisely chosen standards for geographic information users is reflected in three primary themes illustrated in Figure 2.

During the rescue and recovery operations in New York City associated with the events of 9/11/01, standards played a key role in the ability to share data across system platforms and to make rapid changes to existing systems to fit the

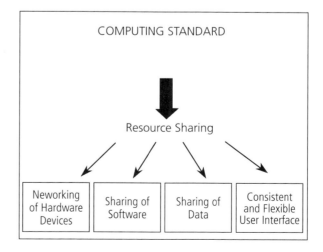

Figure 1: Standards allow sharing of resources

immediate need. The use of industry standards made it much easier to bring volunteer workers up to speed on the operation of the mapping systems, as many of them were familiar with the concepts being applied and were therefore able to adapt quickly to the environment in the Emergency Mapping and Data Center.

updating, upgrading, and effective use of computer systems and databases.

For designers and developers of geographic information systems, the question is not whether standards should be adopted. The challenge is to choose suitable standards and a sensible approach for their implementation to facilitate

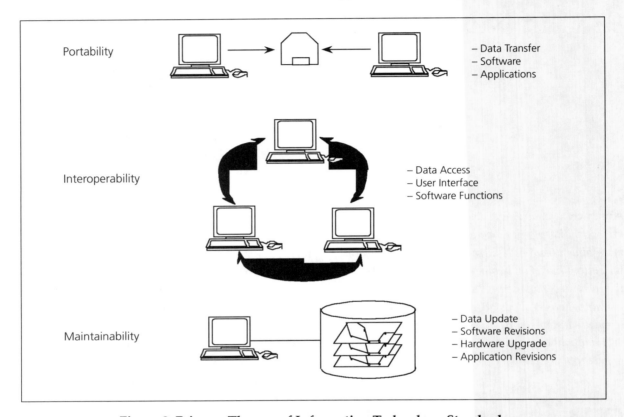

Figure 2: Primary Themes of Information Technology Standards

In the above figure, the following definitions apply:

1) **Portability**, with the concept of "interchangeable parts" implies an ability to use and move data, software, and custom applications among multiple computers and operating system environments without retooling or reformatting.

2) **Interoperability** and **information access** impacts the ability of computers, networks, and users to connect and retrieve information from multiple systems.

3) **Maintainability** addresses the use of standards to promote longterm and efficient

sharing of information and to make systems easier to support and maintain.

New York City GIS utility background

The City of New York utilizes a number of GIS software programs to support departmental functions. Software from Environmental Systems Research Institute (ESRI), GE Smallworld, Intergraph, Autodesk, and MapInfo are all entrenched in the various Mayoral agencies. Applications have been developed and user communities trained on these products. Past attempts at reducing the number of vendor platforms have met with resistance due to the substantial investments already made in these systems. Such changes require analysis of the

New York City GIS Utility Standards		
Theme	**Applied Standard(s)**	**Comments**
Map Accuracy	ASPRS* Accuracy Standards for Large-Scale Maps	Spatial accuracy standard for physical base map
Cartographic Appearance	Internally developed	"PrettyMap" program determined City standards for map appearance
System Architecture	Oracle (Spatial) IBM OS 390 SUN OS Windows 2000	Multitiered architecture utilizes IBM mainframe as data server; SUN Unix as application servers; Windows as development environment
Quality Assurance/Quality Control	ANSI sampling standards ISO 9002 Internal standards	Data uploaded by departments is put through various QA/QC routines
Applications Development	COM Java ISP Internal standards	All applications must comply with standards set by DoITT and other City agencies

Table 1

proposed standard(s) in relation to the goals of the department, along with careful analysis of the cost of application migration, data modifications, personnel retraining, and change management.

In 1999, the City completed a Citywide GIS Strategic Plan that included a vision of a shared "GIS Utility." This utility would act as a central repository for key spatial data layers with means provided for the various departments to download data as needed for their various applications and upload updated information as appropriate. Since the City was already an established user of Oracle software, Oracle was chosen as the database management system. The Department of Information Technology and Telecommunications (DoITT) has taken the

lead in the design and implementation of the GIS Utility. A key aspect of Oracle is its ability to store and manage graphic (map) data and to interface with all of the major GIS packages in use by the City, thus providing a means by which DoITT could focus its GIS development efforts on a single standard while still meeting the needs of the wider departmental GIS user community.

Since the completion of the study, the City has been developing the GIS Utility database through the acquisition of digital aerial imagery (digital orthophotos), accurate street centerlines, property data, and water/sewer utility data. These data layers are in various stages of development and continue to evolve. To ensure accuracy and usability, DoITT has implemented a number of standards that impact a wide range of data and application characteristics. These standards control such things as map accuracy, cartographic appearance, system architecture, quality control, and applications development. Some of the key standards employed by the GIS Utility are summarized in Table 1

The table illustrates the wide range of standards that are required to design, implement, and operate a government spatial information system. Another key area where standardization had taken place was addressing. New York City contains a large number of addresses and even though there are rules for assigning them, there are also many cases where exceptions to the rules have been granted over time. Fortunately, the City had developed a mainframe application and database called "Geosupport" which carried all addresses, aliases, street intersections, and other geographic information in tabular format. Geosupport has been in use since the 1970's and has been maintained to a high level of reliability by the Department of City Planning. Geosupport is an unusually good address database by U.S. municipal standards.

In the spring of 2001, the GIS Utility was contacted by the Mayor's Office of Emergency

---

"...the efficient execution of these steps was facilitated by the application and data standards that had been put in place by DoITT and other agencies."

Management (OEM) to implement a web-based GIS application to provide public information on locations of City-run "cooling centers" for citizens who lack access to airconditioned facilities during summer heat waves. The application would also have pages for "heating centers" during winter cold periods, as well as evacuation instructions during the hurricane season. The evolution of this application from design through implementation, followed by modification in response to the events of 9/11, provides insight into the positive impact that standards can have when applied appropriately.

The emergency management online locator system

One of the most serious hazards in New York City is storm surge caused by coastal storms and hurricanes. Summer heat waves and severe winter cold are also major problems. In response to these issues, the Office of Emergency Management (OEM) contracted with PlanGraphics to design and implement the Emergency Management Online Locator System (EMOLS) to allow New York City citizens to access emergency information through an interactive map on the Internet. EMOLS contains three modules: 1) Hurricane Evacuation provides information on hurricane evacuation methods and routes; 2) Coastal Storm and Emergency Shelters provides information on City heating shelters during severe winter cold periods; 3) Cooling Centers provides information on City cooling shelters during summer heat emergencies. The various modules are activated seasonally by OEM.

The design and implementation of EMOLS required numerous steps. However, the efficient execution of these steps was facilitated by the application and data standards that had been put in place by DoITT and other agencies. Key steps in the process included:

- Requirement Analysis and Design
- Government Architecture and Standards Compliance Review
- System Design
- Database Design and Development
- System and Software Configuration
- Application Development
- Regression, Stress Testing, Production
- Maintenance and Support

The Egovernment architecture standards and procedures had a major impact on the efficient development of EMOLS. DoITT had been working to develop egovernment standards during the months leading up to the EMOLS project. The Mayor's Office of New Media (ONM) had set up standards for web development including development languages, architecture, and graphical guidelines for web page design. ONM reviewed the EMOLS design at key stages to insure compliance with all web publishing standards. Additionally, the GIS Utility team used

> *"The presence of and close adherence to City standards allowed EMOLS and its supporting architecture, including data, to be designed and implemented rapidly."*

their own standards to ensure that the data being used to support the application were in compliance with DoITT requirements. The key data layers used to support EMOLS include:

- NYC Base Map Data
- NYC Street Centerline Data with Address Ranges (LION)
- Shelters
- Zip Codes
- Evacuation Zones
- Transportation Data

The presence of and close adherence to City standards allowed EMOLS and its supporting architecture, including data, to be designed and implemented rapidly. The project was initiated in February 2001 and the initial rollout of the Cooling Center web site occurred in July. Mayor Giuliani rolled out the Hurricane Evacuation site at a press conference in late August, 2001, just a few weeks before the events of 9/11.

EMOLS in the aftermath of the 9/11 attack

Late in the evening of September 10, 2001, PlanGraphics staff was putting the finishing touches on the latest modifications of EMOLS. One staff member was in the OEM offices at 7 World Trade Center until 11:00 p.m. that night working on the server that was housed there. The next morning, during the commuter rush, two airplanes slammed into the main World Trade Center towers and brought them down, thus creating the largest emergency in the history of New York City.

At that time, EMOLS was the only GIS-enabled web application that the Office of Emergency Management had. It's successful rollout just weeks before had given it significant public exposure and therefore it was the logical choice as a conduit to provide emergency information about the area around the catastrophe. Time was of the essence as the requirements for modifying EMOLS were set forth. The key functional requirements included:

- Geocoding by street intersection or address
- Map interface
- Utility outage information

EMOLS is built on ESRI's ArcIMS web mapping software, which is one of the City's standard web packages. Java is used as the programming language. As the new requirements where documented, the PlanGraphics team was able to save time through their familiarity with the ONM web standards, which control the major aspects of web page design including frames, text fonts, colors, window sizes, etc. This base of standards, already implemented for the original EMOLS, allowed the team to focus only on the items that needed changing as opposed to a "ground up" design of a new web site. Dubbed the "Interactive Map for Emergency Information (IMEI)," this first major modification of EMOLS took one week from notice to proceed until the rollout of a new website. Most of that time was consumed with coordination activity associated with gathering information from numerous sources, including private firms who were wary of publishing their data.

IMEI was a resounding success. The main purpose of the application was to provide users with information about electric, gas, water, sewer, and telephone outages. Information was gathered by GIS personnel in the City's Emergency Mapping and Data Center and approved by OEM for distribution. Users would log onto the web, type in an address, and have a map displayed that showed their location relative to outage areas, which were drawn as polygons.

Conclusion

Standards serve as an essential foundation for making information systems and databases easier to use, more responsive, and less costly. When instituting changes within an organization of any size, an analysis of the changes the proposed standards would initiate in terms of goals, costs, and training should be conducted. Once a strong standardization framework is built, networks can be adapted quickly to respond to the needs of a specific situation—whether that situation is a change in customer preferences or an emergency impacting an entire city.

36

Operator Strategies for Maximizing the Benefits of Standardisation

KEITH DICKERSON
BT

Abstract: *The recession in the telecommunications (telecom) industry has meant that the traditional telecommunications operators (BT, AT&T, FT, etc.) have found it difficult to provide the resources needed to participate effectively in the standards process. Thus, they are not influencing international standards to get what is needed to build the next generation of telecom networks. This could mean that the introduction of new services is delayed and that customers may have to pay more for their services than is necessary. A clear priority now is to re-engage the operators in standardisation so that the equipment needed to build their 21st Century Networks is standardized to operator requirements. This is the only way to get network build costs down to a level where operators can afford to install it. This paper looks at ways of achieving this goal.*

Where Have All the Operators Gone?

Telecom operators on both sides of the Atlantic used to be very prominent in standards bodies, giving guidance to ensure that standards met operator and end user requirements. They provided the requirements for new standards and ensured that they were developed in a framework that led to efficient implementation. This has now all changed. The overcapacity and subsequent downturn in the telecom industry has led to a mass withdrawal of operators from participation in standardisation. Today, standards participation is dominated by vendors, most of which develop and

> *"Today, standards participation is dominated by vendors, most of which develop and standardize bottom-up solutions that do not meet operator needs."*

standardize bottom-up solutions that do not meet operator needs. In particular, vendors' solutions do not interwork successfully nor do they provide the appropriate mechanisms for Quality of Service (QoS) and manageability that telecommunications operators need.

The 21st Century Network

The 21st Century Network (21CN) is BT's initiative to design and implement the next generation of telecom networks. It will provide multimedia, video, and data services to customers as well as traditional PSTN (telephony) services. In the ITU and ETSI this is known as the Next Generation Network (or NGN). In designing the 21st Century Network, it must be remembered that customers of public networks pay for services, not bandwidth or technology. They want services that meet their needs at an acceptable quality and at a fair and understood price; they do not want speech dropouts and distortions, video pictures that break up regularly, or frequent instant message advertisements on their SIP (Session Initiation Protocol) phones! Appropriate technology and standards must be developed to enable this to be achieved at an acceptable cost.

The 21st Century Network will be based on the following core concepts:

- An IP-based core network for all services, which uses an enhanced form of Multi-Protocol Label Switching (MPLS) to provide "connections" and therefore an acceptable QoS for real-time services

- SIP as the protocol of choice for establishment of call-based sessions (e.g., Voice over IP-VoIP, multimedia, etc.), including presence management

- A mobility architecture based on 3GPP with extensions for Wi-Fi, broadband access, etc. This will mean that there will be little distinction between fixed and mobile networks within 5-10 years

- Use of IPv6 either upon introduction of 21CN or as soon as possible afterwards. This will be essential for the enhanced addressing, autoconfiguration, and security features, and a mandatory feature of the 3GPP transport architecture

- A residential access network converging on a DSL-based Multi-Service Access Node (MSAN)

- Open APIs that will allow third party application providers to deliver services over the BT core network

- A common intelligence layer controlling both IP (data) and PSTN (real-time) services

- A standards-based home gateway providing seamless access from wide area networks to home networking services

- Operational Support Systems (OSS) based on a common set of components for all services (not stovepipes) and using directories, middleware, and B2B Gateway technology to provide communication between these services

From the above, the standards developments that will be most critical to the success of the 21st Century Network are:

- Mobility – a 3GPP mobility architecture extended to cover Wi-Fi and fixed Broadband access

- A multiservice, carrier-scale core, enabled by an underlying "MPLSv2" network

- Session-based QoS

- Session Control – SIP with full multimedia capability provided end-to-end across corporate and home networks

- Manageability – a commoditised, componentised OSS to radically reduce management costs

- Billing and charging (data interchange billing) between operators

- Security – authentication across different networks, operators, and technologies

- Home Gateways/Networks for easy access to broadband and multimedia services

So What Are the Problems with Standardisation?

OK, so all this 21st Century Network stuff sounds great! Why can't we have it tomorrow and rely on the traditional standards processes for the standards we need for implementation? Well, there are several problems, as described in the following sections.

Operators don't have enough influence over standards

Operators used to drive the formal standards process in the telecommunications area. Due to overcapacity in the marketplace and the subsequent economic downturn, the operators have had to reduce staffing levels drastically and (with some exceptions) have withdrawn from the standards process. This has resulted in a vicious circle where vendors have to second guess what the operators need, leading to bottom-up solutions that don't interwork successfully or meet operators needs. An example of this is Diffserv, which works reasonably well within a corporate or enterprise network. However, because there are no standardized classes of services between operators, it does not work for traffic sent between operator domains. An even more problematic example is fault management—a situation in which the IETF rarely considers operator requirements.

But why do operators need to be present in standards bodies in the first place? The question that I'm often asked is "If operators provide most of the buying power for telecommunications equipment in both Europe and the US, then why don't the vendors simply listen to what we want and build it to our requirements?" The reasons are complex and include the following:

1. Due to the economic downturn in fixed telecommunications services, the traditional telecom operators are simply not buying equipment at present. Switches are not being replaced and new capacity is only installed to provide fixed-line ADSL-based broadband (providing a connection straight to an Internet Service Provider). Apart from ADSL, there are no new services. Of course, this is a circular argument. If there was an accepted vision for a new multiservice network that provided a means for operators to generate revenue from it (or at least enough to pay for its installation and replace costly legacy service provision), then equipment buying would restart.

2. Over the last few years the operators have become accustomed to the competitive model of "competing in their own backyards." This practice has led to a lack of cooperation between operators on standards. Some say that this model and lack of cooperation were a primary cause of the telecom recession in the first place. However, it is clear that, in the future, operators will only get what they want if they cooperate to provide common requirements for standards.

3. The IETF has been the driving force for the standardisation of the new IP-based networks, which will provide a basis for the next generation of telecom networks.

"...it is clear that, in the future, operators will only get what they want if they cooperate to provide common requirements for standards."

Unfortunately, the IETF is working to a different business model and, thus, providing standards that do not meet the needs of the telecom operators. Because vendors dominate the IETF, they have the ability to develop any "standard" they desire through "rough consensus and running code" (a process that requires demonstration of interoperable running code from at least two different vendors).[1] This is covered in more detail later.

There are so many fora and consortia these days!

There are many fora and consortia working at different levels in numerous overlapping technology areas relevant to ICT and the 21st Century Network. Over 500 are listed in web-based catalogues of fora and consortia such as ETSI's FORAwatch http://www.etsi.org/forawatch/, and, at one time (before the collapse of the dot com bubble), new fora and consortia were being created at the rate of at least one a week! It is impossible for operators to keep track of all of these, and it is not clear to an operator (or even to a vendor) which group to work with for the standards they need. Vendors often create new fora to obtain a significant influence in the marketplace and to ensure that any resulting technical standards are based on their own product specifications.

However, following the economic downturn, both vendors and operators want to reduce costs and therefore decrease the number of fora and consortia they participate in. Subsequently, they are (either covertly or outwardly) encouraging fora and consortia in similar technology areas to merge. This was the rationale behind the merger in 2002 of seven smaller fora (including WAP Forum and LIF) to create the Open Mobile Alliance (OMA). While OMA is not yet working fully effectively as a single body, it has created a critical mass of players in the mobile applications marketplace that cannot be ignored. Operators and vendors can join the OMA, confident they will be contributing to standards that will be used in real products and services and are also more likely to interoperate successfully.

Unfortunately, although desirable from a top-down perspective, mergers can't always be achieved and do not always make sense. Fora are created for many different reasons. They are often started to perform a marketing or education role instead of simply to work on standards. Reasons for creating a new forum include:

- the wish to promote a new technology (e.g., the Metro Ethernet Forum—MEF)
- to promote interoperability between standards (e.g., the Multiservice Switching Forum—MSF)
- to promote operator requirements (e.g., FS-VDSL)
- because the formal standards bodies have refused to pick up the issues (e.g., DSL Forum)

The IETF doesn't work anymore

The stated aim of the IETF is to create standards that are in the best interests of the Internet ("The purpose of the IETF is to create high quality, relevant, and timely standards for the Internet.")[2] This simple statement often does not take operator requirements into account because, to create a successful public network, you not only have to ensure interoperability between applications and services, but you must also standardize the interfaces between operators, provide protocols that enable charging for services, and supply sufficient real-time performance information that allows effective network management and QoS maintenance. The focus of the IETF on the Internet means that it will never consider the full requirements of the 21st Century Network (or NGN). And, it appears that the IETF never intends to, as evidenced in this statement: "It is important that this is for the Internet and does not include everything that happens to use IP. IP is being used in a myriad of real-world applications, such as controlling street lights, but the IETF does not standardize those applications." This is especially true in "service surround" areas such as (interoperator) billing and charging, QoS, management, and security. The situation is actually worse than it appears—the IETF claims that the NGN *is* the Internet, and that any other core network is a competing network to the Internet. The problem with this approach is that it won't generate the return on investment needed to build the NGN in the first place (the Internet itself was kick-started using generous funding from the US Defense Department)!

The IPR morass

One of the most important things to do when creating a new standards body or forum is to get the IPR policy right. This can make the difference between a smooth running and productive

---

"One of the most important things to do when creating a new standards body or forum is to get the IPR policy right."

---

forum and one that can't and doesn't function effectively. It has been suggested that traditional standards bodies no longer work due to a complex mass of claims and counterclaims for IPR that are considered essential to a standard's implementation.[3] These claims can delay that implementation by up to four years, putting the future of traditional standards bodies at stake. In the future, only SDOs (Standards Development Organizations) with successful IPR policies will survive.

The two major flavors of IPR policy are Royalty Free (RF) and Fair, Reasonable, and Non-Discriminatory (FRAND). FRAND (sometimes known as RAND) is the traditional model for IPR that has worked well for many years. Under this model, a "timely" declaration of any IPR thought to be essential to a standard under development must be made so that potential users can consider likely licensing royalties. Once the standard has been published, licenses must be issued fairly to all applicants, and the IPR holder cannot refuse to license the IPR to certain companies (non-discriminatory). If, during the standards development process, these terms are considered too onerous, there is an opportunity to specify alternative (possibly IPR-free, but less effective) technologies in the standard instead. However, standards bodies using the FRAND model have been accused of allowing IPR holders to withhold declarations until a standard is agreed upon, allowing the holders to make a "late" declaration so that unexpected royalties have to be paid (ambushing). In practice, the operation of a FRAND IPR policy is fraught with pitfalls because it depends on what is considered "fair and reasonable," whether declaration is necessary for all IPR or only that considered "essential" (without a clear definition of *essential*), and whether penalties are applied for non-declaration or for non-timely declaration.

For these reasons, fora and consortia are increasingly moving towards an RF model. In the pure RF model, any IPR essential to the use of a standard must be licensable without payment. Alternatively, any IPR thought to be essential to a standard under development must be declared within a specified time (e.g., three months). Any essential IPR that is not declared within the specified time frame becomes null and void, allowing organization members to freely use the resulting standards without payment. The W3C and IETF have recently made moves toward an RF policy, and fora such as OSGi and Liberty Alliance were expressly created with this policy in the first place. Sometimes exceptions are allowed. For example, W3C allows exceptions to its RF policy if a significant license holder has IPR that would otherwise constitute a roadblock to further development of a standard. This points to a major failing of the RF model—companies that have significant IPR

in a standard under development will simply not join or will withdraw from membership of that body, often resulting in the establishment of a de facto or proprietary standard instead of a more open standard.

So How Can We Get the Standards Needed to Build the 21st Century Network?

There are several routes of increasing complexity to get the job done more effectively, as described below.

Coordinate the existing bodies better

Coordination between standards bodies and fora is patchy to say the least. While the role some bodies play in the standards process is generally well recognised, the IETF in the development of IP-based protocols (but not architectures) or W3C in the development of Web-based protocols are good examples, others are in direct competition. This has become worse since the "convergence" of the telecom, broadcasting, IT, and media industries, starting in the early 1990s. Today, there is a danger that bodies such as CEN, CENELEC and ETSI (in Europe) or ISO, IEC, and ITU (globally) will develop standards and so called "new deliverables" that compete with each other, thus wasting the industry resources used to develop them. It was for this reason that the ICT Standards Board (ICTSB) was set up in 1995. This involves collaboration between the three European Standards Organizations (ESOs) and approximately 15 fora and consortia in relevant areas including W3C, ISOC (the parent of IETF), TMF, DVB, and The Open Group. It therefore acts as a bridge between the formal standards bodies and the fora working in related areas. The ICTSB's mission is to analyze standards requirements from any competent source based on market needs, translate these into coherent standards work programmes, allocate work items to its members, and monitor progress to ensure the job is done. It has so far worked on standards for electronic signatures, Design for All, and, more recently, has embarked on intelligent transport systems.

The ICTSB only applies to standards bodies and fora that have some kind of European presence. An "Association of ICT Standards Consortia" at a global level (if it could actually agree on what to do!) could provide a place to share information on work programmes and set up a common portal for users worldwide to obtain information on standards, etc. The ITU Informal Forums Summit (IFS) held in San Francisco in July 2003 [3] had similar objectives, although it cannot completely fulfill this role with its schedule of meetings every two years. Led by the Director of ITU-T, this meeting brought together chairpersons or board members from 36 fora and consortia, together with the Chairs of eight ITU-T Study Groups, to improve collaboration between fora and ITU so that the required standards for NGN implementation can be produced.

An alternative approach is for a body such as the Multiservice Switching Forum (MSF) to play the role of a system verification house that ensures interoperability between key NGN components and systems. The MSF addresses interface standards between the Access Network, Call Server, and Gateways, along with providing protocol profiling, implementation agreements, and verification at interoperability events such as GMI2004. This forces vendors to prove that the paper interface specifications actually work (at their expense), reducing the risk for operators of early deployment.

Use formal and informal standards bodies appropriately

We must accept that, despite their increasing number, fora and consortia have a valid place in the standards development lifecycle and will be around for many years to come. They often catalyze the development of technologies and specifications that are essential to the next generation of telecommunications equipment, and should therefore be supported provided they have the buy-in of the major players in their field.

However, selecting a small number of fora to use for major components of the 21st Century Network is desirable. The first step could be for the telecom operators as a group to select

and agree to use only those fora and consortia that are best suited to generate the essential specifications needed! This sounds easy but is not as straightforward as it sounds, as fora and consortia in the same technology area are often operating at different levels. For example, as has

---

"The first step could be for the telecom operators as a group to select and agree to use only those fora and consortia that are best suited to generate the essential specifications needed!"

---

already been observed in the OSS area, although the TMF acts as the focus for the generation of new ideas and work, it also relies on specifications from bodies such as OSS-J. In addition, fora and consortia that are not "chosen" may still continue to work—they have been created by vendors, not operators, after all, and will feel they still have a job to do and a valid role to play! They will obviously continue to produce specifications that may compete with those from the "chosen" fora. Therefore, resources from the operators will still be needed to monitor these fora for the applicability of any new developments. In order to minimize the impact of these fora, operators would need to provide strong statements of intent declaring that only standards from their preferred fora would be acceptable and used in procurement.

Therefore, we need to take an extra step and encourage fora to close down or merge with those in the "chosen" areas. A successful example of this strategy can be seen in "Layer 2" standards. Here the MPLS Forum and the Frame Relay Forum have recently merged to form the MPLS and Frame Relay Alliance. Since a true Layer 2 forum covering all aspects would be of more use to the operators, the ATM Forum, some parts of the DSL Forum, and eventually the Metro Ethernet Forum should be encouraged to join this alliance as well. Considering the varied interests and possibly different IPR policies of the major stakeholders, getting this agreement will not be easy.

Use bodies such as ATIS to promote needed standards

A partial solution to this dilemma is to involve the vendors as well as the operators when choosing fora to work with. The ATIS (Alliance for Telecommunications Industry Solutions) is one example of where this could be successfully implemented givin its large membership of operators and vendors, including a TOPS (Technical Operations) Council of leading telecom operator Chief Technology Officers (CTOs). The ATIS has agreed on five priority standards areas:

- Wide area Ethernet
- Security
- Data interchange billing
- Mobile wireless services
- Voice over IP

Focus groups, which have been set up for each of these five areas, are defining the way forward from a business perspective, attempting to eliminate overlapping initiatives and fill gaps.

Unfortunately the fee for ATIS membership, as a US standards development organization, makes it prohibitively expensive for non-US based operators to join since they already have to pay similar membership fees to European standards bodies such as ETSI. In fact, ETSI can be considered to play a similar role in Europe, having as much or more influence in some areas (such as mobile systems), although lagging in other areas such as Wide Area Ethernet and OSS.

Creating service provider requirements fora

Bodies such as the MPLS and Frame Relay Alliance now place a high priority on operator requirements and have set up a Service Provider Requirements Forum. While time will tell how effective this will be, initially it seems to give the operators an efficient way to communicate their requirements to vendors.

A previous incarnation of these ideas was embodied in FSAN (Full Services Access Network). Set up by the telecom operators in 1997 to promote multi-vendor specifications for access networks, it has successfully steered the development of DSL standards in the access network. FSAN's most recent venture was FS-VDSL, which has now completed its work on VDSL and transferred to the ITU-T to become a Focus Group of SG16 (see below).

Promoting forum specifications to formal standards

Once a standard is established in a particular market, it makes sense to try to globalize it so that it is applicable to equipment anywhere in the world. Standards globalization reduces the costs for all operators (provided regulatory or cultural constraints don't mean they can't use it), because it enables them to buy equipment from any vendor. It also makes sense for vendors, as they can then potentially sell their equipment to all operators! In addition, specifications from fora are not generally recognised by regulators whereas formal standards are. It therefore makes sense to try to promote fora specifications in formal standards bodies, which are more open, neutral, transparent, and permanent. This is particularly necessary in the IT area where formal standardisation just does not work any more. Examples of successful processes include:

- European DVB agreement with ETSI
- Fast Track and PAS procedures in ISO/IEC JTC1
- Focus Group (A.7) procedure in ITU-T (which has led to the transfer of FS-VDSL to an SG16 Focus Group)

There are clear advantages of combining the working methods of the fora (better governance,

---

"However, an agreement is needed that allows formal standards bodies to take up consortium specifications in a more systematic and transparent way."

---

participation, speed, consensus between real actors, etc.) with the quality of the formal bodies (experience, public enquiry process, better ability to maintain, etc.).

However, an agreement is needed that allows

formal standards bodies to take up consortium specifications in a more systematic and transparent way. Setting up the previously mentioned "Association of ICT Standards Consortia," backed by formal and informal bodies, could help to achieve this.

Harnessing the IETF

We need to use the IETF for the things they are best at doing and conduct the rest of the systems and architecture work for the 21st Century Network elsewhere. The IETF has provided the basic protocol standards (e.g., SIP) that serve as building blocks for standards and architectures developed in other standards bodies such as 3GPP and ITU. The re-use of IETF standards allows equipment and services to be provided globally and, therefore, provides cost reductions. Departure from IETF standards should only occur when absolutely necessary, such as when developing enhanced security, QoS, service control, and fault management. The operators have clear needs in these areas that must be met if the network is to succeed. For example, operators need extensions to SIP to meet the needs of real-time and multimedia services in NGN. Our approach will be to work with other European operators (initially) and through ATIS to agree on joint requirements and ensure that these contributions are agreed upon in standards bodies such as 3GPP and ETSI TISPAN. We will then work with vendors in IETF to align these with existing protocols and prevent future divergences.

Encourage royalty free IPR policies

As described in the previous section, the market is moving inexorably towards RF—especially for IT, applications, and eBusiness areas—and simultaneously towards proprietary solutions to avoid the IPR morass. SMEs in particular seem to feel that if they buy from Microsoft or another large recognised systems supplier, they will be immune from IPR licensing claims.

Insisting on an RF IPR policy for all standards bodies may be counterproductive, as essential components of a standard may then be withheld by a significant license holder, potentially causing a roadblock to further development of that standard. In fact, insistence on RF policies could actually encourage the very thing that they are meant to prevent—lots of hidden IPR claims by companies who are not participating in the standards work! On the other hand, we must discourage companies from declaring IPR as "essential," especially since the rules make it easy for them to do so. Many times, the IPR turns out not to be essential after all. Declarations of non-essential IPR should be discouraged, and IPR declarations in standards bodies should be the exception rather than the rule. Therefore, the ideal IPR policy may be a mixture of RF and FRAND, which encourages RF but allows for exceptions. This is perhaps best expressed in the CEN and CENELEC IPR policy, which follows rules developed by ISO and IEC. These policies expect RF to be the norm, but adds: "If in exceptional cases, technical reasons justify the preparation of a European Standard in terms which include the use of a patented item, there is no objection in principle to such a step, even if the terms are such that there are no alternative means of compliance." It then goes on to specify standard FRAND terms.

Conclusion

The 21st Century Network will only be possible if the telecom operators can afford to build it, and to cap and eventually close down their expensive legacy service-dedicated networks. Standards must help us do this. We must ensure that standards are developed in the most efficient way to meet the needs of the operators. In this way, everyone wins— vendors, operators, and end users. Operators get the standards they need to build the networks along with an adequate return-on-investment, vendors sell lots of equipment, and customers get attractive services at a lower price. We must work together to make it happen.

Glossary

21CN   BT's 21st Century Network programme

3GPP   Third Generation Partnership Project (a consortium of five standards bodies including ETSI's creation of standards for Third Generation mobile networks)

ATIS — Alliance for Telecommunications Industry Solutions (a US-based organization committed to rapidly developing and promoting technical and operations standards for the ICT industry worldwide using a pragmatic, flexible, and open approach)

B2B — Business to Business

CEN — Conseil Européen pour la Normalisation

CENELEC — European Committee for Electrotechnical Standardization

Diffserv — Differentiated Services (an IETF protocol to support applications by differentiating classes of service for Internet traffic)

DSL — Digital Subscriber Line (basis of high-speed digital access over copper systems)

Design for All "… the design of products and environments to be usable by all people, to the greatest extent possible, without the need for adaption or specialized design." —from The ICT Standards Board Web site, http://www.ict.etsi.fr/activities_Design.htm

DVB — Digital Video Broadcasting

ESO — European Standards Organization

ETSI — European Telecommunications Standards Institute (home of the GSM standards and the TISPAN project)

FRAND — Fair, Reasonable and Non-Discriminatory (sometimes known as RAND)

FSAN — Full Service Access Network (consortium of operators drafting multi-vendor specifications for access networks)

FS-VDSL — Full Service very high speed Digital Subscriber Line

GMI2004 — Global MSF Interoperability demonstration

GSM — Global System for Mobile (basis of Second Generation mobile services throughout most of world)

HPNA — Home Phoneline Networking Alliance (working towards the adoption of a single, unified phone-line networking standard)

ICT — Information and Communications Technologies

ICTSB — ICT Standards Board (coordinates European standards development – the author is the chairman)

IEC — International Electrotechnical Commission

IEEE 802.11b — Higher Speed Physical Layer Extension in the 2.4 GHz band (the most commonly used Wi-Fi standard)

IETF — Internet Engineering Task Force (the originator of the IP protocol)

IP — Internet Protocol (the basis of all next generation voice and data networks)

IPR — Intellectual Property Rights (covering copyright, patents, and trademarks)

IPv6 — Version six of the Internet Protocol

ISO — International Organization for Standardization

ISOC — The Internet Society (parent body of IETF)

ITU — International Telecommunication Union (the originator of most globally recognised telecommunications standards)

LIF — Location Interoperability Forum

MPLS — Multi-Protocol Label Switching (IETF standard for providing connection-oriented IP services)

MSAN — Multi-Service Access Node

MSF — Multiservice Switching Forum

NGN — Next (or New) Generation Network (term used in ETSI and ITU)

OSS	Operational Support Systems (the components that a company uses to run its network and business)
PSTN	Public Switched Telephone Network (sometimes known as POTS); taken here to mean all existing circuit switched public networks including those based on ISDN and GSM
QoS	Quality of Service (defines the characteristics of a service, e.g., latency, error rate)
RF	Royalty Free (referring to IPR included in a standard)
SDO	Standards Development Organization (any organization that develops recognised standards)
SIP	Session Initiation Protocol (used to set up VoIP and multimedia calls over an IP-based network)
TMF	TeleManagement Forum (the origin of many new OSS standards/ concepts)
VDSL	Very high speed Digital Subscriber Line (basis of providing >1 Mbit/s services to customers)
VoIP	Voice over IP (a method of transporting speech over the Internet)
WAP	Wireless Access Protocol
Wi-Fi	Wireless Fidelity: a set of standards based on IEEE 802.11 for wireless local area access

Notes

[1] RFC 2026 "The Internet Standards Process," Revision 3, October 1996.

[2] "The IETF Mission and Social Contract," IESG proposed statement on the IETF mission, October 2003.

[3] ITU-T Informal Forums Summit (IFS), San Francisco, July 24-25 2003.

37

Standards in Search Engine Advertising Information Exchange and Arbitrage

GARY KREMEN

Grant Media, LLC

Abstract: *On the surface, everyone is for standards in the same way they are for motherhood and apple pie. Investigate deeper, however, and examine what we know as the "ground truth."[1] We find that motherhood has its costs (ask any mother of a two year old) as does apple pie (just look at the amount of "bad" cholesterol that someone who eats too much apple pie has). The same holds true for standards, whether they are set by formal committees or informal rules, majority market power leaders, or ad hoc methods. By examining how standards are implemented "on the ground," one can get a sense of their costs and benefits in a given marketplace. A real world example is the increasing exchange of advertising related information between PPC (pay per click) advertisements and search engines' advertising results. Our Company, Grant Media, LLC, operates one of the top 10 international focused search engines on the Internet:* http://www.Sex.Com *("Sex.Com"), while simultaneously operating one of the biggest wholesale non-adult search engines on the Internet:* http://www.GalaxySearch.Com *("GalaxySearch"). Combined, they perform over 25 million searches per day, growing at the rate of three percent per month, and are directly or indirectly connected to almost every major search engine in the world.*

What Is the Domain and Scope of Our Analysis?

The nomenclature surrounding search engines is confusing to both the "newbie" and veteran web surfer alike. This is surprising since almost every Internet surfer uses search engines (or an application driven by search engines) many times per day. Search engines and their respective products and services drive the majority of Internet commerce. Without them, the Internet—good, bad, or ugly—would be a different animal than it is currently. In fact, some informal definitions (which are a form of standards) are needed before we can look at the presence of formal standards, informal rules, market power standards, as well as a prevalence of ad hoc standards used in search engine advertising information exchange and arbitrage. The scope of our analysis could be quite extensive, but we are limiting it to certain stakeholders such as surfers ("consumers"), advertisers, affiliates, partners, traffic exchanges, and the like.

Definitions

Search engines. Search engines, such as http://www.Google.Com ("Google"), http://www.

AltaVista.Com ("AltaVista"),[2] and http://www.AllTheWeb.Com ("AllTheWeb") produce free results from search phrase queries that are displayed prominently for the surfer, usually in the middle of the results page. Most of the time these free results are preceded by, surrounded by, intermixed with, or even followed by paid text results or banner advertisements. These paid results are likely using either CPA (cost per action), CPM (cost per thousand), or PPC (pay per click) financial models (discussed later in this chapter). Advertisers, not surfers, pay for the "paid" results. Thus search engines are "free."

The paid search results, from our biased observation point, tend to be as relevant, if not more relevant, than the free search results. This is because most partners (which is a term of art to be defined later), who have advertisers as their clients (other CPM branding campaigns), are directly accountable for their results. For example, if a surfer types in the search phrase "New York City Dating," advertisers who bid on "New York City Dating," "New York Dating," "Dating," or even "Relationships" will have their free listings appear with paid search results. In many so-called search engines, only paid results are returned. They are not true search engines under the strictest standard definition because they feature only paid results. The order in which paid advertiser results appear depends on the advertiser's bidding price. Thus the highest priced listing will appear first.[3] Of course, the advertiser will only pay if the surfer actually clicks on the listing (the title or sometimes the description).

Search engine results are generated by parsing the Internet and showing the most "relevant"[4] results associated with the search phrase query. All listings are frequently displayed in the format of a one-line title and a two-three line summary describing the information associated with the search phrase.

Occasionally the actual URL as well as the price per click associated with the paid adver-

tisement is displayed. From a business perspective, the organization that only displays the *free* search engine results—as opposed to paid search engine results—will not remain in business long. The process of continuously parsing the Internet and, in turn, storing, indexing, and displaying information is too expensive to perform for free.

Results. Results are what *may* be returned from a search phrase query.[5] The information displayed might be based on a free search engine model or paid results. In the standard model, the listings that generate the most profit for the web site are displayed first.[6] If there are free listings, they might appear in other loca-

---

"...paid search results are passed through an intricate web of affiliates, partners, and exchanges before reaching the surfer."

---

tions on the pages that have the paid listings. What is interesting and often surprising to both the "newbie" and veteran web surfer is that paid search results are passed through an intricate web of affiliates, partners, and exchanges before reaching the surfer. The paid search results go to affiliates of search engines (the place where the surfer typed the query), to partners of the affiliate search engine (those sites with paid listings), and back and forth in a transparent and instantaneous manner. The instantaneous element is important as the surfer experience is critical. The longer the surfer waits for search phrase results, the worse the experience. This back and forth is all performed while advertisers change their bids on search phrases in real time. The surfer must click on the title (or sometimes the description) for an advertiser's actual money to be spent (other than in a CPM relationship). In the exchange of paid results, there are opportunities to make arbitrage profits for those who understand all the details of the system, including the affiliates, exchanges, partners, and advertisers.

DBLP: Sherrie Bolin

Sherrie Bolin. List of publications from the DBLP Bibliography Server - FAQ ... 1998.
1, EE, **Sherrie Bolin**: E-commerce: a market analysis and prognostication. ...
www.informatik.uni-trier.de/~ley/db/indices/a-tree/b/Bolin:Sherrie.html - 3k - <u>Cached</u> - <u>Similar pages</u>

ACM StandardView, Volume 6
... Carl Cargill: Editorial. 95-96 Electronic Edition (DOI: 10.1145/324042.324043);
Sherrie Bolin: E-commerce: a market analysis and prognostication. ...
www.informatik.uni-trier.de/~ley/db/journals/standardview/standardview6.html - 14k -
<u>Cached</u> - <u>Similar pages</u>

[PDF] <u>The Nature and Future of ICTStandardization Executive Summary</u>
File Format: PDF/Adobe Acrobat - <u>View as HTML</u>
The Nature and Future of ICT Standardization Executive Summary By **Sherrie Bolin**
ast December, government leaders such as Phillip Bond, US Undersecretary of ...
www.sun.com/software/standards/ICT_Executive_Summary.pdf - <u>Similar pages</u>

[PDF] <u>If you clicked on this link, or read the first line of this ...</u>
File Format: PDF/Adobe Acrobat - <u>View as HTML</u>
... all around the globe." —Phil Bond, Undersecretary of Commerce for Technology
The Nature and Future of ICT Standardization By **Sherrie Bolin** If you clicked on ...
www.sun.com/software/standards/natureandfuture_ICT.pdf - <u>Similar pages</u>

Table 1: Typical results of a free search engine – Google search for "Sherrie Bolin"[7]

Title. The title is a URL, which is the shortest summary of the underlying information generated by the search phrase results. In a completely free search engine, the title is automatically generated in an attempt to best summarize the underlying information. In a PPC search engine, the advertiser writes the title. This (and occasionally the description area) is where the surfer clicks to be taken from the search engine site, through the PPC engine that debits the advertiser's account, to the advertiser, and finally to the actual information. The Title URLs are encoded for use by the PPC engine, which is by convention at the partner's or exchange's site.

http://jump.sex.com/r.cgi?84n83n84n90n91n97n99n97n95n95n561n81n552n559n81n42n
500n552n503n551n49n504n555n553n509n505n559n93n83n81n83n92n93n84n83n98n99
n92n95n90n96n90n84n93n84n97n99n81n90n90n81n90n83n81n98n97n89n84n83n84n9
0n91n97n99n97n95n95n89n84n83n98n99n92n90n91n91n90n84n93n84n97n99n81n90n9
0n81n90n83n81n98n97n93n504n42n509n550n559n509n551n505n

Table 2: Typical title URL that is encoded to prevent fraud, hide advertiser information, etc.

Description: The description is an expanded summary of the results a search engine finds. It is broader than the title. In a PPC search engine, the advertisers write the description. Both the description and title are important as they motivate the surfer to click on a title or occasionally the description. One reason why conversions are higher in text listings than in banners is because they must be read, understood, and then clicked on. [8]

CPA: Cost Per Action. CPA is derived from the number of surfer clicks on a search phrase result (the title or occasionally the description), a banner listing, or other forms of rich media. In this model, advertisers only pay for the surfers who click on their text listing or banner and then sign up, fill out a form, or purchase something on their web site (the action in CPA). This type of advertising has the highest rewards from the advertiser's perspective and the worst accountability from the media owner's perspective. The big risk for the media owner is whether or not they can trust the advertiser. Advertisers may "shave" results or may not tell the truth about the success of an advertising campaign. However, given the "use it or lose it" nature of a search results pages, CPA listings are usually placed at the bottom of the paid listings as a filler. Those that advertise in a CPA traffic manner usually track the conversion statistics very closely and are the most sophisticated of the advertisers; therefore, CPA advertisers are the most accountable of all models of advertising.

CPM: Cost Per Thousand impressions. CPM is derived from old school media advertising based on impressions, not clicks. It does not take advantage of the traceability of Internet commerce, but clearly offers solid branding benefits. This early model is seen when old-line media firms value branding more than any other metric. In a CPM relationship, the more an advertisement is shown (in thousands), the more the advertiser pays. While this method has been somewhat depreciated, it has not fully gone away. For example, GalaxySearch conducts CPM campaigns once every two months or so.

Sponsorships: A form of CPM that does not take into account the number of surfer impressions.

PPC: Pay Per Click. PPC (sometimes known as CPC) search engine advertising is now the most dominant model in the online industry. Advertisers bid on their position; the one who pays the most has the top result. This model is

---

"Pay Per Click...search engine advertising is now the most dominant model in the online industry."

---

used by all the major search engines and is the primary focus of this paper. Advertisers select search phrases, titles, descriptions, and prices per click that they are willing to pay if a surfer clicks on their advertisement. The advertisements are shown after the search phrase query is typed into the search engine or search box. Note the prices showing—a clear sign of a PPC advertisement.

Paid or sponsored advertising: This is another phrase for advertising that is paid for.

Search directories: A page comprised of search phrases, usually with high PPC results.

Affiliate: An affiliate in the search engine world is a site that sources surfers and their corresponding search queries (or traffic). For example, let's say a surfer on an affiliate site types in the search phrase "mortgages." The affiliate site does a query of its own advertisers first (if it has any). Then it does another query, usually in the form of a real-time XML query,[9] to inquire if its partner sites[10] have relevant paid results (including the prices partner sites are willing to pay, titles, descriptions, URLs, etc.) to return to the affiliate site. Sometimes a site is an affiliate and sometimes it is a partner, depending on where the surfers enter their search query. The affiliate site might query more than one partner site. In any case, the affiliate site takes all the partner site listings and their own listings and sorts the

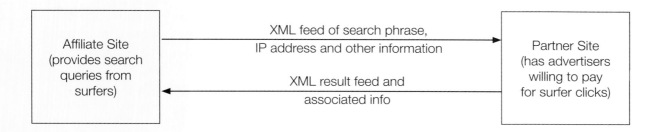

Table 3: Typical relationship between affiliates and partner

results. They are sorted by how much money each result, if clicked on by the surfer, generates for the affiliate site (instead of sorting the results by traditional relevance). A main site uses affiliates as a way to receive more search queries or "traffic" than is actually typed into that site. In the search nomenclature, affiliates provide main sites with more search traffic.

Partners: Partners are sources of paid advertisers. While many search engines have their own paid advertising listings generated by a sales force, advertising agencies, or account managers, they are typically in the business of providing their paid listings to other search engines. In this context, they are partner sites. Again, they can also be affiliate sites depending on where the surfer enters the search query. The underlying XML calls can work both ways. At first approximation (which will change in the next definition of exchanges), in two almost simultaneous queries, a site can first be a partner and then an affiliate.

Exchanges: Exchanges are entities that may sit

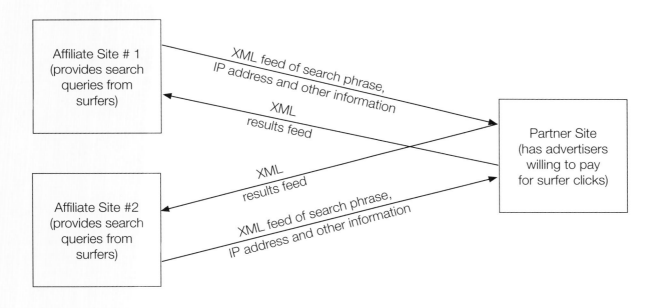

Table 4: Typical partner arrangement with multiple affiliate traffic sources

between affiliates and partners or may be mostly partners or mostly affiliates but talk to each other. Usually a search phrase query is entered at a search site, a search box, or is just displayed based upon a set search phrase query. Then results are generated by querying the site's internal advertising base or its partners' advertisers. The partners, however, also query their partners in the same way that the original search may have come from an affiliate and not the search site itself. Exchanges are like NASDAQ market makers. The entered phrase is considered an affiliate to the exchange. Like most markets, the affiliate will check its own inventory of paid search results first. Then it will go to at least one exchange and see what results and associated prices they have. Those results and prices are determined by the exchange checking its own inventory of advertisers and then querying partner sites that might also have advertisers using XML.

For example, if a surfer types in "Surfing in San Diego" at http://www.Kanoodle.Com, Kanoodle might only have three listings starting at $0.06 and going to $0.04. In this case,

Kanoodle will likely query its partners with this search term. GalaxySearch is one of these partners. Let's say GalaxySearch only has two of its own paid listings for "Surfing in San Diego"— one at $0.20 and another at $0.06. Assuming a 60% revenue share arrangement with Kanoodle, Kanoodle would list the GalaxySearch listing at $0.12 (60% * $0.20) return first, then its owns listing at $0.06, then the next listing at $0.06 ($0.06) in the third position, and finally a GalaxySearch listing at $0.036 (60% * $0.06). As part of GalaxySearch's list finding process, it might also query its own set of proprietary partners (other than Kanoodle to prevent loops) looking for "Surfing in San Diego." If paid listings are found and a "time out" has not occurred, the listings from GalaxySearch's partners will be sent to GalaxySearch at the revenue share arrangement between GalaxySearch and its partners. Then those results from the partner and GalaxySearch's own results are sent to Kanoodle. At this point, Kanoodle sorts all the results by the net revenue it makes and displays the results accordingly.

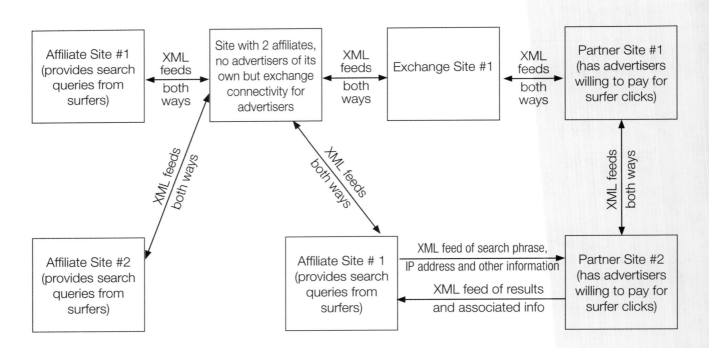

Table 5: Typical arrangement showing complex relationships between players

XML:[11] Extensible Markup Language (XML) is a simple, very flexible text format derived from SGML (ISO 8879). Originally designed to meet the challenges of large-scale electronic publishing, XML is also playing an increasingly important role in the exchange of a wide variety of data on the Web and elsewhere.

Traffic: Another term for surfers or potential customers that might click upon an advertisement.

ROI: Return on Investment. The amount of funds you receive back for a given investment of funds.

What surfers want and the role of standards for the surfers

We have spent some time defining terms in the search engine world. That allows us to get back to the most important item—what do surfers desire? When I started and grew http://www.Match.Com, now the world's largest dating service, I realized that our target customers were not who I expected: amorous men. The true customer's were women between 30 – 45 years-old who desired a long-term committed relationship. If I were able to acquire those customers, the ancillary customers (the other 50%, men) would follow in a disproportionate amount (more than one man for each woman). Thus customer definition is critical for success. In the search engine world, there are several

customers: the search engine value chain (affiliates, partners, exchanges, advertisers) and the surfers. Clearly, the search engines desire financial return, but what do surfers desire? Relevant results speed and results displayed in a format that is compatible with their browser seem to be priorities. Standards either currently or have the potential to deliver on these priorities, as discussed below.

Relevancy of results. In the early days of paid results, consumer advocates worried that surfers would not understand that the position of the search phrase results was not directly linked to relevancy. These consumer advocates pressured search engines to demarcate paid results from free results by using text headers that are clearly visible to surfers such as "sponsored listing" or "paid listings." This demarcation has slowly gone away because either search engines are 100% PPC, clearly demarcating the difference between paid and unpaid results, or they are ignoring the issue. As indicated before, it is not clear if the surfers underlying needs are better met by free search, paid search, or an integration of both.

Speed of results: There are ways to make pages load faster or at least make them appear to be loading faster, including HTML validation, removal of comments, caching networks, and gzip

---

Searched for "Search Engines" (US) ... Found 5,432,303 results.

1. **Submit to 500,00 Search Engines**
   Guaranteed listings and high ranking on the top ten search engines.
   (Cost to advertiser: $ 0.07)

2. **Guaranteed High Rankings on Top Search Engines**
   Obtain a first page listing on the top three search engines.
   (Cost to advertiser: $ 0.06)

3. **Search Engines—Let Us do the Work**
   Getting top placement takes time, knowledge, and skill. Let us do the work!
   (Cost to advertiser: $ 0.06)

Table 6: Typical paid search results noting prices per click

Top 6 of 5897 Total User Agents			
#	Hits and Full Browser Name		Abbreviations for Browser
1	53.54%	Microsoft Internet Explorer 6.0+	MSIE 6
2	34.56%	Microsoft Internet Explorer 5.0+	MSIE 5
3	2.11%	Netscape-based browsers (older)	Mozilla/4
4	1.72%	Browser associated with UNIX	PHP/4.2.2
5	1.69%	Netscape-based browsers (older)	Mozilla/5
6	1.54%	Microsoft Internet Explorer 4.0+	MSIE 4

Table 7: Microsoft Internet Explorer dominates the browser market—a market-based standard

compression.[12] Unfortunately there are no standards for page loading speeds—a critical area of focus for future standards development.

Results display correctly for their browser:
While the vast majority of surfers use Microsoft Internet Explorer 6.0 with the latest updates, there are others that do not use this browser.

There are so many standards that help the surfer, that one does not know where to start. Here are three representative standards:

- **W3C®:**[13] W3C's standards are some of the most valuable yet neglected standards on the entire Internet. W3C, or the World Wide Web Consortium, is an invaluable source of information. For lack of space and time, we are only going to focus on one segment of its vast collection of standards, policies, guidelines, and recommendations. This one segment, HTML validation, is the process of validating HTML code against the actual standards for HTML. The benefit of being 100% HTML compliant is that a site will appear to run much faster than W3C compliant browsers, which make up many of the browsers in the market place today. W3C compliant pages will also appear faster if they are 100% HTML compliant, because HTML validated pages allow browsers to layout text, images, and other objects simultaneously, rather than waiting

for the entire page to be sent. Additionally, you are almost guaranteed that your pages will display in future browsers.

- **P3P:**[14] Platform for Privacy Preferences is a standard that informs the surfer about a given page and site's privacy policies. For example, it will tell the surfer what the site does with cookies and if it has an arbitration policy. Surfers benefit because adherence to the privacy policies is built into many browsers, including Microsoft IE 6.0. In fact, the surfer can change their preferences for privacy and pages/sites. If there are inconsistencies between pages/sites and the surfer's privacy settings, the surfer will be visually warned.

- **TrustE®:**[15] TrustE is an organization that provides site auditing, establishes dispute resolution practices, and creates privacy policies for advertisers for a fee. In fact, the agreement is a legally binding document. Sites that belong to TrustE display TrustE's logo on their front page. By clicking on their logo, the surfer can verify that the site is actually TrustE compliant and not a counterfeit.

What affiliates want and the role of standards for the affiliates

Affiliates are businesses that make money with traffic (i.e., surfers that type in search phrases). The surfers might be on the affiliate site for a variety of reasons: the site is a portal to pertinent information or is even a joke-of-the-day site. Affiliate sites come in different shapes and sizes; many use the common toolbar add-on, such as the Google toolbar that helps affiliates generate traffic for Google as a partner site.

The standard affiliate site collects surfer traffic and sends the search phrase query, among other things, by XML to partner's sites that have advertising. Affiliates may use their own advertising listings (then they are also partners) or send an XML query to as many as 20 sites. A typical affiliate XML query to Sex.Com from GalaxySearch might look like this:

Sites with advertisers (partner sites) perform many checks to be sure that the traffic going to their advertisers are valid. Many times certain traffic is described under the catch all category of fraud. It is hard to believe, but fraud is a continuum in the industry. It is therefore important to clean search listings by hand checking (as we do at Sex.Com) for accuracy and legality.

Affiliates clearly want the highest prices for their traffic. At the same time, they have the same priorities as surfers: a) relevancy of results; b) speed of results; and c) results displayed correctly in their browser, among others. Because of all the internal links between search engines, it is

http://xml.sex.com/xml.php?Terms=viagra&strict=1&Hits_Per_Page=10&
IP=209.81.7.23&affiliate=www.galaxysearch.com

Table 8: Typical XML query with search term, IPaddress, and affiliate codings

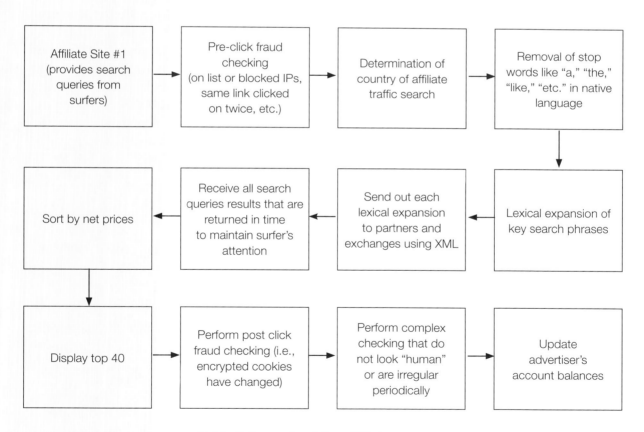

Table 9: Example of the affiliate program

Search Phase Term	Sex.Com Prices for Search Term	ABCSearch.Com ("ABCSearch.Com") Prices	Findology.Com ("Findology.Com") Prices for Search Term
Poker	$0.04	$0.04	$0.18

Table 10: Actual example of how prices vary across search feeds (for a given time)

possible for the same listing to appear more than once. Advertisers do place ads in more than one partner search engine to obtain the best price to performance ratio (measured as "the conversion ratio"). While these ads might have small variations within them, the affiliates (and surfers) want duplicate results or near duplicate results to be removed.

Many of the issues that affect affiliates also impact other stakeholders. These issues will be discussed below, when logical, and in other places if appropriate.

Gross prices vs. net prices

Affiliate or partner advertising prices, passed by XML, can either be the *net* of revenue share percentage or the *gross* of revenue share percentage. This variety makes initial setup more complex than it needs to be and raises an unnecessary barrier to entry. Because some partners prefer the net and others the gross of revenue share percentage in their XML, the process of adding another partner, exchange, or affiliate becomes excruciating painful in terms of time and communication. Thus some relationships are net-based and some are gross-based, which becomes very confusing to the implementer and the accounting department. Although standardizing prices so that they are all based on either the net or the gross of revenue share percentage should be an easy process, it unfortunately has not been done.

Fraud

Whether a click is a robot or a real human searcher has been touched upon lightly already. We are going to defer discussion of the lack of standards involved in this important issue until later.

Making money under tight margins

When you are a partner, by definition "you own the advertiser," which means that you have an account management relationship with them and earn at least a large part (40% minimum) of the revenue share. This account management relationship is quite powerful and is the most loyal part of the entire value chain in search engine advertising. Advertisers do not want to be "ripped off" and they (and their agencies, if they have them) experiment with other partners. However, once they are happy with a particular partner, there is a natural inertia to stay with the partner that they receive their traffic from. Affiliates and exchanges want as much of the remaining revenue share as possible. This is why per click accounting, fraud accounting, and other accounting standards are important. Industry-wide standards other than the partner's statistics are usually, but not always, considered the statistics (other than fraud) to work from.

What the exchange wants and the role of standards for the exchange

Reconciliation

It is critical for an exchange to understand why a counterparty did not receive a payment for a given click and recognize if a click is real or

---

"The lack of standards hurts the money-making potential of all parties, especially exchanges where margins are thinner."

---

fraudulent. Reconciliation should be done on a daily, if not weekly, basis. This is another area in which affiliates, exchanges, and partners desire standards but none have been agreed upon. The lack of standards hurts the money-making potential of all parties, especially exchanges where margins are thinner. A good standard would enable every click to have a unique, encrypted ID so that affiliates, sites, exchanges, partners, and advertisers could reconcile the clicks exactly. There is a growing industry in third-party PPC advertising tracking software that might lead to industry standards in this area.

Counterparty risks

Typically at the end of the month, the partner or exchange site owes the affiliate site money for the traffic or search queries that were clicked on. As we have discussed previously, many times an affiliate has listings and the surfer's search query comes from the partner. As with the global swaps market, payments should be netted out between affiliates, exchanges, and partners on a daily basis. Unfortunately, the norm now is to make payments 30-45 days after the end of the month. This has resulted in several cases in which parties did not receive payment from "bad actors." Obviously, there is an urgent need for standards listing "bad" actions as discussed below.

Fraud

Whether a click is a robot or a real human searcher has been touched upon lightly already. We are going to defer discussion of the lack of standards involved in this important issue until later.

24/7 operations

While there are multiple exchanges and direct connections between many affiliates and partners, an exchange needs to be especially vigilant with respect to its operations. If an exchange is thought of as multiple XML feeds that operate in both directions and prices change rapidly throughout the entire network, the exchange goes online and offline. This fluctuation in prices does not serve the partners main customer, the advertiser. Uptime (defined as the time the relevant system is actually up and running for use by its partners and affiliates) standards need to be set by: a) advertisers, and met by their part-

ners; b) partners and met by their exchanges (if any); c) by exchanges and met by their sites; and d) sites and met by the affiliates.

What partners want and the role of standards for partners

High quality traffic

Unlike affiliates and exchanges, partners live and die by the ROI generated by their advertisers.[16] So when the quality of traffic decreases (judged by the quality of surfers who sign up, fill out a form, or purchase something on a web site) due to fraud, advertisers are hurt. Thus the development of traffic standards is in their partner's best interest—unfortunately, no such standards exist today. Emerging standards include "good traffic"/"fraud traffic" ratios (hard to define because there is no definition in the fraud world) and "tagging" of every click so that the entire value chain knows which partners, exchanges, sites, and affiliates convert the best.

Other

Like exchange and affiliates, partners place a priority on 24/7 operations, fraud, counterparty risks, reconciliation, making money under tight margins, gross versus net prices, etc.

Standards that work across all players

Passing of IP address in XML strings

In the beginning, XML requests only consisted of the search phrase that was being searched for. Quickly, to be able to spot real-time click

---

"For international traffic, it is usually only sophisticated partners who agree and have internal systems to determine which country's traffic, based on ISO standards, are acceptable for a given advertiser."

---

fraud, the IP address of the surfer was added to the XML string. This enabled detection of certain kinds of fraud in real time (a robot does not change its IP engine). Of course, this is not the complete solution because post-click fraud is still needed.

Standards that partially work across all players

Internationalization

We have already discussed fraud as being a continuum. For international traffic, it is usually only sophisticated partners who agree and have internal systems to determine which country's traffic, based on ISO standards, [17] are acceptable for a given advertiser. Thus there is a standard, but only a few partners have the sophistication to implement it.

Standards that do not work or seem never to be standardized

Fraud and fraud codes

We have mentioned the role of fraud before. It strongly affects every segment of the industry other than the surfer. Advertisers do not want to pay for traffic that does not convert. Partners do not want advertisers who complain about low conversion rates. Affiliates want to get paid for the traffic, which they will not receive if the partner determines the click is a "fraudulent" click. The exchanges get caught in the middle between partners and affiliates and end up giving some of the already slim arbitrage profits away to each group.

Below is an abbreviated list of some common fraud events. Even though they look simple, partners, affiliates, exchanges, and advertisers do not agree upon what does and does not constitute "fraud." Their definitions are different, parameters associated with the definitions are different, and the actions to perform when "fraud" conditions happen are not standardized.

There are probably over 100 possible situations that could be defined as fraud. Surprisingly, there are no common definitions of fraud even in situations that look cut and dry. A good example is a double click— a surfer clicking on the same link twice or more. Is it fraud? More likely the affiliates, exchange, partner, or advertiser was too slow in responding to the surfer's query. Is it then fair to say that two clicks on a link in one second is likely the result of an impatient human, while 100 clicks on the same link is nonhuman behavior and clearly fraud? Should the advertisers (or partner or exchange) be charged for the second click? Should it be charged for click 3-100? Unfortunately, along with the lack of standards that define fraud, there are no standards for response time.

It should be noted that fraud in this context

Table 11: Some examples of potential "frauds"

Potential frauds	What is going on?
Surfer clicks on same link twice, as links have encrypted time stamps	Sign of someone or something (robot) trying to deplete funds in someone else's account. Or it just might be a slow link. Advertiser is not charged for second click.
Clicks happen proportionately to only the most expensive words	Clearly the sign of someone (or something – robot) trying to make money. Local advertiser is not charged for second click.
Different IP address between search and click and cookies not accepted or are changed.	Several large ISPs surprisingly change their surfers' IP address mid-session. However, the cookies do not change. If the cookies are not accepted or changed, it is the sign of a robot.
Time between search and click is too rapid for a human.	Clearly the sign of someone (or something—robot) trying to make money. Local advertiser is not charged for second click.

does not necessarily imply a malevolent act; it might simply be a situation that reduces advertiser conversion. For example, sending a partner site traffic from Canada when they requested only US traffic is probably just a mistake and not a malevolent act. Sending a partner site traffic from a US proxy that has a Canadian surfer (such as what happens from time-to-time with America Online) is another one of those indeterminate conditions—there is no right or wrong answer. The current ad hoc standard uses the partner's numbers for the number of clicks, prices, and thus payments unless the differences are financially material. In that case, an average "good" click number is used. If there was a standards setting body, the situations that constitute fraud could be more clearly defined and reconciliations between advertisers, partners, exchanges, and affiliates could be improved.

On the surface, it seems there is a common interest among all parties—advertisers, partners, exchanges, and affiliates—in standardizing fraud definitions. Surprisingly, this is not the case. The pat reason is because there are always companies that benefit by deviating from the standard, as customers (which in the search engine world could be advertisers, partners, exchanges, sites, and their affiliates) might have needs that differ from the actual standard.

Byte language

Many people on the Internet are able to use English, whose alphabet uses single byte characters. Non-English speaking computer surfers often use non-English computer characters such as two-byte characters. Affiliates, exchanges, partners, and advertisers could operate in non-English characters to a varying degree. At Sex. Com, we use two-byte characters if the surfer comes to the site directly. But we cannot force our affiliate partners to do so even in easy-to-accommodate languages like German and Spanish. Obviously, this problem would best be resolved through standards.

Gross prices vs. net prices

This problem, discussed previously, presents a large problem for all stakeholders.

Counterparty risks

Typically at the end of the month, the partner or exchange site owes the affiliate site money for the traffic or search queries that were clicked on. As we have discussed previously, many times an affiliate has listings and the surfer's search query comes from the partner.

Fractional amount

There are not any standards for rounding prices, as exemplified in the following common case: A partner has a listing at $0.06. The partner gives its affiliates 60% revenue share. Thus the partner will get $0.024 and the affiliate $0.036 for the $0.06 advertisement. Affiliates, exchanges, partners, and advertisers do all sorts of actions such as retaining the actual numbers, rounding up or down at random, round in a way that is favorable to them, truncating, etc. No wonder the industry has standards issues!

"Bad actors"

There are several types of bad actors: a) there are those affiliates, partners, and exchanges that do not pay on time, if ever; and b) there are those with reputations for not being honest or fair in reconciling which clicks were pre-clicks, post-clicks, and post-processing fraudulent traffic. There are many affiliates with a large percent of fraudulent traffic. It is easy to sign up as an affiliate (of course, partner sites say they perform due diligence on potential affiliates) and write programs that will send traffic to mimic human traffic. It is not surprising that this happens, especially the practice of blending in human traffic to make the nonhuman traffic more obscure. While we discussed the non-standardization fraud codes and the benefits that would accrue with their standardization, we have not discussed what to do with those parties who continually have higher than normal fraud amounts. A list of bad actors as a standard may be needed.

The biggest challenge of working with traffic containing higher than normal fraud is that the advertisers (unless they are CPM based) will get less conversions than normal. Consequently, they will drop their bid prices, use another search engine, or refrain from advertising.

Why there is not a "do not fly" list

The easiest solution would be to create a list of bad affiliates that includes their names, IP addresses, ISP, and other characteristics. This would be similar to a "do not fly" list for the industry. Again, the misconception of motherhood and apple pie enters. One could logically ask who would be against keeping a list of bad merchants, just like Visa® and MasterCard® do? **Standards can sometimes be viewed as a competitive disadvantage.** Similar to the airline industry that did not share their "do not fly" list unless pressured from the Federal Government, people view their list of "bad apples" as propriety information and do not want to share it with competitors or worry about legal issues involved in blacklisting.

Open Issues and How to Improve Things

Standards are created, distributed, and updated in many ways. In our market, market forces that are profit-linked are the strongest drivers behind changes in standards. The paid search engine advertising market is in a rapid consolidation period. For example, Overture purchased AltaVista, which, in turn, was purchased by Yahoo. Espotting (http://www.espotting.com) was purchased by Findwhat (http://www.findwhat.com), and Google purchased Sprinks (http://www.sprinks.com). The consolidation by competitive tier one players like Overture, Yahoo, and Google modifies the behavior of tier two players, such as the Find-What / Espotting transaction. At the same time,

Kanoodle is growing by raising venture capital as "Mamma" (http://www.Mamma.com) and is now owned by Intasys Corporation, a public company that is even changing its corporate name to Mamma.com to demonstrate its focus on the search engine market. Microsoft has announced it will conduct its own PPC offering.

It is currently unknown what effect this consolidation process will have on the search engine advertising information exchange and arbitrage. As direct competitors purchase parties who once worked together, it will take some time for the exchange arrangements to be examined. In fact, exchanges might grow if, for example, Yahoo decides it does not want to work directly with Google but will do so through an exchange. This use of an exchange as an intermediary (again

---

"It is possible that with this new consolidated search engine interconnection era, corporate policies and politics will prove a more important factor than cooperation and, strangely enough, profit maximization (achieved when everyone interconnects in all ways possible)."

---

like a NASDAQ market maker) may not immediately be visible to new management, but new management is faster to get rid of complex win-win relationships that do not have transparent benefits. As industries consolidate, they do get bigger. But after a while, growth plateaus as

Tier 1	Tier 2	Tier 3
Yahoo/Overture	Dogpile	GalaxySearch
Google	Mamma	Search123
FindWhat/Espotting	Sex.Com	Findology

Table 12: Examples of search engine tiering (levels of importance)

consolidation becomes more challenging due to: a) general inertia; b) worries about antitrust and collusion charges; c) a belief that their solution is better than all other parties; and d) concerns for creating standards that hurt themselves. It is possible that with this new consolidated search engine interconnection era, corporate policies and politics will prove a more important factor than cooperation and, strangely enough, profit maximization (achieved when everyone interconnects in all ways possible).

Conclusion and Summary

Standardization in the search engine advertising information exchange and arbitrage market is a good, though esoteric, example of formal written standards, informally exchanged standards, market share majority standards, as well as a proponderance of ad hoc standards. There are no direct standard bodies, but some of the stakeholder participants follow, to varying degrees, the activities of standards organizations in their field. Some standards started out as bilateral arrangements between parties that grew as more entities desired to interconnect with each other. However, unlike the Bell System with old Bellcore[18] unilaterial standards,

forces in this market change day-to-day and are the true drivers behind setting search engine information and arbitrage standards. Given that not everyone desires to link with everyone else (both directly and indirectly), that some market participants have more power than others, and other participants engage in questionable practices (from a partner perspective), standards have also become fragmented. Our belief is that, in today's market, standards evolve not when they make sense in an academic formula but when there are win-win chracteristics to them and they make sense as profit maximization tools for stakeholders.

Copyright © Gary Kremen

Special thanks and shout out to:

Cokos, John, http://www.IWebSoftware.com, creators of the Hyperseek software, the best off the shelf PPC software in existence.

Klopf, Steven, COO Grant Media, LLC. Making it work while I get time to think

Tay, Marvin, CTO Grant Media, LLC. Making it work through real world implementation

---

Notes

[1] The dictionary definition of "ground truth" is data taken from the actual area being studied. Ground truth is a term first used in geology and now in politics. It is usually the opposite of what an academic thinks. In this context, the reference is to what is actually happening with search engines, directories, affiliates, partners and surfers on the Internet now.

[2] Now owned by Overture, which in turn is now being purchased by Yahoo.

[3] Not everyone supports that algorithm. For example, Google also takes into consideration which advertisements get clicked on the most in addition to who pays the most. It is said that this is to get around a patent that Overture owns. Some say Overture maximizes short-term profit by their algorithm and Google maximizes long-term profit by their algorithm.

[4] Of course, one person's opinion of relevant results is not another person's opinion of relevant results. This is a problem that is currently unsolvable.

[5] Not always true. Sex.Com and GalaxySearch sell on a very, very limited CPA basis when there are no search results for some rarely encountered countries.

[6] See endnote 3.

[7] When I was invited to contribute an article, I conducted a search on the book's editor to determine her qualifications. I chose to display these (partial) results as an example of a typical search that an Internet user might conduct.

[8] "Conversion" by informal standards is defined as the percentage of clicks that actually sign up, fill out a form, or purchase something on an advertiser's web site.

[9] Extensible Markup Language is a kind of sophisticated comma separate file schema.

[10] Partner Sites: Other sites with advertising that serve search engines with advertising and may be search engines themselves.

[11] http://www.w3.org/XML/

[12] Gzip compression: A GNU compression utility, which reduces the size of a file.

[13] http://validator.w3.org/

[14] http://www.w3.org/P3P/

[15] http://www.truste.org/

[16] By "live and die," if an advertiser is using a partner, or an advertising agency is using a partner for the advertisers, and if the traffic does not convert, they could "die" and lose that account."

[17] http://www.iso.org/iso/en/prods-services/iso3166ma/02iso-3166-code-lists/index.html

[18] http://telephonyonline.com/ar/telecom_bellcore/index.htm

Bibliography

Kremen, Gary, et. El. Patent #5706434, Integrated request-response system and method generating responses to request objects formatted according to various communication protocols. The underlying concepts were invented on or before April 12, 1994.

Kremen, Gary, "20 Outstanding Adult Business Practices," Ynotmasters.Com, http://ynot-news.ynotmasters.com/issues/091103/page3.html (YNOT Network, LP San Diego, California, September 11, 2003,), Page 1

38

A Case for Standards: Lessons Learned From a Start-Up's Involvement in Life Sciences Standards

SCOTT MARKEL

Lion bioscience Inc.

MICHAEL DICKSON

Lexinomics, LLC

Abstract: *NetGenics was a small start-up company focused on developing software in the life sciences domain, primarily for pharmaceutical companies. As part of this development effort NetGenics was heavily involved in the Life Sciences Research Domain Task Force at the Object Management Group. This chapter will explore the details of that involvement, including specific technology adoption efforts and the roles that we played, with an emphasis on lessons learned.*

Introduction

This chapter will present a case for the use of standards in the life sciences community. NetGenics (now a part of LION bioscience Inc.) was a small start-up company actively involved in the Object Management Group (OMG). We provide background information about both NetGenics and the OMG, including history, organizational structure, and the roles that key individuals played. Next we give some detailed case studies of individual specifications. This is followed by a detailed look at the lessons we learned. We cover what our customers and coworkers thought, what we think worked, and what we think didn't work. We close with some comments about the future of the Life Sciences Research (LSR) Domain Task Force and the current set of technology adoptions underway.

NetGenics Background

NetGenics as a company

NetGenics was founded as a venture capital backed corporation in 1996 by Manuel Glynias and Dr. Walter Gilbert. The company mission was to develop and market analysis software to pharmaceutical and biotechnology corporations specifically to enhance their early stage research and development drug discovery efforts. NetGenics proposed to do this by utilizing the then emerging capabilities of Java and the World Wide Web to provide a rich user environment for integration and presentation of life sciences R&D data.

At the time NetGenics was founded, much of the bioinformatics software used in drug discovery R&D was internally developed or developed to support a specific academic or institutional research effort. Most of this software used command line interfaces and ran on Unix based computers. Executing an analytical pipeline often required hand editing and transformation of the data from one tool to the next to accommodate the plethora of input and output formats in use across analytical tools. Output formats (and therefore presentation formats) were equally varied. There was no real integration across any of the tools and data being utilized for research. The ability for researchers to collaborate and share data was severely limited by this essentially manual analysis process. In order to address this research bottleneck, NetGenics developed and marketed SYNERGY, a project and team centered point and click environment that integrated a variety of types of R&D data and analysis algorithms. SYNERGY was task based and team oriented. Team members could easily execute an analysis pipeline without in depth knowledge of file formats or command line syntax. Collaboration was encouraged through the ability to share annotated research and analysis results within team centered project workspaces. Changes to a research artifact were immediately visible to other researchers in real time. This sort of electronic "white board" made research across groups or sites possible. It also freed up expensive informaticians from simple data formatting support tasks and allowed them to extend SYNERGY or to engage in other informatics research.

In developing SYNERGY, we looked at available distributed object technologies in order to be able to leverage the desktop Java and HTML browser environment for presentation while still executing the sometimes data- and processor-intensive analytical calculations on the Unix servers. We examined and discarded RMI (Remote Method Invocation) as a possibility due to concerns about scalability across multiple geographically distributed deployment sites and the need to support development in C or C++ on the Unix servers. Since we needed to tie together desktop PCs, including Apple Macintoshes, which were common in R&D groups at that time, and Unix servers, Microsoft COM was not an option due to its Windows-centric deployment model. This left CORBA® as the logical choice; it addressed our cross-platform and cross-language concerns, was object oriented, and widely available.

NetGenics and standards

As we designed our objects and classes and the interactions between them, we learned how to use CORBA Interface Definition Language (IDL) to specify efficiently the distributed object behavior to support the novel real-time updates we wanted our system to support. We were using some pretty bleeding edge technology (and we did get bloody a few times). In the process of trying to understand how best to utilize the technologies we'd chosen, we started looking for existing patterns and quickly found the specifications and existing work done within the OMG (Object Management Group) to be helpful. Early efforts at sales also made it clear that, while we were solving an important problem, the IT groups were often uncomfortable with aspects of the technology we'd chosen. Clearly we needed to educate on the benefits of the technology choices we had made.

Why would a startup organization get involved with or care about standards development and compliance? A lack of any sort of standard for interchange or analysis of life science data had traditionally been a huge barrier to integration of this data. We wanted to make NetGenics and SYNERGY synonymous with the ability to provide this easy integration. We also wanted to increase the buyer's savvy within drug discovery R&D and make them demand a solidly engineered, integrated approach vs. the ad hoc set of tools and data they traditionally worked with. On the other hand, NetGen-

---

"If we could make compliance with standards an important check box criterion for purchases and help to drive the definition of these standards, we felt we could ensure a leadership position in our developing market segment."

---

ics was not in a position to build and supply every analytical tool or data type that might be useful within the drug development analytical pipeline. If we could make compliance with standards an important check box criterion for purchases and help to drive the definition of these standards, we felt we could ensure a leadership position in our developing market segment. We worked to develop broad acceptance of our SYNERGY product and a standards based approach within the market. We did this by joining the OMG, participating in the Life Sciences Research (LSR, more on this below) Domain Task Force to develop relevant standards, and through education and training efforts targeted to our customers. Participation in LSR added marketing value to NetGenics (and now LION) by displaying the company's leadership and innovation in the marketplace.

As NetGenics developed and grew and as we started to pick up customers, we saw an increased need to support a research effort that would be able to pursue longer term projects (such as standards activities) while the core development activities were being driven by sales. Our goal with the creation of the research group was to provide a mechanism for quick prototypes to be generated to facilitate exploration into new product areas that might have an impact on the business, and to transfer those pieces of research into the core development organization in a way that didn't negatively impact the release driven schedules the core development team followed. We also used the research team as the home within the company for standards work because of the time commitment required to track the standards process. We didn't want to hamper development with tracking a developing standard.

NetGenics' SYNERGY product was initially focused on sequence analysis and this topic was the first to be addressed within the LSR at the OMG. At the time the work on a standard for sequence analysis started, we had already shipped SYNERGY, which included objects to represent the various data types and results used to provide sequence analysis capabilities. Our initial submission (OMG's adoption process typically consists of initial and revised submissions) was loosely based on the implementation used in SYNERGY. At the time we felt that we could improve upon the existing interfaces in the product and use the standardization efforts to do so. In retrospect this was probably a mistake. The resulting standard interfaces never

made it into our products and when we did implement the standard interfaces we discovered problems that might have been avoided had we submitted and focused on the production interfaces. We also found that the simple interfaces in use in SYNERGY were entirely adequate to support the needs of the product. Sometimes simpler is better!

NetGenics was an active submitter to a number of standards processes (called "Request for Proposals" or "RFP" in OMG parlance) issued by the LSR. We developed implementations for many of the standards we participated in within our research group and took elements of the standards into our products. Over time, CORBA was replaced by other middleware technologies (Java platform technologies—J2EE, web services) and the earlier work that had been done using CORBA Interface Definition Language (IDL) as the normative specifications became more useful as models rather than directly implemented interfaces. The current Model Driven Architecture® (MDA®) based approach now being used to develop standards within the OMG and specifically within the LSR addresses the problems we saw with changing platform technologies impacting the usability of the standards. We saw benefits from the standards process however, even in those cases where we

---

"Because we derived the implementations from a well-defined platform independent model, we were able to easily reuse the implementation across differing transport technologies without the need to rewrite large portions of the component."

---

could not directly use the standardized interfaces. One specific example is the query service implementation originally in SYNERGY and carried into second-generation products. The query service implementation is modeled closely after the CORBAServices' QueryService defined within the OMG. The initial implementation in

SYNERGY was built using CORBA. The second-generation query service component supported CORBA, Enterprise Java Beans (EJB), and Web Service interfaces. Because we derived the implementations from a well-defined platform independent model, we were able to easily reuse the implementation across differing transport technologies without the need to rewrite large portions of the component.

NetGenics actively participated in the governance of the OMG at a number of levels. Mr. Dickson held a seat on the Board of Directors for a period of time during NetGenics' involvement in the OMG. NetGenics sought out a position on the board because we felt that the OMG and standards were important to the success of our business. NetGenics developed a reputation in our market for strong technical expertise and solid software engineering, and the authors feel this was at least in part due to our visible participation in the OMG and the LSR. In his role as CTO and Sr. VP of Product Development at NetGenics, Mike actively promoted its involvement in standards activities internally within the company and externally to our target market. Dr. Markel held and continues to act as a co-chair of Life Science Research Domain Task Force (LSR-DTF) for successor company LION bioscience. In this role Scott, as co-chair, has advocated for the needs of the LSR within the OMG and works with member organizations interested in the Life Sciences to make sure that the road map, standards proposals, and submitted and adopted standards represents the needs of the life science community.

NetGenics today

In January of 2002 NetGenics was acquired by LION bioscience Inc. As of the writing of this chapter, LION continues active involvement within the OMG and a number of the software components developed by NetGenics as a company play a key role in LION's product line.

History of the LSR

The Life Sciences Research (LSR) Domain Task Force (DTF) is a part of the Object Management Group's Domain Technology Committee (DTC).

Object Management Group

The Object Management Group™ (OMG™) was founded in April 1989 as a not-for-profit corporation to develop and promote interoperability specifications for the software industry. The consortium includes hundreds of member organizations and is best known for standard specifications including CORBA® (Common Object Request Broker Architecture), CORBA/IIOP™, the UML™ (Unified Modeling Language™), XMI® (XML Metadata Interchange), and MOF™ (Meta Object Facility).

The OMG was formed to create a component-based software marketplace by accelerating the introduction of standardized object software. The organization's charter includes the establishment of industry guidelines and detailed object management specifications to provide a common framework for application development. Conformance to these specifications will make it possible to develop a heterogeneous computing environment across all major hardware platforms and operating systems. Implementations of OMG specifications can be found on many operating systems across the world today.

The OMG's series of specifications detail the necessary standard interfaces for Distributed Object Computing. Its widely popular Internet protocol, IIOP (Internet Inter-ORB Protocol), is being used as the infrastructure for hundreds of technology companies. OMG specifications are used worldwide to develop and deploy distributed applications for vertical markets, including Life Sciences Research, Manufacturing, Finance, Telecommunications, Electronic Commerce, Real-time systems, and Health Care.

The OMG defines object management as software development that models the real world through representation of "objects." These objects are the encapsulation of the attributes, relationships, and methods of software identifiable program components. A key benefit of an object-oriented system is its ability to expand in functionality by extending existing components and adding new objects to the system. Object management results in faster application development, easier maintenance, enormous scalability, and reusable software.

The OMG is structured into three major bodies: the Platform Technology Committee (PTC), the Domain Technology Committee (DTC), and the Architecture Board. The consistency and technical integrity of work produced in the PTC and DTC is managed by an overarching Architectural Board. Within the Technology Committees and Architectural Board rest all of the Task Forces, Special Interest Groups (SIGs), and Working Groups that drive the technology adoption process of the OMG.

The Founding of LSR

Representatives of biotechnology software vendors, pharmaceuticals and biotechnology companies, and academia interested in promoting component-based software development in

Table 1: OMG structure

Architecture Board	Platform Technology Committee	Domain Technology Committee
Liaison Subcommittee (SC)	Product Standard Definition SC	Business Enterprise Integration Domain Task Force (DTF)
Object & Reference Model SC	Analysis & Design Platform Task Force (PTF)	Consultation, Command, Control, Communications and Intelligence (C4I) DTF
Business Rules Special Interest Group (SIG)	Middleware and Related Services PTF	Finance DTF
Java Community Process SIG	Real-time, Embedded, & Specialized Systems PTF	Geospatial and Imagery Value Added Services DTF
MDA Users SIG	Agents Platform SIG (PSIG)	Healthcare DTF
Security SIG	Benchmarking PSIG	Life Sciences Research DTF
Test & Validation SIG	Common Warehouse Metadata Interchange PSIG	Manufacturing Technology and Industrial Systems DTF
Web Services SIG	Digital Asset Management PSIG	Space DTF
	Japan PSIG	Telecommunications DTF
	Korea PSIG	Transportation DTF
	Legacy Transformation PSIG	Analytical Data Management Domain SIG (DSIG)
	Model Integrated Computing PSIG	Distributed Simulation DSIG
	Ontology PSIG	eGovernment DSIG
		Human Resources DSIG
		Software Radio DSIG
		Super Distributed Objects DSIG
		Systems Engineering DSIG

life sciences research met in Philadelphia on 5 - 6 August 1997. The attendees voted to apply to the Object Management Group (OMG) for recognition as a Domain Special Interest Group (DSIG) for Life Sciences Research at the next regular OMG meeting, to be held in Dublin, Ireland, 22-26 September 1997. The attendees also developed and approved initial statements of mission and goals for the DSIG and elected as acting DSIG co-chairs: David Benton (Smith-Kline Beecham), Nat Goodman (Jackson Laboratory), Eric Neumann (NetGenics), and Tim Slidel (European Bioinformatics Institute). The four initial co-chairs represented a pharma, an academic lab, a vendor, and a European organization. Later on LSR dropped to three co-chairs, but it has always kept the broad representation.

The initial mission statement was:

- To improve the quality and utility of software and information systems used in Life Sciences Research through use of interoperable distributed object technology.

- To encourage the development of interoperable software tools and services in Life Sciences Research.

- To use the Object Management Group (OMG) technology adoption process to standardize interfaces for software tools, services, frameworks, and components in Life Sciences Research.

- To communicate the requirements of the Life Sciences Research domain to the Platform Technical Committee.

- To coordinate with OMG Task Forces and Special Interest Groups, and other standards organizations and information providers to ensure common standards.

LSR as a Domain Special Interest Group

LSR was officially created as a Domain Special Interest Group on 26 September 1997. DSIGs are created under a parent Domain Task Force. LSR's parent was the CORBAmed DTF (now Healthcare DTF). LSR's first main task was writing and publicizing an initial Request for Infor-

mation (RFI). OMG is largely organized around Task Forces, so SIGs allow groups to get started without having to deal with all of the organizational issues.

Four initial Working Groups (WG) were established: Web-page WG, RFI review WG (to publicize the RFI and to review responses), Sequence Analysis WG (to develop a draft sequence analysis RFP), and Roadmap WG. The goal of the Roadmap WG was to develop a roadmap document outlining subdomains within the life sciences research domain and possible timescales for their inclusion in the standards process. This WG continues as the Architecture & Roadmap WG.

LSR as a Domain Task Force

LSR was promoted to a Domain Task Force on 3 April 1998. The co-chairs were David Benton (SmithKline Beecham), Eric Neumann (NetGenics), and Tim Slidel (European Bioinformatics Institute). Since then Tim Clark (Millennium Pharmaceuticals), Karl Konnerth (Incyte), Martin Senger (European Bioinformatics Institute), and Scott have also been co-chairs.

The primary work of a Task Force is to promote technology adoptions through the issuance of Requests for Proposals. When LSR has needed more information before writing an RFP, the members have often issued an RFI first.

Issued RFIs:
- Life Sciences Research (CORBAmed RFI 4)
- Entity Differentiation Service
- Gene Expression
- Macromolecular Structure
- Chemical Entity Representation and Interface Definition
- Clinical Trials Laboratory Data Interchange
- Life Sciences Research 2
- Chemical Sample Management, Representation, and Interface Definition

Issued RFPs:
- Biomolecular Sequence Analysis (adopted)
- Genomic Maps (adopted)
- Bibliographic Query Service (adopted)
- Macromolecular Structure (adopted)

- Clinical Trials Laboratory Information Exchange (withdrawn)
- Entity Identification Service (withdrawn)
- Gene Expression (adopted)
- Chemical Structure Access and Representation (active)
- Laboratory Equipment Control Interface Specification (adopted)
- Biomolecular Sequence Analysis Entities (withdrawn)
- Laboratory Activity Broker (withdrawn)
- Chemical Sample Management (withdrawn)
- Life Sciences Identifiers (active)
- Biochemical Pathways (active)
- Gene Expression Query Service (active)
- Single Nucleotide Polymorphisms (active)
- Life Sciences Analysis Engine (active)
- Compound Collection (active)

Some of these RFPs efforts are described below.

Our roles at OMG

We have held positions at many different levels within LSR and OMG. These positions have given us a broad view of the activities and issues.

Scott represented NetGenics as the Architecture & Roadmap WG chair. A previous NetGenics employee, Eric Neumann, also held this position. There was a successful effort on an initial roadmap document in 1999. There have been incremental changes since then, driven by participant interest. Leading this WG gave NetGenics a key opportunity to influence LSR's direction. Scott continues in this position, now representing LION.

Scott also represented NetGenics as an LSR co-chair. Eric Neumann had also represented NetGenics as an LSR co-chair. The reasons for wanting a representative in this position are the same as for the Architecture & Roadmap WG chair, but also leverages procedural knowledge acquired during the Biomolecular Sequence Analysis effort. Co-chairs are often asked to speak at conferences, to provide quotes for trade periodicals, and to assist OMG staff in membership recruitment. Scott continues in this position,

now representing LION, working with David Benton (GlaxoSmithKline) and Martin Senger (European Bioinformatics Institute).

In 2000, Scott was asked to consider running for a seat on OMG's Architecture Board. This group is responsible for the consistency and technical integrity of technology adoptions. After some internal discussion at NetGenics, Mike supported Scott in running for the AB. Being elected would have allowed Scott to participate at a higher level, with more visibility for NetGenics and for Scott. This would have allowed him to leverage his architectural and OMG procedural knowledge. He lost the election so, in the end, it didn't have an impact on NetGenics.

A few months later Mike was encouraged to run for a seat on OMG's Board of Directors. The selection measurement criteria include checking that the company maintains attendance at four out of every five consecutive OMG meetings, a place on at least one Task Force voting list, a record of submission to at least one adoption process in the last two years, an elected chair position (TF, SIG, SC or AB), and demonstrated public support of adopted OMG technologies of the Group (e.g., via press releases & advertising). Mike was elected to a three year term in September 2000. According to OMG Board Chairperson, Dr. Richard Soley, "Mike was selected because of NetGenics' strong support of OMG, the OMG process and OMG technologies, and for the key insights he will bring to the board in the area of life sciences standards." This was a good position for Mike and more visibility for NetGenics. Scott inherited this position from Mike when he left LION earlier this year.

Case Studies within the LSR

This section highlights some specific RFP efforts.

Biomolecular Sequence Analysis (BSA)

The BSA RFP was the first for the LSR community. This was also the first standards development experience for many individuals. There were five initial submissions involving eight organizations. The final revised submission was done by Concept Five Technologies, EMBL-EBI (European Bioinformatics Institute), Genome Informatics Corporation, Millennium Pharmaceuticals, Neomorphic Software, and NetGenics. The final submission was designed largely from scratch. Specifying best-of-breed solutions is hard. The individual initial submissions were self-consistent, so taking pieces from each didn't necessarily work. In addition, negotiations can often lead to lowest common denominator solutions, which are not always the best technical

---

"...negotiations can often lead to lowest common denominator solutions, which are not always the best technical approaches."

---

approaches. Another issue was that different organizations can have very different success criteria. NetGenics defined success as positive impact on our products and business. The BSA specification includes two IDL (Interface Definition Language) modules, one for domain objects and one for an analysis engine (job control, etc.). The domain objects were based on a prioritized list gleaned from the set of initial submissions and augmented by LSR input. Not all items on the list made it into the submission. This led to issuing the Biomolecular Sequence Analysis Entities RFP two years later.

Genomic maps

The Genomic Maps RFP was issued after work had started on BSA, but finished concurrently. Many players were the same (EBI, Millennium, NetGenics). This allowed the group to go much faster. There were some key differences in how strongly the parties thought that existing OMG technologies (e.g., CORBA Services) should be used. The final implementation was done by GlaxoSmithKline. The submitters were either no longer interested (Millennium, NetGenics) or had lost key individuals (EBI). The submission included a nice controlled vocabulary module. To our knowledge the specification is not being used.

Bibliographic Query Service (BQS)

The BQS specification was a single organization effort by EBI. It was nicely done, leveraging the Dublin Core. NetGenics liked the approach and decided it was not necessary to contribute directly. Parts of BQS have been incorporated into BioJava and BioPerl, two Open Source efforts.

Biomolecular Sequence Analysis Entities (BSANE)

The BSANE RFP was issued as a follow-on to BSA. The RFP asked for additional domain objects that the BSA submitters didn't get to. The BSANE work was largely overtaken by Open Source efforts (e.g., BioJava and BioCORBA). Scott made presentations at two Bioinformatics Open Source Conferences (satellite meeting to the annual Intelligent Systems for Molecular Biology conference) to try to get the Open Source community to join the BSANE effort. At that time the Open Source community in life sciences was too fragmented to make this happen even though EBI and NetGenics based their initial submission on BioJava.

Gene expression

The Gene Expression specification includes the Microarray Gene Expression Object Model and Markup Language (MAGE-OM/ML). There were three initial submissions. Rosetta represented their GEML (Gene Expression Markup Language) community and brought extensive industry experience. EBI represented the Open Source Microarray Gene Expression Database (MGED) group and its Microarray Markup Language (MAML). MAML had richer science than GEML. NetGenics had a CORBA-based initial submission but was supportive of an XML-based revised submission. Though Scott helped with an MDA-like approach for the revised submission, NetGenics dropped out early in the revised submission phase. We liked the approach as it was and our help was no longer needed. In addition, we no longer saw a business need to include a gene expression product. We think this is the best example yet of how well standards can work in life sciences domain, especially the coordinated interaction of the LSR and Open Source community.

Macromolecular Structures (MMS)

The MMS technology adoption was another single organization effort, this time by the San Diego Supercomputer Center. NetGenics had an initial submission, but withdrew when it became clear that we didn't have a business need in this area. NetGenics would have liked an approach that could have been leveraged more (e.g., data structures that could have been used in the Chemical Structure Access & Representation submission), but the adopted approach certainly solves the Protein Data Bank problem it was intended to solve.

Chemical structure access and representation

This RFP was issued at the same time as Gene Expression. It has followed a similar MDA-like approach. The UML model was obtained by reverse engineering Chemical Markup Language (CML). The submission effort by Intelligent Solutions and LION (initially NetGenics) is almost finished.

Lessons Learned

NetGenics' involvement in standards on the whole was a positive experience. Based on our original business goals of increased visibility and a reputation for being innovative and technically sound, we would judge the activities as successful. On the other hand, the bioinformatics market itself did not develop as expected and in many ways the success of the LSR was equally impacted by this lack of maturity. All of this activity really taught us some very important lessons about how to get the maximum value from standards efforts. In this section we'd like to highlight some successes, as well as some things we'd do differently if we did it again.

What our customers thought

This was a critical reason we got involved in standards in the first place. We felt that the marketplace was fragmented and could be better served by at least standardized interfaces

that would have facilitated integration across tools and data within the life sciences. A critical element for this to happen was direct involvement by the customers we hoped to serve. If the customers demanded standards-conforming products, then vendors would have incentive to implement the standards in their products. The fact that even NetGenics never fully integrated

---

"Other than a few of the larger pharmaceutical companies, customer participation was and remains low."

---

the standardized interfaces into our products is an indication of the lack of real emphasis the marketplace put on the standards being produced. Other than a few of the larger pharmaceutical companies, customer participation was and remains low.

What our coworkers thought

Inside NetGenics the standards efforts were often viewed as a "research" project and not directly leveraged into development. This was partly caused by the initial desire to "improve" on the interfaces used in our SYNERGY products rather than use them directly as the basis for our standards submission. By starting with interface definitions that were different from our products we found it difficult, as time progressed and as they moved further apart, to reconcile the new standard interfaces with those in the products. Also, the interfaces in SYNERGY actually proved adequate to address the requirements in the original submission so that we could have based our submission on production experience and possibly avoided some of the theoretical arguments that arose during the standards development process. Of course, convincing the other submitters of this may have been harder.

The early standards work was focused on CORBA interfaces as opposed to the model driven approach being used within the OMG and the LSR now. This also proved problematic as the development team lobbied over time to move to J2EE based implementations as our development moved to Java. A similar shift occurred as web services became the "new thing" in life sciences. As the shift away from CORBA occurred, it seemed as if the early CORBA-centric standards work might not be able to be directly leveraged. In fairness however, we were able to use some of the patterns expressed in the CORBA interfaces and carry them forward. On the other hand, the later standards work using the MDA based approach for specifying standards is much less tied to a specific implementation approach and therefore will be easier to leverage in future projects.

What worked

NetGenics, through our involvement in the LSR and OMG, did develop a reputation for providing leadership for standards in the life sciences. Over several years of activities within the LSR, we developed an understanding of the submission process and were able to mentor and help other submitters. We also developed

---

"The standards efforts we engaged in allowed us to demonstrate to the market our interest, expertise, and focus on integration capabilities over tools and data."

---

a reputation for savvy use of technology and strong IT and production software development expertise through the leadership at the OMG and the presentations and training (CORBA focused training for life sciences companies) we developed and delivered. The standards efforts we engaged in allowed us to demonstrate to the market our interest, expertise, and focus on integration capabilities over tools and data.

NetGenics was also able to use our standards efforts as an effective recruiting tool. Scott joined NetGenics after attending an OMG meeting representing a customer organization. We also engaged some summer interns to do the initial implementation of one of the standards submissions. A number of these interns went on to become permanent NetGenics employees and

brought their knowledge of the standard interfaces into the development group. In this way we were able to recover and use at least some of the implementation of the standardized interfaces. Similarly a number of the individuals directly involved in the standards development work developed a more widely known reputation due to the exposure that participation in the LSR afforded them.

One of the largest benefits from participation in standards development came from exposure to new and differing ideas around how to solve integration problems in the life sciences. In addition to the large body of existing standardized work already at the OMG (the Common Object Services and other standardized domain interfaces provided a wealth of successful implementation patterns to draw from), the process of resolving multiple initial submissions down to a single final submission provoked a dialog that often required the resolution of vast differences in approach. This dialog really allowed for the exploration of new ideas and approaches that we might not have been exposed to otherwise. There was of course a cost to this interaction in time and in adaptation of existing software, but the dialog itself was beneficial and resulted in better implementation in the production software we produced in many cases.

It should be noted that we've also been pleasantly surprised at the number of individuals and organizations that are aware of the LSR standards and have either used them directly or as starting points for internal development efforts. We routinely hear comments like this at technical conferences. After LION acquired NetGenics, we visited the other development sites in Europe and the US and found that LION had used the domain objects in the Biomolecular Sequence Analysis specification as a starting point. They had also used parts of the analysis interfaces.

One of the clear benefits we realized by using an existing forum (in our case the OMG) for definition of the standards was a clear, well defined process for definition and adoption of standards. There had been numerous ad-hoc attempts in the past at creating life sciences "standards." Most of these have proven to be unsuccessful due to the lack of an existing adoption process. As noted, changes in the implementation approach (away from CORBA) commonly used for life sciences software have limited the usefulness of some of the early LSR work. Later MDA-based standards have received much broader adoption. The MAGE-OM Gene Expression work is an example of a widely used, collaboratively developed life sciences standard that clearly benefited from the well defined OMG adoption process.

What didn't work

One area that proved problematic when attempting to develop life sciences standards was a tendency to leave the RFPs used to guide the standards definition very broadly scoped. Initially, based on discussions in early LSR meetings, it was felt that a more focused scope would limit the creativity of the submitters. Unfortunately, in our experience, the broad scope made the reconciliation of the initial submissions more difficult and ultimately limited the usefulness of the resulting interfaces. The initial RFP considered, Biomolecular Sequence Analysis, suffered from a lack of definition of some base biological objects. This encouraged each submitter to invent his own. Ultimately, this required the submitters to reach agreement on these base objects before the sequence analysis problems could be addressed. The biological objects as defined also retained a bias towards sequence analysis since that was the context used when they were defined. It's possible that with a differently worded RFP, the domain objects would have been defined more broadly and available for use in later submissions.

Another problem we've already noted was the separation between the standard interfaces and those used in NetGenics' production products. We tended to view the standards work as a way to improve on what we'd done in the products. Unfortunately this sort of revolutionary approach is often much harder to embrace when production deadlines are being faced. If

we had used the production interfaces as a starting point and instead allowed the standards to evolve from that point, we might have had more success getting the standard interfaces into our products and functional. This also would have provided us with a real test bed to identify and address implementation issues with the standard interfaces (such as performance, scalability, and implementation problems due to an ill-defined inheritance structure in some of the classes).

Probably the biggest single "failing" with our efforts to develop standards was the low-level involvement of the customer (pharmaceutical and biotechnology) companies we wished to serve. To a large degree the organizations involved in the standards were vendors (either corporations like NetGenics who wished to sell products into this marketplace or institutes and research organizations that were suppliers of tools and data). A small number of forward thinking customer organizations did participate, but involvement directly in the standards development was low. At a minimum, more influence on the road map of the LSR by consumers of the standards would have been beneficial. Ideally, direct involvement in discussions on the content of the standards would have occurred.

Conclusions

NetGenics got involved in standards development initially to further its business interests. A nearly total lack of standardization in our target marketplace made easy integration of tools and data nearly impossible. NetGenics did see some benefit from the forum the LSR provided for discussion and development of standards, but some of the business benefits we hoped for were never fully realized. We did benefit from the injection of new ideas into our research and product development efforts, and the recruiting access and career development exposure that participation afforded. A small company especially can make its mark by driving standards to expand the market, taking a leadership position to become first entrant in a standardized market and a recognized driver of standards, and visibly move the market and drive the direction.

While theory remains untested due to changes in the marketplace, the authors at least feel that had we based our standards submissions more closely on our existing products and less on a "research" based approach we might have seen greater benefits from the standards program. We also saw limited usefulness from early CORBA specific standards due to changes in the implementation technology (movement to extend beyond CORBA in the life sciences). The current MDA based standards have addressed that problem. At least the first few specifications developed in this way within the LSR seem to be finding a higher level of acceptance than we'd seen previously.

Another area that we feel needs attention is a better defined scope in the initial RFPs that are issued. There is a tendency, due to the time that standardization takes, to try to include more material in the RFP. In those cases where the RFP's scope was well defined and the proposed and adopted standard material was based on existing implementation or practice, broader acceptance of the adopted standard has been achieved.

Future of the LSR

The LSR has some very dedicated and talented participants from a variety of organizations. The MAGE specification is a superb example of how the LSR can work together with Open Source efforts to produce widely accepted technology. One of the main reasons for this is the Model Driven Architecture approach championed by OMG. By focusing on the models and allowing the middleware approaches to vary as widely as necessary, the new specifications from

LSR have a much better chance for success in the life sciences community.

The RFP efforts now underway include:
- Life Sciences Identifiers
- Biochemical Pathways
- Gene Expression Query Service
- Single Nucleotide Polymorphisms
- Life Sciences Analysis Engine
- Compound Collection

We encourage you to join these efforts.

Acknowledgements

We'd like to thank David Benton, Mark Canales, Manuel Glynias, Darryl León, Richard Soley, and Hartmut Voss for their encouragement and constructive criticism of early versions of this chapter.

Bibliography

Benton, David, Karl Konnerth, Scott Markel. The OMG Life Sciences Research Domain Task Force. ACM SIGBIO, December 2000, Volume 20, Number 3, pp. 14-21.

BioJava web site: http://www.biojava.org.

BioCORBA web site: http://www.biocorba.org.

Life Sciences Research Domain Task Force web site: http://lsr.omg.org.

Object Management Group web site: http://www.omg.org.

Model Driven Architecture web site: http://mda.omg.org.

Spellman, Paul et al. Design and implementation of microarray gene expression markup language (MAGE-ML). Genome Biology 2002 Aug 23; 3(9).

39

Data Standards and Mortgage Credit Reporting

Mike Bixby
Bixby Consulting Inc.

Greg Alvord
Gallagher Financial Systems

Abstract: *Data standards have been used in the mortgage credit reporting for the last decade. Their use has allowed mortgage lenders to more easily choose credit reporting services based on the best price, service, and quality. At the same time, data standards can have a dual effect on their users. Because data is provided in the same format, standards can lull the users into accepting that the quality of the data from different sources is also the same. Having data in a standard format can make it easier to identify differences in data provided from two sources. There can be many benefits from the adoption of data standards, but the need for clearly understanding the meaning of the data and its proper application never diminishes.*

Introduction

"**D**ata standards help the smaller companies play in the same ball field as the larger companies, and they help the larger companies be as nimble as the smaller ones."

This statement was made by Michael Petree, Senior Vice President of First Franklin Direct, at a recent Mortgage Bankers Association conference panel session. For service consumers (lenders) like First Franklin Direct, data standards can also make it simpler to switch to, or add, service providers who support a common data standard. For service providers (credit report providers), supporting a data standard can expand their potential customer base to all service consumers that are also able to support the standard. The service providers who can offer the best price, quality, or service will still be able to distinguish themselves from their competitors.

In the mortgage credit reporting industry, the credit report data is the product being sold.

> *"Data standards help the smaller companies play in the same ball field as the larger companies, and they help the larger companies be as nimble as the smaller ones."*

When lenders are able to receive industry standard credit report data from multiple sources, they may naturally tend to assume that since the same format is used across the industry, the resulting credit report data will also be the same. This may not always be the case, especially for credit reports containing late payments, collections, or other adverse data. These differences can affect whether or not a particular lender offers credit to an applicant and on what terms. Fortunately, the standardized data format can also make it easier for lenders to compare the quality and accuracy of the underlying data.

This article will explore these effects and others that mortgage credit reporting data standards have had on both the credit reporting service providers and the lenders who are the consumers of these services.

Background

This section will go into a fair amount of background information about credit reporting, because it helps bring out some of the significant, nontechnical issues regarding data standards.

Identifying the players

"Credit Bureau," "Credit Reporting Agency," "Credit Reseller," and "Credit Repository" are all terms that are used inconsistently in legislation, data standards, and marketing materials to describe the players in mortgage credit reporting. It's probably good to start by identifying these players with consistent labels and defining their roles.

The *"credit data repositories"* are the companies that collect, store, and report financial credit data on individuals in the United States. *Equifax, Experian,* and *Trans Union* are the three primary credit data repositories.

The *"credit bureau vendor"* is the agency that creates the credit report for the lender. They are also sometimes referred to as the "credit reporting agency" (CRA) or the "credit vendor." For consistency, in this article we will refer to these companies as the credit bureau vendors. *Advantage Credit, Chase Credit Systems, Equifax Mortgage Services, Factual Data, First American Credco, FNIS Credit Services, LandAmerica Info1, LandSafe,* and *The Credit Network (TCN)* are examples of credit bureau vendors.

"Borrower" and *"applicant"* are often used interchangeably in mortgage industry discussions, but both are labels for the same person. When individuals first apply for a loan they are applicants. When they receive the loan they become borrowers. In the Mortgage Industry Standards Maintenance Organization (MISMO) standards, the borrower label won out over applicant because having the status of being an "applicant" only lasts a matter of weeks, whereas being a "borrower" can last for decades.

How a credit report is prepared

The process of producing a credit report begins with the collection and storage of the credit data. This is the function of the credit data repositories. Equifax, Experian, and Trans Union collect monthly financial and public record data reported by financial lenders, collection agencies, and the federal, state, and local courts. When the data is stored by the credit data repositories, it is organized into "credit files" — one for each person. Over a period of time, as payments are made and account balances are updated, a "credit history" is built up within each credit file. This snapshot of the individual's current credit status and total debt, combined with the payment history, provide the raw data that mortgage lenders use to determine whether or not an individual is a good, bad, or median credit risk.

The next step in the process is to request the applicant's credit report from a credit bureau vendor. Not too long ago, the requests were sent by fax or mail or were submitted over the phone. Today, credit requests are generally sent as electronic transactions that use either proprietary or public data formats. When a credit bureau vendor receives the request, their software will generate and transmit one credit request to each credit data repository that was selected. Each of these requests must be in the proprietary data format specified by the credit data repository.

The credit data repository locates the credit file data that matches the name, address, SSN, and date of birth that was submitted in the credit request. If a "credit score" was requested by the lender then it is also generated at this point. It is calculated by looking at the borrower's credit file and comparing its payment history and other factors with historical data from hundreds of thousands of past credit files. The "credit score" is a mathematical assessment of the borrower's likelihood of making timely payments on future credit accounts. The higher the score, the better the credit risk the borrower represents to a future lender, a little bit like handicapping a horse race. When the credit data and credit score have been obtained, this data is converted into the credit data repository's proprietary credit data format and returned to the credit bureau.

After the credit bureau vendor receives the requested credit file data from the credit data repositories, **additional processing is done by the credit bureau vendor's software to produce a final credit report that matches the lender's specifications.** Since a credit file is requested from each credit data repository for most mortgage credit reports, the data from the three sources is combined into a single report. Duplicate liability records (e.g., a "Sears" account reported by Equifax, Experian, and Trans Union) are identified and then removed and/or combined into a single, more complete liability record. The credit data is often converted into some type of printable or human-readable format, as well as reformatted into the public or proprietary credit data format used by the lender's loan processing software.

The resulting credit report transaction is returned to the lender who made the original request. The entire request and response process normally takes less than 20 seconds, or more typically, less time than it took to read this paragraph.

Qualifying the applicant

How the lender comes to a decision to offer credit varies depending on their target market of potential borrowers. Lenders who offer credit only to the "prime" market may only look at the credit score and some summary data returned on the credit report as the basis for their decision. Lenders who are in the "subprime" market may look at the score, but focus much more on the details about the number of late payments and any collections, foreclosures, bankruptcies, liens, etc. The quality of the credit report data can be critical for the sub-prime market as we will see later in the article.

At some point, a decision is made to offer credit to the applicant, not offer credit to the applicant, or offer credit but with stipulations (e.g., applicant must pay off debt first or deliver proof of income, show tax returns, etc.). If credit is offered, the interest rate, points, and terms options are also usually set at this point and then the mortgage origination process begins. If credit is not offered or offered with stipulations, the lender and/or applicant will normally review the credit report to check if there are any errors that could affect the decision to issue credit. There are procedures for reporting errors to the credit bureau vendors so that they can be verified and then corrected by the credit data repositories in the applicant's credit file. The updated credit file is then "rescored" and reissued to the lender so that the loan applicant can requalify using the updated credit report.

Development of the Credit Reporting Data Standards

ASC X12 EDI credit reporting standards

The Accredited Standards Committee (ASC) is the U.S. standards body that coordinates the development, maintenance, and publication of Electronic Data Interchange (EDI) standards. The first public credit reporting data standards used in the mortgage industry were developed in the early 1990s. Volunteers from credit bureau vendors and lenders formed a Credit Reporting Work Group to develop data transactions that

"The first public credit reporting data standards used in the mortgage industry were developed in the early 1990s."

would allow the ordering of a mortgage credit report and the delivery of the credit report data.

The credit request transaction was released by ASC as the X12.833 Mortgage Credit Report Order. This transaction allowed the lender or mortgage broker to send the borrower data and other ancillary information needed to request a credit report from a credit bureau vendor.

There were two X12 transactions used for the response transaction from the credit bureau vendor back to the lender. The X12.200 Mortgage Credit Report transaction contained the credit report data – liabilities, public records, credit scores, etc. The X12.864 Text Message transaction was used to transmit human-readable "text" versions of the credit report that could be viewed or printed by the lender.

Since ASC encourages the reuse of existing data structures, the Credit Reporting Work Group incorporated many of the common data structures that had already been developed. While reusing existing structures allowed the new credit transactions to be developed more quickly, it also meant that some of the existing data structures contained data elements and coded values that did not have any relevance to the credit reporting transactions. X12 Credit Reporting Implementation Guides were created to specify which segments should be built when creating one of the credit reporting transactions.

The X12 EDI transactions were originally designed for high volume "batch processing" commonly used in large mainframe computer environments. With the acceptance of the use of personal computers in small, medium, and large businesses in the 1980s and 1990s, data translation software that allowed the X12 transactions to be used in smaller volume environments became available. X12 data translation software was relatively expensive, and writing custom software to use or create X12 transactions was a labor-intensive effort. But because of the need and the benefit of using business to business data transactions that used a standard format, X12 was implemented enthusiastically by medium to large size lenders and a fair number of the larger credit bureau vendors.

Once the credit bureau vendor has developed software to accept the X12 833 Credit Request and deliver the X12 200 Credit Report and/or X12 864 Text Message transactions with a lender, it should be simple to add other lenders as customers whose systems also used the same X12 data formats. Like any standard, the X12 specification defines how the data *should* look in a data

file. In actual practice, when lenders or credit bureau vendors implement a standard, they create a data file based on their interpretation of what the X12 specification says. This can lead to minor, but annoying, differences in expectations that need to be resolved in one way or another.

Of course, there have always been differences, sometimes big and sometimes small, between what is defined as a standard and the real world adherence to the standard. That's as true with X12 standards as it is with any other standard such as the Ten Commandments, Roberts Rules of Order, or the English Language. But even with the time it takes to identify and resolve deviations from the standard, the X12 transactions greatly reduced the amount of time

---

"...the X12 transactions greatly reduced the amount of time from the signing of a sales agreement to the first "live" credit transaction."

---

from the signing of a sales agreement to the first "live" credit transaction. Sometimes there is a religious fervor about the proper interpretation of the standard. Since each transaction in the realm of electronic commerce represents money being exchanged, it is usually wiser for implementers to focus on doing what it takes to begin exchanging and processing transactions as soon as possible.

Newer standards have evolved for credit reporting transactions, but the X12 Credit Reporting standards are still in use today and their use will probably continue for years to come. The compact X12 transaction files allow for fast transmission and efficient data storage. Companies that are successfully processing large volumes of X12 transactions may find it hard to justify converting to another data standard just because it's "new."

XML—The Extensible Markup Language

The "buzz" regarding the Extensible Markup Language, or XML, began in earnest around 1999 when it was approved as a standard by the

World Wide Web Consortium (W3C). Here is an example of XML data, which is obviously an address organized into Street, City, State, and Postal Code components.

XML Data Format:

```
<ADDRESS Street="401 9th ST NW"
City="Washington" StateCode="DC"
PostalCode="20004"/>
```

"Washington" is clearly labeled as being a City. "DC" is clearly a State Code, and "20004" is a Postal Code. As you can see, XML is not rocket science. It provides a flexible, easy to build and maintain framework for describing and organizing data. The representation of this same data in an X12 format might appear as shown below. It's easy for anyone familiar with city names and common address formats to determine that this is address data containing a street name, city, state, and postal code.

X12 Data Format:

```
N3~401 9th ST NW
N4~Washington~DC~20004
```

Here are sample X12 and XML representations of the same court record from a credit report. This less common data is not easily deciphered in the X12 format as it is in the XML format

X12 Data Format:

```
RO~03~01~3~14~7541~LS~31~1099999~23
DTP~270~D8~20020104
DTP~621~D8~20020313
DTP~666~D8~20020313
DTP~234~CM~200203
```

XML Data Format:

```
<CREDIT_PUBLIC_RECORD _
Type="Judgment"
_DispositionType="Satisfied"
_DispositionDate="2002-03"
_FiledDate="2002-01-04"
_ReportedDate="2002-03-13"
_PaidDate="2002-03-13"
_DocketIdentifier="1099999"
_LegalObligationAmount="7541"
_PaymentFrequencyType="LumpSum"/>
```

For the X12 data, an implementation guides is needed to decode and understand its content. Even without looking at an implementation guide, it is as easy to understand the meaning of the XML data today as it will be ten or twenty years from now. This is an important trait for mortgage data that may be archived for up to thirty-seven years. Easy readability is also an asset during software development and testing, and whenever there are production issues that need resolution by a customer service representative.

XML has been widely embraced by the software industry. Software that supports XML is readily available and relatively inexpensive. New standards are being developed using XML as their definition framework. Some of these are vertical market standards like the MISMO XML Automated Underwriting System transaction, and many have horizontal market application like the Web Services standards, designed to simplify the access to software services across computer and operating system platforms.

So is XML the all knowing, all powerful, magic solution to all of the world's data processing problems? Not quite. For one thing, the XML representation of a set of data is considerably larger than the X12 representation of the same data, as the previous example showed. The

> *"XML standards can either become a lingua franca or a Tower of Babel, or both"*

XML format was clearly represented with 255 characters of data, while the X12 representation only required a compact 115 characters of data. In addition, because XML data files are so easy to create and implement, companies have been quick to implement their own custom XML data formats for use inside and outside their companies. XML standards can either become a *lingua franca* or a Tower of Babel, or both.

MISMO XML standards

For the mortgage industry, the promise and

potential hazards of XML led to the creation of MISMO — the Mortgage Industry Standards Maintenance Organization (www.mismo.org). In Spanish, "mismo" means "the same." The goal of MISMO is to create data structures that are "the same" and easily recognized between business partners. Like the X12 standards development effort, MISMO is made up of companies and individuals volunteering their time, effort, and business knowledge to create a data standard that hopefully is beneficial to all of the users of the standards.

After its creation in late 1999, one of the first tasks that MISMO tackled was to create a *Logical Data Dictionary* (LDD) for all of the business data that is exchanged between mortgage industry partners. This mortgage industry dictionary is probably the most valuable product that MISMO has produced for the simple reason that business data that has been clearly defined and agreed on by the industry participants is more likely to be used in a correct and consistent manner.

For example, the generic term *"Loan Amount"* could have a slightly different meaning depending on where it is used in the mortgage process. On the mortgage loan application form, the applicant is requesting a "loan amount." At the closing, the borrower signs a note agreeing to pay back a specified "loan amount" to the mortgage lender. The loan amount that the borrower requested on the loan application may not end up being the same as the amount that the lender is agreeing to loan to the borrower. Discussions among the participants in this early stage of MISMO led to the creation of two separate terms for loan amount in the MISMO LDD. The definition of each data element also includes its location on the Universal Residential Loan Application (URLA):

- **Borrower Requested Loan Amount** — the total dollar amount of the mortgage note that is being requested by the borrower. This amount may include financed PMI (private mortgage insurance), MIP (mortgage insurance premium), and Funding Fees. It is collected on the URLA in Section I (Amount) and in Section VII, line 'o'.

- **Base Loan Amount** — the amount to be loaned to the borrower, not including PMI, MIP, or Funding Fee. It is collected on the URLA in Section VII, line 'm'.

The MISMO LDD is an invaluable resource for companies who are well established in the mortgage industry and, even more so, for companies that are just beginning. Although the information present in the MISMO LDD is commonly known among the folks familiar with the business side of the mortgage industry, it is extremely educational for newcomers and can help them avoid expensive mistakes. Like any language dictionary, the MISMO LDD is always growing and evolving. It is the foundation for data structures that have already been developed and those that will be developed in the future, whether they use the XML framework or some other standard.

The first data structures produced, *MISMO Version 1*, revolved around the concept of an electronic loan package. The idea was that loan data from the various mortgage process areas could eventually be merged into an individual loan "package" like pieces of a pie. One segment of the "pie" might contain loan application data. Other segments might hold credit report data, mortgage insurance data, title data, appraisal data, loan data, etc. In the center of the "pie" was "core data" that was common to all mortgage process areas, such as borrower and property information.

(The industry's response: "If we're going to use XML to transact business, shouldn't we build formats that are optimized for that purpose?")

In mid-2001, the first *MISMO Version 2* standards were published. In MISMO Version 2, there was a deliberate move towards more "transactional" structures. Rather than focusing on the building of a single loan package, MISMO Version 2 was more oriented towards electronic commerce—exchanging business data as transactions. For example, there is a transaction for requesting an automated underwriting decision. There are others for requesting credit reports, appraisals, flood certifications, mortgage insurance, and title insurance. Other transactions are built to provide the response data to the request transactions, such as the actual credit report data, appraisal data, etc.

(The industry's response: "Great! We've got transactions, but how are we going to consolidate all of this information into a single loan file, so that it can be recorded and archived?")

The architecture for MISMO Version 3 is currently under development. In the computer industry, "Version 3" is a marketing label that translates as "this is the one that finally works as it's supposed to." It's hard to say at this point, but this version will probably end up as some type of blend of the "loan-centric" approach of MISMO Version 1 and the "transactional" view of MISMO Version 2. MISMO Version 3 will also correct some inconsistencies and errors, but mostly it will allow for a more precise definition of what is considered to be valid data.

The Effects of Implementing MISMO XML Data Standards

*Data standards have
leveled the playing field*

For companies like credit bureaus vendors whose product is the credit data, the use of data standards removes the uniqueness that distinguishes one company's product from a competitor's product. When the processed credit data is formatted according to the MISMO XML

"Using common data standards reduces the number of factors that distinguish one credit bureau vendor from another. Therefore, price, customer service, and the accuracy of the data become the most important selling points when a credit bureau vendor approaches a lender."

---

standards and implementation guides, there should normally be little difference between the content of a credit report produced by a two

billion dollar company and that produced by a two million dollar company. Using common data standards reduces the number of factors that distinguish one credit bureau vendor from another. Therefore, price, customer service, and the accuracy of the data become the most important selling points when a credit bureau vendor approaches a lender.

The first wave of companies to implement the MISMO XML credit standards were mostly smaller companies who were looking to gain recognition and market share by demonstrating their ability to implement a leading edge, state of the art technology. Some of the established leaders in the industry also became early adopters to take advantage of the quick product development times that the steadily growing library of XML software tools offered. With the introduction of MISMO Version 2, the pace of adoption picked up when the MISMO Automated Underwriting System (AUS) standards were endorsed by both Fannie Mae and Freddie Mac. These two government sponsored enterprises purchase the bulk of home mortgages and mortgage related securities, and are vital to the success of the mortgage industry.

*Data standards can mask
data quality problems*

Data standards can give the false impression that underlying data is more accurate just because it is presented in a standard way. The standards may just be adding another layer of translation, which gives an additional opportunity for the incorrect or misleading conversion of information that often occurs in the translation process. There are a number of stages in which potential confusion and errors can be introduced as the credit data is converted from one data format to another. Two of the stages are especially critical.

The first critical stage occurs when the original loan account data and public record data are reported to the credit data repositories, Equifax, Experian, and Trans Union. This data is normally reported to the credit data repositories using a data standard, called "Metro 2." In this stage, the credit grantors must convert their own internal account data and payment history data into the Metro 2 format. Whenever data is converted from one format to another, it frequently happens that for some old data there is not an "exact fit" in the new format.

For example, if a credit account balance is 120 days past due and a portion of the balance is charged off by the credit grantor, should "120 Days Past Due" or "Charge-Off" be recorded as the account's current status? This is just one example of the numerous "decision points" that credit grantors deal with when writing software to convert their internal data into the Metro 2 format. The standards body that maintains the Metro 2 standard, the Computer Industry Data Association (CDIA), does an admirable job of addressing these types of questions in their documentation and their "Metro 2 Accuracy Workshops." But with the sheer number of large and small credit grantors, collection agencies, and courts reporting data, along with the size and complexity of the Metro 2 standard, there are bound to be inconsistencies and errors in the data being reported to the credit data repositories.

Each of the credit data repositories then converts the Metro 2 format data into their own unique, proprietary data storage formats. When a credit report is requested by a credit bureau's customer, another data translation takes place when the credit data repository retrieves the credit data from their databases and prepares the credit report format that is transmitted to the credit bureau vendor.

The second critical stage of data transformation takes place during processing of the credit data by the credit bureau vendor. Since the current trend in the mortgage industry is to request credit files from all three credit data repositories, there will be a lot of data from the three credit data repositories that will be duplicated. The credit bureau software first identifies which liability accounts and public records are duplicated. If all of the duplicates are not identified, then the borrower could appear to have more debt than they really have.

Once duplicates are identified, most credit bureau vendors begin a process called "blending" or "merging" of the data from the duplicates. This process is almost more of an art than a science and has a number of "decision points" that can have a significant effect on the content of the "merged" data record. Because of this, the final mortgage credit report data can have significant differences from one credit bureau vendor to another.

These effects are usually minimal for a credit report on a borrower that has a fairly "clean" payment history. But credit reports for borrowers with collections, large numbers of late payments, etc. are scrutinized much more closely by the lenders who offer credit to those with less than perfect payment histories. The differences from one credit bureau vendor's credit report to another's can affect whether or not the applicant is offered a loan, along with the interest rate and "points" options that are presented to the applicant.

Here's an area where the data standards can help the lender ask the right questions about the credit report data and make the right choices about how that data is used in making their underwriting decisions.

Data standards can help expose data quality problems

For a lender, specifying the use of a standard data format among its credit bureau vendors can be helpful in uncovering data inconsisten-

---

"When the lender began getting MISMO XML formats from both credit bureau vendors, they were able to easily compare the credit data for the first time."

---

cies. A few months ago, a major sub-prime lender converted to exclusive use of the MISMO XML Version 2 Credit Reporting data format. Previously, they had used a proprietary credit report format from one credit bureau vendor and the MISMO XML credit report from another. When the lender began getting MISMO XML formats from both credit bureau vendors, they were able to easily compare the credit data for the first time. When requesting a credit report on the same individual from both credit bureau vendors, one credit bureau's report indicated that there were six liabilities with a current status of "collection," while the other credit bureau vendor's data showed 17 liabilities with a current status of "collection." When the lender compared other credit reports, they consistently found these types of differences from the two different credit bureau vendors, even though the reports were generated from the same credit repository data.

The differences were significant enough that the lender's Automated Underwriting System (AUS) might approve loans using one vendor's credit reports, but reject them or trigger higher interest rates or "points" when using credit reports issued by the other vendor for the same credit repository data. This situation did not come to light until they started getting credit data from both credit bureau vendors using the MISMO Version 2 Credit Reporting standards.

Further investigation showed that when one credit bureau vendor's software merged the duplicate liabilities from the three credit data repositories into a single liability, it used the payment status from the most recent duplicate liability for the "merged" liability. The other credit bureau vendor's software used the most adverse payment status of all of the duplicates for the "merged" liability, regardless of the date that it was reported, which resulted in more liabilities being reported with a current status of "collection."

Having credit data available in a common data format allows lenders to identify these types of differences, determine their origins, and exercise the proper due diligence before using the credit data for their underwriting decisions.

Conclusion

This isn't really the conclusion, because there are enough other issues that affect the content and quality of a credit report to fill a book. But for this particular article, this is the time to take inventory.

DO standards benefit us?

- Standards define how things should be.
- Standards enable us to see things the same way.
- Standards benefit those who need them.
- They impart understandable information.
- It takes discipline to adhere to them.
- Standards are a facade. They can hide what's underneath.
- Standards can make deviations, differences, and flaws more obvious.
- Focusing too much on standards can keep you from exploring better options.

Regardless of your industry, any of these answers may apply. Data standards are essential for any industry that combines data from multiple sources. Companies need to remember that just because data is presented in a standard format, it does not mean they can relax their due diligence in verifying the quality and meaning of the data before they use it in their own applications. At the beginning of this chapter, we included a quote stating that data standards level the playing field, bringing advantages to small and large companies alike. Companies and industries who recognize that data standards— or any standards—not only change the playing field, but significantly enlarge it, are destined to lead in the evolving marketplace.

Copyright @ Mike Bixby & Greg Alvord

40

Health Informatics Standardisation— Cooperation Not Conflict

ADRIAN V. STOKES

CAT Ltd.

Abstract: *Although health is a major industry sector, there was relatively little standardisation until the early 1990s, far later than comparable sectors. In the last decade, there has been a significant growth in standardisation in this field, both in formal standards bodies and elsewhere (notably industry consortia). One particular feature of this work has been the cooperation between the two arenas leading to faster development of standards, better standards, and ones that are readily accepted by industry. This article examines the development of standardisation in health informatics with particular emphasis on that cooperation and the results of it.*

Introduction

There are many mechanisms for defining standards, from internal company ones to formal, internationally agreed upon ones. These mechanisms are not mutually exclusive and, indeed, there is often conflict and the production of competing standards. Much is made of this— it is often reported that the formal standards-making process is far too unresponsive to user needs and takes far too long; conversely, the less formal mechanisms such as consortia of manufacturers are reported to produce standards that are not rigidly defined and have interworking problems.

Over the last few years, there has been a growing realisation that the truth is between the two extremes and that the huge investment required for standardisation cannot be duplicated, triplicated, or worse. Also, there are relatively few people who wish to be involved in the standards-making process and this rare resource must not be wasted.

As a result, the formal (*"de jure"*) standards bodies have been introducing mechanisms such

> *"Over the last few years, there has been a growing realisation that the truth is between the two extremes and that the huge investment required for standardisation cannot be duplicated, triplicated, or worse."*

as Workshops and Fast-Track procedures in order to obviate many of the criticisms of their processes. Similarly, the other standards-makers (*"de facto"*) are often feeding their results into the formal processes to obtain the imprimatur and rigid formalism of the international bodies.

One of the best examples of the convergence of the various standards processes is in health informatics and this is described in the remainder of this paper.

Background

For such a large, major industry sector, standardisation in healthcare started extremely late—far later than in other major sectors such as banking. Indeed, much of the work in this field has taken place only over the last decade.

This is not to say that there was not work being undertaken in the field, but it relied on separate, generally uncoordinated, initiatives often undertaken by a very small number of people—sometimes just individuals.

Early initiatives

Perhaps the major early initiative was that of the MEDIX project in the mid-1980s, under the auspices of the Institute of Electrical and Electronics Engineers (IEEE), an international professional body based in the USA. Other initiatives in the USA included a consortium of manufacturers (HL7) on messaging, the American Society for Testing and Materials (ASTM), and cooperation between a professional organisation, the American College of Radiologists (ACR), and a trade body, the National Electronic Manufacturers' Association (NEMA), resulting in the DICOM imaging standard. These bodies are described below.

There was also active standardisation work in Japan (especially in the imaging field) and in Australia and New Zealand (which resulted in the setting up of a Joint Technical Committee for Health Informatics between the two countries).

In the late 1980s, it was clear that there was little coordinated work in standardisation in health informatics, especially in Europe. Despite the undoubted advantages of such standardisation, the field was substantially behind other industry sectors.

The European Commission Mandate

In 1989, to provide an impetus for such work, the European Commission issued a "Mandate" (BC-IT-SI-05) for the *"Study and Investigation of the problems related to Standardisation in Medical Informatics."* The mandate was separated into two parts; part A resulted in the establishment of a Technical Committee (TC 251) of the principal European standards body, the Comité Européen de Normalisation (CEN).

The second part of the Mandate, dealing with the open systems aspects of medical informatics, culminated in the establishment of an EWOS (European Workshop for Open Systems) Expert Group on Healthcare—EWOS/EG MED—in early 1991. EWOS/EG MED had formal liaison status with CEN/TC 251 and operated in almost exactly the same way in relation to TC 251 as if it were another TC 251 Working Group.

Much of the early work of CEN/TC 251 used the EDIFACT (Electronic Data Interchange for Administration Commerce and Transport) syntax and the Western European EDIFACT Board (WEEB) Message Development Group for Healthcare (WEEB/MD9) also had formal liaison status with CEN/TC 251.

In 1998, EWOS was closed down and a new organisation—based largely on the EWOS model—was set up as part of CEN. This was known as CEN/ISSS (Information Society Standardization System) and its purpose was to facilitate workshops to develop CEN Workshop Agreements (CWAs), which are similar to pre-standards. To date, no Workshops have been set up in the health informatics field. Following the closure of EWOS, some of the work of EG MED was abandoned while the remainder was transferred to various TC 251 Working Groups.

The logical development from these initiatives was for a full International Committee to be set up in health informatics and there was general agreement that this should be done. Following initial planning meetings, a proposal was made to ISO to set up a Technical Committee and ISO/TC 215 was established in January 1998.

Other Standards Bodies

ASTM

The American Society for Testing and Materials is a not-for-profit organisation that develops standards in various areas by agreement between interested parties (*cf.* the international Workshop processes). In the field of health informatics, the relevant Committee is E31. ASTM provided the Secretariat of ISO/TC 215 for the first five years of its existence.

CAP

The College of American Pathologists is a US professional society and is accredited by ANSI for the development of standards. In the field of healthcare standards, it is perhaps best known for the SNOMED (Systematized Nomenclature of Medicine) terminology and coding scheme and, more recently, SNOMED-CT (SNOMED Clinical Terms) based on collaboration with the UK National Health Service.

DICOM

The American College of Radiology and the National Electrical Manufacturers' Association worked together to produce a standard for imaging, known as DICOM (Digital Imaging and Communications in Medicine). The standard is now developed under the auspices of the DICOM Standards Committee. Its goals are *"to achieve interoperability and to improve workflow efficiency between imaging systems and other information systems in healthcare environments worldwide."* This body has a formal liaison with ISO/TC 215. DICOM has also set up a joint working group with HL7 (see below) and has cooperated closely with two Japanese bodies, JIRA (the Japan Industries Association of Radiological Systems) and MEDIS-DC (the Medical Information System Development Centre). It is also an ANSI accredited standards developer.

Health Level 7 - HL7

HL7 is another organisation accredited by the American National Standards Institute as a Standards Development Organisation. Founded in 1987, like similar organisations it is a not-for-profit consortium of manufacturers and other interested parties. The specific domain that it addresses is clinical and administrative data.

The name of the organisation derives from the upper (seventh) layer of the ISO Reference Model of Open Systems Interconnection (RM-OSI)[1]—the application layer.

There are currently 20 international affiliates. The total membership of HL7 is about 2500 and this membership covers the major healthcare information systems vendors.

HL7 is not a formal liaison member of ISO/TC 215 although there is close cooperation between the organisations. Indeed, there is a pilot project arranged between the ISO Technical Management Board and HL7 that HL7 standards will be published jointly by ISO and HL7. Similarly, a Memorandum of Understanding has been developed between CEN/TC 251 and HL7.

IEEE

The Institute of Electrical and Electronics Engineers is an international professional body, based in the USA. It is perhaps best known for the IEEE 802 series of standards ("Ethernet") but it has also been extremely active in the field of healthcare. Indeed, one of the major early initiatives in healthcare standardisation was IEEE's Project 1157 (also known as MEDIX).

The second significant initiative is Project 1073. This is concerned with "point of care" devices. There is extremely close cooperation between the IEEE work and ISO/TC 215 (through WG 2/SG 1), and the IEEE 1073 standards are being fed into ISO as full international standards (in the ISO 11073 series reflecting the IEEE number). A taxonomy has been developed to map between the IEEE references and the ISO numbering scheme.

IHE

IHE (Integrating the Healthcare Enterprise) is another initiative from two US professional societies, the Radiological Society of North America (RSNA) and the Healthcare Information and Management Systems Society (HIMSS). The goal of standardisation is for various implementations to be able to interwork. The purpose of IHE is to encourage integration of healthcare systems by the development of profiles (subsets of standards) and to provide facilities (on an annual basis) for vendors and others in the healthcare community to demonstrate interworking. There are IHE demonstrations in various countries, including a number in Europe and Japan.

Although the origins of IHE were in imaging, it now covers most aspects of healthcare.

Early Cooperation

One principal reason for requiring standardisation is the fact that markets are global and manufacturers are generally unwilling to make products for small areas such as individual countries or even entire regions of the world. Thus it is vital that standards developers cooperate and do not produce competing standards (usually on the "Not Invented Here" basis). It

---

"One principal reason for requiring standardisation is the fact that markets are global and manufacturers are generally unwilling to make products for small areas such as individual countries or even entire regions of the world. "

---

can be seen that the structure for the development of standards in healthcare is very complex. While there are liaisons between the various organisations, it is clear there is a need for full cooperation.

An extremely good example of early cooperation in this field was in the area of medical imaging. Not long after CEN/TC 251 was set up, one of the mandates it was given was to develop a standard for medical imaging. A Project Team was set up and did a considerable amount of work. In the meantime, DICOM (see above) was developing its own *de facto* standards. The Project Team leader was also involved in that standardisation effort and realised that there was considerable overlap in the work and that it was in no one's interest for the result to be two competing standards, one in the USA and one in Europe. After considerable discussion, it was agreed that the CEN Project Team would, in principle, abandon its existing work and adopt the DICOM standard. Because the DICOM standard was oriented towards the USA, some changes were needed and these were willingly accepted. Also, not all parts of the standard were

relevant to Europe so the European standard only adopted those parts that were relevant. Finally, priorities in Europe were somewhat different from those in the USA so European workers in this field developed parts of the DICOM standard (in cooperation with the USA but with a clear European lead).

After some problems with Intellectual Property Rights and version control, and certain formalities regarding access to the standard, it was adopted as *"Medical image and related data interchange format standards" (ENV 12052:1995)*.

A second example was in the field of bedside medical devices. This fell within the remit of EWOS/EG MED and contact was made with the IEEE committee working in this field (IEEE 1073). At that time, the draft standards were very much oriented to the USA (including, for example, references to "American Wire Ga[u]ge"). EWOS/EG MED agreed to "internationalise" the standards and considerable work was done. When EWOS was abolished, this work was taken over by CEN/TC 251/WG 4. Also, when ISO/TC 215 was formed, this work fell within the scope of TC 215/WG 2/SG 1. Most meetings of the CEN and ISO Working Groups are held jointly, with the main participants in the IEEE process also attending (as full members).

It was agreed that the results would be published as multiple parts of an ISO standard and, in fact, it was agreed by the ISO Council that the documents were to be known as ISO/IEEE standards to emphasise the joint development (they were also being published by IEEE). Close collaboration is continuing to develop further parts of the standard, some in the CEN Working Group, some in the IEEE and others jointly.

Cooperation with HL7

Perhaps the main area of potential conflict was in the field of messaging and communication between systems. In Europe, it was decided to adopt the EDIFACT [2] syntax and a number of messages were developed, particularly in the UK. Following early work, it was decided that the relevant models would be developed in a completely syntax-independent manner, then mapped into the relevant syntax (an early study of interchange formats recommended three syntaxes, including EDIFACT).

In the USA, an industry consortium, HL7 (see above) had been formed and was developing its own messages in a much more *ad hoc* fashion, not basing them on a specific data model. Also, its syntax was "home-grown" but, like EDIFACT, was character based.

Although HL7 started out in the USA, a number of "international affiliates" were set up and fed in each country's requirements into the standards.

There was considerable tension between proponents of HL7 and of the European message development work. Furthermore, within ISO/TC 215, work was starting to develop on a full international standard that would have overlapped the existing work. The main areas of conflict were that HL7 (version 2) was not based on a theoretical data model and it was so broad that there were problems of compatibility. On the other hand, HL7 had the support of many manufacturers of healthcare systems and few, if any, wished to implement different standards for the USA and for Europe.

Many of these problems were overcome in the development of version 3 of HL7, which was based on a very formal model (the Reference Implementation Model (RIM)) and on reuseable data types (archetypes), a very similar approach to that adopted in Europe.

Following very considerable discussion, the ISO Council developed an agreement with HL7 stating that HL7 standards could be "fast-tracked" into ISO in a similar way to that for the IEEE standards mentioned above. This involved recognition by HL7 of the formal standards process and by ISO of the requirements of industry.

At the ISO TC 215 Plenary Meeting meeting in Oslo in May 2003, a number of significant resolutions were passed. These included ISO requesting HL7 to submit their Clinical Document Architecture (CDA), Version 2.5 of the HL7 standard and the Reference Implementation Model into ISO. Because of the agreement between HL7 and ISO, these drafts will be "fast-tracked."

Summary and Conclusions

The development of competing standards results in a great deal of nugatory work and the better/best standards are not necessarily the ones that are finally adopted (e.g. standards for videotapes or TCP/IP vs. OSI). Furthermore, features that are in the "losing" standards are unlikely to be included in the "winning" ones and hence the chance to improve those standards is lost.

The only sensible way forward is for the proponents of competing standards to collaborate closely and to produce standards that are technically sound and will be widely adopted, having the support of all interested parties.

The development of health informatics standards in recent years has shown how such cooperation may be achieved and demonstrates the significant advantages of this approach.

Notes

[1] "Information technology - Open Systems Interconnection - Basic Reference Model", International Organization for Standardization, ISO/IEC 7498.

[2] "Electronic data interchange for administration, commerce and transport (EDIFACT) - Application level syntax rules", International Organization for Standardization, ISO 9735.

41

The Havoc of Non-Interoperability

MARK REICHARDT

Open GIS Consortium (OGC)

Abstract: *A recent Delphi Group Study, "The Value of Standards" (June 2003),*[1] *gathered the responses of more than 800 end users, software vendors, and service providers to identify current attitudes and expectations for software standards. Delphi's conclusions were striking: "There is a clear and sudden shift in attitudes towards software standards. The climate of economic constraint and risk aversion along with the mandate to integrate systems on both sides of the firewall has created a sea change in the sense of imperative to adopt software standards. .... The results portray a shifting landscape where **standards will provide the foundation for long term advances in the way software is built, bought and deployed.**" [Emphasis mine.] The Open GIS Consortium (OGC),*[2] *an innovative public-private partnership, has worked for a decade to cause such change in the domain of digital geographic information and geoprocessing. "Economic constraint and risk aversion," always important drivers in the geospatial domain, are increasingly important as agencies and businesses face recession and national security threats. In this paper, we look at how standards are creating a new geospatial information space and discuss how the methods employed by the Open GIS Consortium to enable interoperability in the spatial technology domain provide a model for the way standards will be built, adopted, and deployed.*

Introduction— The Potential for Havoc

It is always good to take a positive approach in trying to convey an idea, and indeed, this paper is about very encouraging progress. So I address "havoc" at the outset to be done with it. By "havoc," I refer mainly to Webster's "great confusion and disorder," though I shall also make reference to Webster's "wide and general destruction" definition.[3]

Our world is going through a communications revolution on top of a computing revolution, and the many technology issues this involves frequently cause confusion in the corporate technology decision making process. In a period of rapid change, it has been difficult for people to stay sufficiently informed to make good decisions about technology. The technology has been immature as well as overwhelming in volume, hype, and rate of appearance in new products. Thus, in hindsight, we often see that resources have been applied less effectively than they might have been. This sense of confusion and disorder has been amplified by the latest phase in the communications revolution in which almost all computers have been attached to a vast network. The Net is potentially a wonderful thing, but besides unleashing evils like viruses and spam, it has shown that our applications often don't work very well together. That is, they are often non-interoperable."

Non-interoperability impedes the sharing of data and the sharing of computing resources, causing more resources than necessary to be expended on data, software, and hardware. Since the Delphi report states that organizations today are under "economic constraints," the issue of non-interoperability is one that obviously needs to be resolved quickly.

The report also states that organizations are risk-averse. Non-interoperability increases technology risks, which are a function of 1) the probability that a technology will not deliver its expected benefit and 2) the consequence to the system (and users) of the technology not delivering that benefit. Risk assessment must take into account evolving requirements and support costs.[4] Some technology risks derive from being locked in to one vendor, others from choosing a standard that the market later abandons.

The most dire risks associated with non-interoperability are real-world risks. Today, lives and property depend on digital information flowing smoothly from one information system

---

"The most dire risks associated with non-interoperability are real-world risks. Today, lives and property depend on digital information flowing smoothly from one information system to another."

---

to another. Public safety, disaster management, and military applications increasingly depend on communication between dissimilar systems used by groups with different but related missions. No single organization produces all the data (so it's inconsistent) and no single vendor provides all the systems (so the systems use different system architectures, which are usually based on different proprietary interfaces). Thus, there is the potential for real world havoc.

In this section, we first consider the particularly difficult interoperability challenges of geographic information and geoprocessing software. Then we look at a scenario that illustrates the dangerous but all too common real world trouble that ensues when those challenges are not met.

Sources of geoprocessing non-interoperability

Few kinds of information are more complex than information about the location, shape of, and relationships among geographic features and phenomenon. One reason is that there are many fundamentally different kinds of *geoprocessing systems*, that is, systems for creating, storing, retrieving, processing, and displaying geospatial data. These include vector and raster geographic information systems (GIS) and systems for Earth imaging (imaging devices on satellites and airplanes), computer-aided design (CAD) (for roads, sewers, bridges, etc.), navigation, surveying, cartography, location based services (delivered, for example, via cell phones that can give directions and report about what's nearby), facilities management, etc. Numerous vendors work within each of these technology domains who did not, until they joined OGC, consult with their competitors to form agreements on how the data should be structured and how the systems might communicate. This lack of communication coupled with the many different ways of measuring and mathematically representing the Earth produced a complex and non-interoperable geoprocessing environment. Added to that "havoc" are the user-side semantic issues: Without coordination, no two highway departments, for example, will use the same attribute schemas, measurement types, and data types in describing a road. Their "metadata" (data describing their data sets) will also use different schemas, making automated data discovery and data sharing difficult.

Scenario

Suppose a gasoline truck hits a utility pole where a state highway intersects a county road. Gasoline spills and burns, some of it running into a storm drain that empties into a stream. The utility pole, owned by the electric utility and used also by a cable company and a phone company, falls amid a tangle of wires. Traffic backs up in all directions. People are injured and the fire is spreading to nearby properties.

In considering the information sharing one would like to see in this scenario, we begin by merely listing the government and private entities that might have and/or urgently need spatial information: the state and local police, the ambulance company, the local fire department, the company that employs the truck driver, the company that does the hazardous material (HAZMAT) transportation monitoring, the state and local highway departments, the local sewer department, field engineering and customer service groups at each of the "wires" companies, the traffic reporters at the local news broadcasting stations, the state department of environmental protection, the owner of the burning property, and perhaps others, including federal authorities such as the Federal Emergency Management Administration (FEMA), the Environmental Protection Agency (EPA), and the National Transportation Safety Board (NTSB). Currently, some of these information flows, particularly those that require only a phone call or that work through proprietary interfaces in tightly coupled systems, work smoothly. But most of the information sharing that involves digital spatial data cannot happen in real time. It often takes hours or days because no single technology provider has "tightly coupled" all those systems nor have all of these providers yet implemented the new OGC Web Services standards that enable "loose coupling" of multiple vendors' applications.

Now imagine a much broader disaster such as a major flood, an earthquake, an explosion, a building collapse in a downtown area, a natural gas pipeline explosion, or a sudden national epidemic. Consider the impact of non-interoperable data on services such as power, water, electricity, sewage, and transportation, along with the impact on safety and repair costs. Suffice it to say that all "spatial data infrastructure" stakeholder groups and the the vendors who serve them have a responsibility to work together to establish interoperable geoprocessing that will help plan for, mitigate, and respond to such real world havoc. As the HAZMAT carriers say, "Information is safety."

The Good News: Open Standards Conquer the Havoc

As the Delphi report states, "There is a clear and sudden shift in attitudes towards software standards." It appears that both intra-enterprise interoperability and inter-enterprise interoperability are now seen to be much more important than just a year or two ago. This is easy to understand given people's experience with non-interoperability havoc and the sudden obviousness of the following logic:

1. *Computing* means to store, retrieve, and process data.

2. To avoid havoc (and to enjoy many positive benefits), our computer systems need to be able to *communicate*.

3. *Communication* means transmitting or exchanging through a common system of symbols, signs, or behavior.

4. *Standardization* means agreeing on a common system.

5. Therefore, we should promote standardization and employ standards in our computer systems.

This realization is perhaps induced by the Internet and Web, whose open standards (HTTP, TCP/IP, XML, etc.) and extraordinary success give us a taste of what interoperability is all about.

Open standards in the geospatial world

To begin this discussion, we must first define the term *open standard*. OGC defines an open standard as one that:

1. is created in an inclusive, international, participatory industry process

2. is owned in common

3. has free rights of distribution. that is, anyone can share it with anyone, free of charge

4. is free and openly available to the public, in all its details

5. does not discriminate, in the license or the standard, against persons or groups

6. is technology neutral—no provision of the license may be predicated on any individual technology or style of interface

By this definition, a de facto standard established by one company, an exclusive group of companies, or a government is not an open standard, even if it is published and available for use by anyone at no charge. The Web must not depend on proprietary standards and the same applies to the "Spatial Web," which OGC defines as the set of all Web-based geoinformation and geoprocessing resources that are accessible through open interfaces.

Open standards are developed by non-exclusive industry consortia and task forces (like the OGC, the World Wide Web Consortium (W3C), the Open Mobile Alliance (OMA), the Internet Engineering Task Force (IETF), and others) as interlocking parts of interoperability frameworks and reference models. These organizations' framework and reference model documents guide developers and integrators in designing customer-specific open architectures, which specify the open data models (information schemas) and open interfaces, protocols, etc. that will meet the needs of particular enterprises based on their user needs, including business models and work flows.

Open standards address user needs that can only be met by cooperation among system vendors. *Overall, users want to maximize the value of past and future investments in systems and data.*[5] [6] In the geospatial world, that general statement points to the following user needs:

1. The need to share and reuse data in order to decrease costs (avoid redundant data collection), obtain additional or better information, and increase the value of data holdings

2. The need to choose the best tool for the job and the related need to reduce technology and procurement risks (i.e., the need to avoid being locked in to one solution or vendor)

3. The need to leverage investments in software and data, such as enabling more people to benefit from using geospatial data across applications without the need for additional training

It happens that the open framework that addresses these basic needs (documented in more detail in any open geoprocessing architecture) makes it possible for vendors to address a whole new array of user needs that require a standards foundation. These additional user needs include:

1. The need to organize geographic data stored in text and on video, audio, and other media

2. The need to access and process on-line sensor data (a sensor is always someplace) from multiple sources

3. The need for Location Based Services that are portable across devices, networks, and providers

4. The need to apply different symbology to data for different applications

5. The need to take advantage of grid computing for geoprocessing applications

The solutions that vendors will offer to fill

"The solutions that vendors will offer to fill these needs must have a standards platform that enables them to establish new markets and new opportunities for growth."

---

these needs must have a standards platform that enables them to establish new markets and new opportunities for growth.

Enabling a New Information Space

Information technology standards are business enablers and channelers just like highways, air traffic rules, business laws, and HAZMAT transportation regulations. The five-point list above demonstrates how a platform of open standards enables innovation and proliferation of new capabilities. Recognizing this, vendors in OGC's consensus process give up their proprietary "lock" on customers in favor of the chance to participate in a greatly expanded market.

Just as the World Wide Web opened up a whole new information space, the OGC-enabled Spatial Web opens up a vastly expanded geospatial information space. Few people a decade ago could imagine the Web-enabled information space. In the same way, few outside of OGC to-

---

"Information technology standards are business enablers and channelers just like highways, air traffic rules, business laws, and HAZMAT transportation regulations."

---

day imagine the greatly expanded geospatial information space that will result from a platform of open standards for geoprocessing. What is and isn't known about location, proximity, spatial distribution, and extent (of assets, suppliers, customers, service providers, purchases, risks, opportunities, etc.) is tremendously important. More importantly, however, is that our information systems are largely blind to such information and incapable of useful spatial calculation and presentation. OGC members believe that "spatial enablement" will have a profound and largely positive impact in the public and private sector, similar to the impact of the Web itself. Ultimately, we believe that spatial enablement will drive new business opportunities and allow new human activities.

Enabling Other New Information Spaces: The OGC Model

One might argue that governments, industries, professions, and disciplines have an absolute obligation to their stakeholders to organize consensus-based strategic "imagineering" for the purpose of creating the shared information framework that will optimally support their work in the future. OGC's experience suggests that this happens best in an inclusive, structured, consensus-based specification process with ample input from prototyping in testbeds and real-world testing in pilot projects. OGC's "Interoperability Initiatives" are testbeds, pilot projects and other short-term, intensive, multiparticipant "spiral engineering" activities that rapidly develop, test, and promote the use of OpenGIS Specifications. Specifications developed initially in testbeds typically are addressed in the OGC Technical Committee, tested in commercial products in pilot projects, and then approved by the OGC Technical committee and Planning Committee. Interoperability Initiatives provide an opportunity for technology user organizations to help guide the direction of technology by providing user interoperability requirements that are the main guiding factor in these initiatives. Other technology domains could use the same methods to quickly develop standards that are quickly implemented in commercial products and tailored to users' interoperability needs.

To ignore this opportunity, leave interoperability to a vendors' de facto standards, or hire consultants to build a "closed" system from the top down, is to condemn stakeholders to more years of havoc. Vendors and consultants will play essential roles, of course, because the actual development, maintenance, customization, and service of software require special skills. Success, however, lies in the ability to engage these experts and other stakeholders in the process mentioned above.

It should be added that data models are an important part of the information space. Geospatial data models are complex and heterogeneous. OGC has developed an XML encoding for spatial data, the Geography Markup Language (GML). When used with XML tools, GML makes it possible to resolve many of the difficulties associated with incompatible data models. The XML tools (prototyped in OGC's Geospatial One-Stop Transportation Pilot and Critical Infrastructure Protection Initiative Phase 2 pilot project) map GML-encoded data from a local model to the national model and vice versa. The data thus becomes as useful as possible to the data sharing partner who uses a different model. Although certain elements of one model cannot map to the other, the XML tools make these inconsistencies plain in all their details so that it is easy for data managers to focus on the critical schema elements that don't map. This makes both data sharing and data coordination much easier. Already, different disciplines, industry sectors localities, and professions are forming data committees to manage data coordination, sometimes in the context of setting up data consortia that negotiate data contributions, access, pricing, etc. This work, too, is part of the consensus work that builds the information space.

Today and in the future user requirements will almost always involve interoperability, that is, communication between different systems. It is thus necessary to pay attention to:

1. The requirements of multiple users and classes of users

2. The details of technical communication standards

3. The ideas, needs, and stated directions of multiple technology providers

The specification process should involve thoughtful consideration of what the community does now, what its members may want to accomplish in the years ahead, and what kind of information flows will be necessary to enable those accomplishments. From these requirement statements, participants construct a framework of interoperability specifications that will support all current and future work. Such an effort is intellectually challenging, socially reward-

---

"With so much at stake, imagine what could be accomplished if a large number of people each took a small step and insisted on open standards in procurements."

---

ing, and empowering for the present and future community. In addition to the process recommended above, it is important to emphasize the crucial role that users play in the move towards open standards. With so much at stake, imagine what could be accomplished if a large number of people each took a small step and insisted on open standards in procurements.

Much more needs to written about this process, which is at the creative leading edge of

standards setting. Additional topics might include:

1. How can OGC's successful technology-steering-through-standards-setting model be employed in broader information technology (IT) domains?

2. How can such a process be employed as a tool of industrial or economic policy?

3. How can such a process be employed as a tool of procurement policy? What guidelines can best leverage the process to ensure fair, application satisfying procurements that yield maximum value for the customer?

4. How can vendors in a consortium like OGC optimize their participation to best promote and stabilize markets?

5. What guidelines, regulations, best practices, etc., might minimize the potential for conflict and abuse in standards activities (anti-trust and anti-competitive behaviors, IPR issues)? Currently, for better or worse, businesses influence the policy decisions of local, national, and international governments. What role can a consortium such as OGC play in ensuring that such influence is moderated to have a wholesome effect?

6. What guidelines can make a standards process most useful as a tool for unification (markets, regions, nations, continents)?

Notes

[2] A Delphi Survey, "The Value of Standards", ©2003 Delphi Group, Ten Post Office Square, Boston, MA 02109

[2] OpenGIS Consortium (OGC): http://www.opengis.org

[3] Merriam Webster, Webster's Ninth New Collegiate Dictionary, 1984

[4] Dave Brown, Technology and Engineering Department, Defense Acquisition University, <davebrown@dau.edu>, "Evolutionary Acquisition and Spiral Development" (presentation, ca 2002)

[5] "The Importance of Going 'Open,'" an Open GIS Consortium (OGC) White Paper, September, 2003

[6] Chuck Heazel, "An Architecture Approach for Web-Enabled Systems," an unpublished article written for OGC, August, 2003

Biographies

About the Editor

Sherrie Bolin is President and CEO of Bolin Communications, a strategic consulting firm specializing in oral and written communications, standardization, strategic planning and implementation, and training and development. Bolin Communications has become the premier provider in standardization consultation, specializing in research and analysis reports, communications strategy designs and implementation, training curriculum development, and executive coaching. By emphasizing a business approach to standardization, Bolin Communications provides each client with the unique package of strategies, implementation plans, and communication methodologies to position their organization in the complex world of standardization.

Ms. Bolin is the creator and editor of *The Standards Edge* series. This series has become one of the most comprehensive resources on critical standards issues in the current environment and now serves as a significant guide to ICT industry leaders, academics, and representatives in the European Union, Japan, and the US Congress. Ms. Bolin is currently at work on additional books in *The Standards Edge* series, which examine separate strategic standardization issues. http://www.bolincommunications.com

About the Contributors

Alderman, Ray

Ray Alderman has served as Executive Director at VITA (VMEbus International Trade Association) since 1998. The organization promotes the VMEbus and the concept of open technology.

Prior to VITA, Alderman served as CEO of PEP Modular Computers, the technical director of VITA, and as a partner in two start up organizations that built computer systems for communications, military, industrial controls, transportation, and medical applications. He received his BS from the University of North Carolina and has conducted graduate work in business and computer science at the same university.

Alvord, Greg

Greg Alvord is Business-To-Business Architect for Gallagher Financial Systems. He also serves as vice chairman of the Mortgage Industry Standards Maintenance Organization (MISMO) Architecture Committee.

Alvord has worked for both lenders and vendors in the financial industry for the past ten years. With years of experience in health care, computer security, and computer science, Greg advises all of Gallagher Financial Systems' clients on how to incorporate new technologies into their production environments.

Greg is a private member of OASIS, a cross industry standards organization, and is a member of the XML Digital Signature Technical Committee. He is also a member of ACM, the academic computer science professional organization, and the American Bar Association Information Security Committee of the Science and Technology Division.

Amit, Aharon

Aharon Amit became IEC General Secretary on 1 January 1999, having served as IEC Deputy General Secretary since 1996.

Between 1971-1994, Amit held management positions in the electronics and telecommunication industries in Israel, the U.S.A., the Fiji Islands, and the UK. He has a degree in Aeronautical Engineering from the Israel Institute of Technology and attended courses towards a Masters in Aeronautical Engineering, and M.B.A. at New York University. He also attended Harvard Business School in 1984.

Bassetti, Ann

Ann Bassetti is an Associate Technical Fellow with The Boeing Company. She has long been actively involved in promoting web technology standards and is currently serving on the World Wide Web Consortium (W3C) Advisory Board.

Bixby, Mike

Mike Bixby is the founder of Bixby Consulting Inc., which provides consulting, data integration, and on-demand data translation services. In 1997, he was contracted to design and develop a business-to-business server framework for INFO1, now one of the nation's top four mortgage credit reporting bureaus. This framework allows INFO1 to seamlessly transact business with lenders using any of the dozens of public and proprietary credit data formats in use today, which include XML, X12, Fannie Mae, and a variety of flat file formats. (INFO1 is now known as LandAmerica Info1, since it was acquired in September 2003.)

In 1999, Mike wrote an XML Credit Reporting specification, which evolved into the MISMO Credit Reporting specification that is widely used today. Mike has represented INFO1 on the MISMO Governance committee since MISMO was formed. He also serves as co-chair of the Credit Reporting Work Group and participates actively in the Architecture, Schema, Core Data, and Enveloping Work Groups. He is also the author of the MISMO XML General Information and Credit Reporting Implementation Guides and a frequent speaker at mortgage industry conferences.

Bond, Phillip J.

Phillip J. Bond was sworn in as Under Secretary of Commerce for Technology on October 30, 2001. He was nominated by President George W. Bush on September 4, and confirmed by the United States Senate on October 23, 2001. From January 2002 through January 2003, Bond served concurrently as Chief of Staff to Commerce Secretary Don Evans. In his dual role, Bond worked closely with the Secretary to increase market access for US goods and services and further advance America's technological leadership at home and around the world.

Under Secretary Bond serves as the principal advisor to Secretary Evans on science and technology policy to maximize technology's contribution to America's economic growth. In this context, Mr. Bond's primary responsibilities are to supervise policy development and direction among the Office of Technology Policy (OTP), the National Institute of Standards and Technology (NIST), and the National Technical Information Service (NTIS). He also serves on four committees of the President's National Science and Technology Council (NSTC), a Cabinet-level council established by the President to coordinate science, space, and technology policy within the Federal research and development enterprise.

One of Mr. Bond's top priorities has been to transform the Technology Administration into the preeminent portal between the federal government and the U.S. technology industry. In that regard, he directs TA efforts to advocate on behalf of U.S. technology in the federal policy-making process. Some of the high priority issues that he is involved in include support for American innovation and entrepreneurship; the converging fields of nanotechnology, biotechnology, information technology and the cognitive sciences; strengthening U.S. technology cooperation with other countries, especially in areas such as standards development; education and training of a high tech U.S. workforce; and an array of issues of concern to the telecommunications and information technology industries.

Bunje, Carl

Carl Bunje is an Associate Technical Fellow with The Boeing Company. He has been active for years in a number of IT standards organizations, including The Open Group and the Distributed Management Task Force (DMTF), and is currently chair of The Open Group Customer Council.

Cargill, Carl F.

Carl F. Cargill is Sun's Director of Standards, where he manages Sun's standardization strategies, activities, and portfolio. He has been at this activity (standardization) for nearly twenty years, and has written two books (*Information Technology Standardization: Theory, Process, and Organizations* and *Open Systems Standardization: A Business Approach*), several chapters in other books on the subject, and the "Standards" entry in the Van Nostrand Reinhold "Encyclopedia of Computer Science." He was the Editor-in-Chief of StandardView, ACM's journal of Standardization, and has written scores of articles on the subject of standardization and its practical applications.

He is a member of the W3C Advisory Board, a member of the Board of Directors of the Open GIS Consortium and the Open Systems Gateway Initiative, and Chairman of the Strategic Planning Committee of the Information Technology Industry Council. He has been a member of the Coordinating Committee and General Assembly of ECMA, as well as a member of the BoD at the Object Management Group and the Open Mobile Alliance. Prior to rejoining Sun, he was the Director of Standards at Netscape, and a standards strategist at both Sun and Digital Equipment Corporation.

Croswell, Peter L.

Peter Croswell is an Executive Consultant with PlanGraphics, Inc., an independent GIS consulting firm. He has managed or been a major participant in more than 120 GIS planning, design, and implementation projects for government agencies and private firms in North America, Europe, China, and the Middle East. He has specific experience in GIS management and the effective application of information technology standards in GIS implementation and operations. Croswell is a former president of the Urban and Regional information Systems Association (URISA), a member of the National Emergency Number Association (NENA), and is certified as an ASPRS Mapping Scientist and a PMI Project Management Professional. He is a contributing author to several books and many published papers on GIS and information technology.

Davidson, Alan B.

Alan B. Davidson is Associate Director at the Center for Democracy and Technology (CDT), a Washington, D.C. non-profit group working to promote civil liberties and human rights on the Internet and other new digital media. Mr. Davidson leads CDT's Internet free expression and digital copyright projects, and efforts to promote democratic values and individual rights within Internet governance and technical standards bodies.

Mr. Davidson was a computer scientist before entering the policy world. A graduate of the Massachusetts Institute of Technology, he received an S.B. in Mathematics and Computer Science and an S.M. in Technology and Policy. Mr. Davidson worked on technology and policy issues at the U.S. Congress Office of Technology Assessment and for the White House Office of Policy Development. Mr. Davidson attended law school at Yale.

Deutsch, Donald R.

Dr. Donald Deutsch is currently Vice President of Standards Strategy and Architecture for Oracle Corporation in Redwood Shores, CA., and a

25-year veteran of the Information Technology industry. For over 20 years, Don has chaired the committee charged with defining the standard that all relational database management system products support, the INCITS H2 Technical Committee on Database (a.k.a., the ANSI SQL Committee). In addition to leading H2's development of database language SQL specifications, he represents Oracle at the executive/policy level in various consortia as well as in formal standards bodies including the INCITS Executive Board, the Executive Committee for the Java Community Process, and the W3C Advisory Board. The American National Standards Institute (ANSI) recognized Dr. Deutsch for his leadership of national and international information technology standardization as the 2002 recipient of the Edward Lohse Information Technology Medal.

Prior to joining Oracle, he held senior software engineering management positions with Sybase and the Information Services Division of General Electric Co. He has published numerous articles and papers, and co-authored an undergraduate textbook on Database Concepts. In addition, the National Bureau of Standards published his doctoral research on Modeling and Measurement of Database Management Systems.

Dickerson, Keith

Keith Dickerson has worked in the ICT industry for 25 years and is currently head of Standards for the BT Group of companies, as part of the Office of the CTO. He provides direction to BT's standards activities, identifying key technologies to BT and the standards required to support them. He is responsible for developing strategies for participation in bodies such as ITU, CEN, ETSI, IETF, TMF, W3C, OMA, and many others. He is also a member of the Internet Society (ISOC). Since February 1997, Keith has been the CEN ICT Rapporteur and Chairman of the CEN/ISSS Forum, which manages and sets direction for the CEN/ISSS workshop programme. He has led work on Telecommunications and Information Architecture in ETSI and currently serves on ETSI's board. Keith is also Chairman of the ICT Standards Board (ICTSB), the body which

coordinates the standards activities of the three European Standards Organizations and 15 fora and consortia.

Dickson, Michael

Michael Dickson has over 20 years of experience in systems software and distributed computing applications development. He was the principal architect and later the CTO and Sr. VP of Product Development at NetGenics. Mr. Dickson is the President of Lexinomics, LLC; a small consulting and software development firm specializing in web based software that leverages semantic content to facilitate search, retrieval, and mining of information.

Egyedi, Tineke

Tineke Mirjam Egyedi is senior researcher on standardization in the ICT department of the Delft University of Technology, the Netherlands. She received her Ph.D. in 1996 and has worked as a researcher and consultant since (e.g., Dutch Ministry of Transport and Water Works; KPN Research; Royal Institute of Technology in Stockholm, Sweden; the European Commission; University of Maastricht; Sun Microsystems; and Delft University of Technology). She has published widely, co-edited a few books, and guest-edited special journal issues. She is presently the associate editor of *The International Journal of IT Standards & Standardization Research (JITSR)* and a member of the editorial board of Computer Standards & Interfaces.

Among other things, she was organiser of the European Academy for Standardization (EURAS) 2001 workshop on Standards, Compatibility and Infrastructure Development, and chaired the 3rd IEEE conference on Standardization and Innovation in Information Technology (SIIT2003). She was recently elected vice-president of EURAS.

Garcia, D. Linda

Dr. Linda Garcia joined Georgetown University's Communication, Culture & Technology program in 1996 and served as Research Professor and Associate Director before becoming Director in 2001.

Previously, she was Project Director and Senior Associate at the Office of Technology Assessment of the US Congress where Dr. Garcia directed studies on electronic commerce, intellectual property rights, national and international telecommunications policy, standards development, and telecommunication and economic development.

Dr. Garcia holds a Ph.D. in Social Science and Informatics from the University of Amsterdam (1997), an M.A. in Philosophy - Comparative Government/International Politics and Social Forces from Columbia University (1968), an M.A. in International Affairs from Columbia University (1965), and a B.A. in International Relations and Economics from Syracuse University (1963).

Gingell, Rob

Rob Gingell is a Sun Fellow and Vice President at Sun Microsystems where he serves as Chief Engineer. Since 1990 he has been involved in a variety of standards efforts in a variety of roles, including author and editor of several standards as well as serving on the boards of several industry organizations. He currently serves as Chair of the Java Community Process.

Goodden, Richard

Richard Goodden is Vice President of PlanGraphics, Inc., an independent GIS consulting firm. Based near Washington, D.C., he has managed or been a major participant in numerous GIS planning, design, and implementation projects for government agencies and private firms in North America, China (PRC), the Middle East, and the United Kingdom. Mr. Goodden has been a key consultant to the City of New York since 1995 on their GIS efforts and was an active participant in the GIS response to the attacks of 9/11. He has a technical background in aerial mapping and is an ASPRS Certified Photogrammetrist.

Hatfield, Dale N.

Dale N. Hatfield is currently an independent consultant and Adjunct Professor in the Department of Interdisciplinary Telecommunications at the University of Colorado at Boulder. Between December 2000 and April 2002, Hatfield served as Chair of the Department.

Prior to joining the University of Colorado, Hatfield was the Chief of the Office of Engineering and Technology at the Federal Communications Commission and, immediately before that, he was Chief Technologist at the Agency. He retired from the Commission and government service in December 2000.

Hatfield has nearly four decades of experience in telecommunications policy and regulation, spectrum management, and related areas. He has received numerous awards including the Department of Commerce Silver Medal for contributions to domestic communications satellite policy and the Attorney General's Distinguished Service Award. More recently, he received the Distinguished Engineer award from the University of Colorado at Boulder and was elected to the Wireless Hall of Fame in the United States.

Hebner, Robert E.

Dr. Robert E. Hebner is the Director of the Center for Electromechanics at the University of Texas at Austin. Before joining the University of Texas, he was a researcher and manager at the National Institute of Standards and Technology (NIST), an agency of the U.S. Department of Commerce. As a researcher, he has co-authored more than 70 technical papers. He has held a number of management positions including Acting Director of NIST. He also worked in the Office of Management and Budget to help prepare the technology portions of the Administration's 1990 budget and at the Advanced Research Projects Agency of the Department of Defense, where he developed programs to stimulate technical advances in semiconductor manufacturing.

Hill, John

John Hill has spent 27 years in the Information and Communications Technology industry with the past 15 years in industry standards. He is currently employed by Sun Microsystems where he is responsible for implementing strategies to improve the efficiency and effectiveness of ICT standardization.

While with Sun Microsystems, AMP, Compaq,

and Unisys, Hill obtained extensive experience in industry standards, software and hardware engineering, data processing operations, strategic marketing, and technical negotiation. He has influenced industry standards for computer programming languages and operating systems. Throughout his career, Hill has participated actively and held numerous elected positions in a wide range of standardization organizations including ECMA, JTC 1/ SC22, INCITS, JTC 1 TAG, IEEE, and VITA.

Hill has received numerous awards including the 1998 National Committee for Information Technology Standards Chairman's Award, the IEEE Certificate of Appreciation (1996), and *The Wall Street Journal* Award in 1971 for a research paper entitled "The Economic Cost of the Oil Import Quota, 1959-1970."

Johnson, Larry L.

Larry Johnson, an Enterprise Systems Architecture Consultant specializing in technical collaboration, has designed and coordinated the integration architecture for the seamless deployment of software products and services in customer environments; facilitated collaborative advanced technology programs; and served as software standards representative for organizations such as the National Centers of Manufacturing Sciences, Texas Instruments, and MSC. Software. He served on the Object Management Group's (OMG) Board of Directors for three years and was co-chair of the OMG Manufacturing Domain Task Force for six years. Larry was co-chair/facilitator for two Joint Product Data Management (PDM) Enablers Submission Teams, and also co-chaired two of the PDM Revision Task Forces in the OMG. At Texas Instruments he was elected Member, Group Technical Staff, where he served as CAD/CAM/CIM Infrastructure Architect for 15 years.

Kamlani, Deepak

Deepak Kamlani is President and CEO of Global Inventures, Inc., a leader in the incubation of technology initiatives and the growth of collaborative communities around these initiatives. Inventures has helped create, structure, and grow communities in the communications infrastructure, broadband connectivity, information technology, service delivery, and multimedia web applications markets. The firm also produces conferences, provides diligence services to venture capital companies, and "C" level technology strategy consulting services to enterprises.

Kamlani's experience is focused on voice, data, and video products and services on enterprise, home, building, and wide area networks that utilize Switched, IP, and wireless infrastructure, and he has held P and L management, senior marketing, product management, and strategy and business development roles for leading US, UK, and Japanese high tech companies. He plans to play in a blues band when he grows up.

Kempf, James

James Kempf has worked in the high tech industry in Silicon Valley since 1983. For 13 years, James worked at Sun Microsystems, involved in the development of mobile computer operating systems and wireless networking, among other areas. In 2001, James moved to DoCoMo Labs USA, which is the US research laboratory for NTT DoCoMo—the leading Japanese cell phone company. Since 1997, James has been active in the IETF, and is currently a member of the Internet Architecture Board and Working Group co-chair of two working groups.

Krechmer, Ken

Ken Krechmer has participated in communications standards development since the mid-1970s. He actively participated in the development of the International Telecommunications Union Recommendations T.30, V.8, V.8bis, V.32, V.32bis, V.34, V.90, and G.994.1. Krechmer was the technical editor of *Communications Standards Review and Communications Standards Summary, 1990–2002.* In 1995 and 2000, he won first prize at the World Standards Day paper competition. He was Program Chair of the Standards and Innovation in Information Technology (SIIT) conferences in 2001 and 2003. Krechmer is a Fellow at the University of Colorado at Boulder, Colorado,

USA, International Center for Standards Research, and a senior member of the IEEE. His current activities are focused on research and teaching about standards.

Kremen, Gary

Gary Kremen has over fifteen years experience with emerging growth companies and developing information technology. He is currently the President and CEO of Grant Media Management Inc., the managing member of Grant Media LLC. Grant Media, LLC is a highly profitable Internet traffic distributor owning numerous web sites, including Galaxysearch.com and Sex.com. Previously, Kremen was President of NetAngels.Com, Inc., a 40 person company solely focused on Internet profiling and personalization. The company merged with Firefly Network, Inc. (Agents, Inc.) in late 1996, which was later merged with Microsoft. From 1993 through March 1996, Kremen founded and was Chairman of the Board of Electric Classifieds, Inc./Match.Com, the leading on-line classifieds advertising technology outsourcing company and perhaps one of the most widely accessed communities on the Internet.

Kremen is a frequent speaker on on-line marketing, business development, and capital raising for emerging growth companies. He is the primary inventor of the seminal US patent for creating Internet web pages dynamically, patent #5706434, and is ranked in the Top 100 Internet Entrepreneurs according to *MicroTimes Magazine*.

Leidner, Alan

Assistant Commissioner Alan Leidner currently serves as Director of the New York City GIS Utility within the Department of Information Technology and Telecommunications. Mr. Leidner has worked for NYC government for the past thirty-five years. Following the attack on the World Trade Center, Mr. Leidner directed the Emergency Mapping and Data Center (EMDC) for the City's Office of Emergency Management.

Liikanen, Erkki

On 16 September 1999, Mr. Erkki Liikanen was appointed as Member of the European Commission responsible for enterprise and information society.

Prior to his current appointment, Mr. Liikanen served (from 1995 to 1999) as Member of the European Commission, responsible for budget issues, personnel, and internal administration. From 1990–1994 Mr. Liikanen was the Ambassador Extraordinary and Plenipotentiary from Finland to the European Union. During that period Finland negotiated the Accession to the European Union.

Mr. Liikanen was elected to the Finnish Parliament in 1972 at the age of 21. He served there until his appointment at Foreign Office in 1990. From 1987 to 1990 he was Minister of Finance of Finland. From 1976 to 1979 Mr. Liikanen was a Member of the Supervisory Board of Televa Corporation. He then chaired the Supervisory Board of Outokumpu Corporation (1983–1988).

Mr. Liikanen was Vice-Chairman of the Parliamentary Trustees of the Bank of Finland in 1983–1987 (also the decision-making body of the Finnish National Fund for Research and Development (Sitra). In addition, he was a Member of the Science and Technology Policy Council of Finland in 1987–1990. Mr. Liikanen has a Masters degree in political science specializing in economics from the University of Helsinki, Finland.

Lofgren, Zoe

Congresswoman Zoe Lofgren represents the 16th District, California. She was elected in 1994 as the only freshman Democrat from west of the Rocky Mountains. Currently, Congresswoman Lofgren serves on the Select Committee on Homeland Security, serving as the Ranking Member of the Subcommittee on Cybersecurity, Science and Research and Development. She also serves on the Committee on the Judiciary: Subcommittee on Courts, the Internet, and Intellectual Property; and the Subcommittee on Immigration and Claims. She also serves on the Committee of Science: Subcommittee on

Environment Technology and Standards and on the Subcommittee on Research. In 2003, Congresswoman Lofgren was elected by her California Democratic colleagues to serve as the Chair of the California Democratic Congressional Delegation.

Her key legislative initiatives include the introduction of legislation to accelerate the development of fusion as a long-term energy source, which was included in the comprehensive House energy bill (H.R. 4). In addition, Lofgren successfully fought to initiate the "e-rate" that provides affordable Internet access for schools, libraries, and rural health centers. She also served as Democratic floor manager for the 21st Century Patent Improvement Act and initiated the SAFE Act to ease export control on encryption.

Congresswoman Lofgren has received numerous awards including the BAYMEC Award (September 2002), the TechNet Founder's Circle Award (May 2000), and was named "Cyber Champion" by the Business Software Alliance.

Markel, Scott

Dr. Scott Markel is a Research Fellow at LION bioscience Inc. where he is responsible for providing scientific and architectural direction in the development of software for the life sciences, including the use and development of standards. He is a co-chair of the Life Sciences Research (LSR) Domain Task Force of the Object Management Group (OMG). He also chairs the LSR's Architecture and Roadmap Working Group and is a member of the OMG Board of Directors. He is on the Editorial Board for Briefings in Bioinformatics.

Prior to working at LION Dr. Markel worked at NetGenics, Johnson & Johnson Pharmaceutical Research & Development, and Sarnoff Corporation. He has a Ph.D. in mathematics from the University of Wisconsin-Madison. He recently co-authored "Sequence Analysis in a Nutshell: A Guide to Common Tools and Databases," published by O'Reilly & Associates.

Marks, Roger B.

Dr. Roger B. Marks is with the National Institute of Standards and Technology (NIST) in Boulder,

Colorado, USA. In 1998, he initiated the effort that led to the IEEE 802.16 Working Group, chairing that standardization group since inception and leading it through the development of the WirelessMAN™ standard for broadband wireless metropolitan area networks. He also serves on the Executive Committee of the IEEE 802 LAN/MAN Standards Committee. Marks received his A.B. in Physics from Princeton and his Ph.D. in Applied Physics from Yale. Author of over 80 publications, he received the 2003 Individual Governmental Vision Award from the Wireless Communications Association and a 1995 IEEE Technical Field Award.

Morris, John B., Jr.

John B. Morris, Jr. is the Director of the Internet Standards, Technology and Policy Project for the Center for Democracy and Technology (CDT). Previously, as a partner in the law firm of Jenner & Block, Mr. Morris litigated groundbreaking cases in Internet and First Amendment law, including the ACLU v. Reno case, in which the Supreme Court unanimously extended to speech on the Internet the highest level of constitutional protection.

Prior to becoming a lawyer, Mr. Morris had significant experience in the computer industry and was a founder of Intelligent Solutions, Inc., which grew to become the leading developer of office management software for Members of the U.S. Congress. Mr. Morris graduated from Yale College and Yale Law School, where he was the Managing Editor of the Yale Law Journal.

Munden, Stephen

Stephen Munden is Head of Stakeholder Policy department at the UK's National Standards Body, British Standards Institution (BSI). The role involves the development and implementation of polices and strategies to meet BSI's public interest obligations. In addition, Mr. Munden is responsible for maintaining close working relationships, ongoing dialogue, and strategic consultation with government, industry, and representatives of societal organisations. He is one of the principle architects of the UK's National Standardization Strategic Framework.

Prior to joining BSI two years ago, he was manager of technical affairs for Eastman Kodak Company's European, African, and Middle Eastern Region, a role that involved using standards to achieve corporate objectives. He holds an MBA (Technology Management) and is a Fellow of the Institute of Quality Assurance.

Noth, Robert W.

As Manager of Engineering Standards for Deere & Company, Bob is responsible for overseeing the development, deployment, utilization, and administration of standards affecting the John Deere product line worldwide.

A graduate of the University of Dubuque with a BA in mathematics, Bob joined Deere in 1965. He has held a variety of positions in Manufacturing Engineering and Management in his career, assuming his current position in 1992.

Bob is active on a global scale in professional societies, trade associations, and standards developing organizations. He is currently a Vice-Chairman of ANSI and chairs the International Policy Committee.

Reed, Carl

Dr. Carl Reed is the Executive Director for the Open GIS Consortium Specification Program. Prior to his current position, Dr. Reed was an independent GIS consultant. Before this, Dr. Reed was VP of Infrastructure Marketing at Intergraph. Before Intergraph, Reed was President and CTO for Genasys II, a GIS software company.

From 1980 until 1986, Reed was GIS Division Manager for Autometric Inc. He obtained his Ph.D. in GIS from SUNY Buffalo in 1979. His accomplishments include designing and implementing two major GIS packages, MOSS and GenaMap. Dr. Reed has published dozens of papers and given numerous GIS conference keynotes. In 1996, in recognition of his contributions to the GIS industry, Dr. Reed was voted by the industry as one of the top ten most influential people in the GIS industry.

Reichardt, Mark

Mark Reichardt serves as Executive Director of the Outreach and Community Adoption Program for the Open GIS Consortium. His responsibilities include the development and implementation of marketing and communications programs and interoperability initiatives to encourage adoption of OGC specifications by technology development and user communities. Mr. Reichardt is also responsible for retaining and growing membership, and encouraging investment in OGC programs.

Mr. Reichardt joined OGC after a 20-year career in mapping with the Department of Defense. His career included several assignments, which included a two-year assignment with the Federal Geographic Data Committee to implement a program focused on building spatial data infrastructure in Africa, South America, Europe, Asia, and the Caribbean.

Scott, Anthony E.

Anthony E. (Tony) Scott is the Chief Technology Officer for GM's Information Systems and Services (IS&S) organization. He joined GM on September 1, 1999. Scott is responsible for defining the information technology computing and telecommunications architecture and standards across all of GM's business globally. He provides leadership in the areas of IT architecture and standards, and emerging technology. His work at GM has included the development of GM's employee portal (a collaboration between GM, Daimler-Chrysler, AOL, Sun Microsystems, and Workscape), development of GM's wireless implementation strategy, and directing GM's involvement in external IT standards bodies and technology consortium organizations. He was named "CTO of the Year – Manufacturing Sector" by Infoworld Magazine in 2001, and is a regular panelist and speaker at a variety of information technology events and seminars.

He joined GM from Bristol-Myers Squibb where he was Vice President, Information Management. Scott also held positions as a Senior Director with Price Waterhouse; Vice President of Engineering with Uniteq Application Systems; and Manager, Worldwide Information Resources with Sun Microsystems.

Sheldon, Jack

Jack Sheldon has worked at the IEC since 1983 and currently occupies the position of Strategic Development Manager, having previously worked in standards development and overseen the transformation of the IEC from a paper-based to a paperless organization.

Prior to joining the IEC he worked as an electronics engineer in a number of European-based IT and telecommunications companies. He has an MA in Natural Sciences from Cambridge University and an MBA from the Open University.

Smith, Mike

Mike Smith was appointed Technical Director of ISO in 1989 and in 1995 also assumed responsibility for the Standards production department and the secretariat of the ISO Technical Management Board. He joined ISO in 1978 as a technical editor, and subsequently was the technical officer responsible for the building and civil engineering field from 1984 to 1987, and for the information technology field from 1987 to 1989.

Smith holds a degree in chemistry from the University of London and worked with the British Standards Institution from 1973 to 1978 in the construction and chemical departments.

Stokes, Adrian V.

Adrian V. Stokes is Chief Executive of CAT Ltd., a small consultancy company specialising in health informatics, standardisation, and computer networking. He worked in the UK National Health Service (NHS) for nearly twenty years and is currently a Non-Executive Director of three NHS organisations. He has been involved in international standardisation for 25 years and has represented the UK at many international standards meetings, including being head of delegation at ISO/IEC JTC 1, ISO/TC 215, and CEN/TC 251.

Dr. Stokes has written thirteen books and over 150 papers on various aspects of computer technology and has lectured in many countries of the world. At University College London he obtained a B.Sc. (First Class Honours) and a Ph.D., and was awarded an honorary Doctorate of Science by the University of Hertfordshire.

He was Visiting Professor at University College Northampton for six years.

Susaki, Ayato

Ayato Susaki is a researcher/consultant at Mitsubishi Research Institute; Science and Technology Research Division. His research field covers public policies, science and technology policies, and R&D/intellectual property strategies.

Takaya, Toru

Toru Takaya is a researcher and consultant at Science and Technology Policy Department, Mitsubishi Research Institute. His research field covers the telecommunications industry, management of technology, and science and technology policies.

Tanaka, Hidehisa

Hidehisa Tanaka is a Senior Researcher at Mitsubishi Research Institute, Inc. in Tokyo, Japan. Since 2002, he has taken charge of coordinating the "Study Group on Standardization and Intellectual Properties" hosted by the Ministry of Economy, Trade, and Industry of Japan. His research includes: (1) the integration of R&D and standard setting, and (2) issues on intellectual properties for the promotion of new business development by enterprises and international competitiveness of Japan.

Terpstra, John H.

John H. Terpstra is CEO/President with PrimaStasys, Inc., a company that mentors information technology companies and facilitates profitable change in practices. John is also CEO of Fabuluss Software, Inc.—an innovative company that is working to popularize next generation desktop productivity enhancements. John is a well-known contributor and visionary in the open source community with a very active commercial focus. He is co-founder of the Samba-Team and a member of the Open Source Software Institute Advisory Board. He has worked with the LSB, Li18nux (now OpenI18N.Org), is a best selling author of *The Official Samba-3 HOWTO and Reference Guide,* ISBN: 0131453556. He has other books in production. John has worked with The SCO Group (previously Caldera Inc.),

TurboLinux Inc., in VP level positions. Prior to moving to the USA in 1999, John founded and managed Aquasoft Pty Ltd (Aust.) for 10 years. He has a Graduate Diploma in Marketing (with Credit), UTS Aust. and an Applied Science Certificate in Chemistry, QUT (Aust.).

Udall, Mark

Mark Udall has represented Colorado's second congressional district in Congress since 1998, and won his last election with 62% of the vote. A member of the House Resources Committee, Udall sits on the Subcommittee on National Parks, Recreation and Public Lands and the Subcommittee on Forests and Forest Health. Udall is also a member of the House Science Committee and sits on the Subcommittee on Space and Aeronautics, and is Ranking Member on the Subcommittee on Environment, Technology and Standards. Udall also sits on the House Agriculture Committee.

Mark made his entrance into politics in 1997 as a representative in the Colorado State House. He graduated from Williams College in 1972 with a bachelor's degree in American Civilization. Mark developed a long and successful career with the Colorado Outward Bound School, as a course director and educator from 1975-85 and as the organization's Executive Director from 1985-95. Mark is an avid mountain climber and has climbed or attempted some of the world's most challenging peaks, including Mt. Everest.

Updegrove, Andrew

Andrew Updegrove, a partner in the Boston law firm of Lucash, Gesmer and Updegrove LLP, has been helping to create standard setting and promotional consortia since 1988. He has been retained by many of the largest technology companies in the world to assist them in forming consortia and has written and spoken frequently on consortia and standard setting. Recently, he gave testimony to the Department of Justice and Federal Trade Commission on the same topics. In 2002, he created www.ConsortiumInfo.org, the most detailed and comprehensive source on the Internet on standard setting and consortia. Mr. Updegrove is a graduate of Yale University and the Cornell University Law School.

Uthurusamy, Ramasamy

Ramasamy Uthurusamy is currently General Director of Emerging Technologies at GM. He received his Ph.D. from Purdue University. He has taught at Purdue University and at the University of Idaho. At GM, he leads the emerging technologies initiatives in the Global Technology Management Group headed by Tony Scott, GM Chief Technology Officer. His professional interests and expertise spans four major areas: Knowledge Discovery in Databases and Data Mining (KDD); Artificial Intelligence; Knowledge Management; and Advanced Web Technologies. He received the "Distinguished Service Award" from ACM SIGKDD for his active involvement in KDD. He received the Charles McCuen Special Achievement Award from General Motors R&D Center for part of his work in GM-specific applications in these areas. He was one of the 2002 Winter Olympics Torchbearers.

Vardakas, Evangelos

Mr. Vardakas joined the Directorate General for Industry of the European Commission with the rank of Director in January 1991. The Commission services under Mr. Vardakas' leadership are responsible for Single market, regulatory environment, standardisation, and New approach.

In January 1984 he was nominated Secretary General (CEO) of CEN, the European Committee for Standardisation. He guided CEN for seven important years, covering the period when reference to standards in the legislation of the European Union was being introduced, and when the first important steps were being taken for the implementation of the "New Approach" in the technical legislation of the European Union. In the 1970s he was instrumental in the establishment of ELOT, the Greek Standards Body and Greek member of ISO and IEC. He served as Deputy Managing Director of ELOT for seven years.

Yamauchi, Toru

Mr. Yamauchi is the Director of Industrial Standards Research Office for METI (Ministry of Economy, Trade, and Industry) and is in charge of standardization policy as a JISC secretariat. His main task is to plan a policy addressing the issues of patents included in standards.

In 1985, Mr. Yamauchi entered MITI (Ministry of International Trade and Industry), Japan. He has been working for industrial technology policy as a senior government official. He earned an M.S degree in Engineering Management, Stanford University, in 2002.

Zevin, Susan F.

Dr. Susan F. Zevin is the Acting Director of the Information Technology Laboratory (ITL) of the National Institute of Standards and Technology (NIST), U. S. Department of Commerce. Prior to joining ITL, Dr. Zevin was with the National Oceanic and Atmospheric Administration (NOAA), serving as the Deputy Assistant Administrator for the National Environmental Satellite Data and Information Service, and as the Deputy Assistant Administrator, National Weather Service. Dr. Zevin received a B.A degree from the University of Pittsburgh, an M.S. from the University of Tel Aviv, and a Ph.D. from the University of Arizona. She was awarded the University of Arizona Alumni Distinguished Citizen Award in 1996. She is a Fellow of the American Meteorological Society.

Zhao, Houlin

Mr. Zhao was elected Director of Telecommunication Standardization Bureau (TSB), International Telecommunication Union (ITU) at the 1998 Plenipotentiary Conference in Minneapolis (USA), and took office on 1 February 1999. Since 1993, he has served as TSB Counsellor for ITU-T Study Group 7 (Data networks and open system communications) and Study Group 8 (Characteristics of telematic systems). He is ITU-T's coordinator with the International Organization for Standardization (ISO), the International Electrotechnical Commission (IEC) and their

Joint Technical Committee 1 (JTC1). His record of maintaining excellent collaboration with these bodies, where he has combined technical expertise, diplomacy, firmness, and flexibility, has ensured that ITU-T's interests are safeguarded in the development of joint standards.

From 1975 to 1986, he worked as an engineer in the Designing Institute of the Chinese Ministry of Posts and Telecommunications, responsible for projects in the areas of telex, data communication, non-voice transmission, telephone switching, and mobile networks. He took an active part in his country's experts meetings on national telecommunication standards. He received a second prize in 1985 for his science and technology achievements in the Ministry of Posts and Telecommunications. In addition, his work in the Departments of Planning, Capital Construction, and Network Maintenance in the Ministry earned him an engineering project prize for his outstanding performance and contributions in the planning, designing, and construction of a number of major national network projects.

Zilles, Stephen N.

Mr. Zilles has had experience in standardization at the international, national, and consortium levels. He joined Adobe Systems to lead their Standard Page Description Language (SPDL) effort and was one of the ISO 10180 (SPDL) editors. While at Adobe he also took a lead role in the development of standards for the management of network and desktop printers and presentation document interchange. He was an author of the SNMP Printer MIB and the DMTF Printer MIF. He has been active in the standardization of the PDF, most recently with CGATS SC 6. Besides his W3C work, he is active in a number of standards related to the electronic distribution of information, including text formatting and presentation: ANSI X3V1, ISO JTC 1/SC 18/WG 8, IETF, CGATS, DDAP, and EDI. He is currently an independent consultant. Prior to joining Adobe Mr. Zilles was with IBM for 29 years.

Acronym Glossary

21CN	21st Century Network
3GPP	Third generation Partnership Project

A

A2LA	American Association for Laboratory Accreditation
ACATS	Advisory Committee on Advanced Television Services
ACIF	Australian Communications Industry Forum
ACR	American College of Radiologists
ADR	Alternative Dispute Resolution
ADSL	Asymmetric digital subscriber line
AFNOR	Association Française de Normalisation
AGMA	American Gear Manufacturers Association
AIAG	Automotive Industries Action Group
AMI-C	Automotive Multimedia Interface Collaboration
ANSI	American National Standards Institute
APEC	Asia Pacific Economic Cooperation
APIs	Application programming interfaces
ASA	American Standards Association
ASAE	American Society of Agricultural Engineers
ASC	Accredited Standards Committee
ASME	American Society of Mechanical Engineers

ASN.1	Abstract Syntax Notation One
ASPRS	Accuracy Standards for Large-Scale Maps
ASTM	American Society for Testing and Materials
ATIS	The Alliance for Telecommunications Industry Solutions
ATM	Asynchronous transfer mode
AUS	Automated Underwriting System (MISMO)

B

B2B	Business to business
BQS	Bibliographic Query Service
BSA	Biomolecular Sequence Analysis
BSANE	Biomolecular Sequence Analysis Entitites
BSI	British Standards Institution

C

CAD	Computer-aided design
CAP	College of American Pathologists
CBI	Confederation of British Industry
CCITT	Previous name of the ITU–T; International Consultative Committee on Telephony and Telegraphy
CDIA	Computer Industry Data Association
CDMA	Code division multiple access
CDT	Center for Democracy and Technology

CEE	International Commission on Rules for the Approval of Electrical Equipment
CEN	European Committee for Standardization (Conseil Européen Normalisation)
CENELEC	European Committee for Electrotechnical Standardization
CGATS	Committee on Graphic Arts Technology Standards (ANSI)
CIFS	Common Internet File System
CLEC	Competitive Local Exchange Carrier
CML	Chemical Markup Language
CMM	Capability Maturity Model
CMRS	Commercial Mobile Radio Service
CMU	Carnegie Mellon University
CMVP	Cryptographic Module Validation Program
CobiT	Control Objectives for Information and Related Technology
CompTIA	Computing Technology Industry Association
CORBA	Common Object Request Broker Architecture (OMG)
COS	Corporation for Open Systems
CPA	Cost per action
CPC	Pay per click
CPM	Cost per thousand
CPTWG	Copy Protection Technical Working Group
CSE	Canadian Security Establishment
CTO	Chief Technical Officers

D

DARPA	Defense Advanced Research Projects Agency
DICOM	Digital Imaging and Communications in Medicine
Diffserv	Differentiated Services (IETF)
DIN	German Institute for Standardization (Deutsche Institut fuer Normung)
DoC	Department of Commerce
DoITT	Department of Information Technology & Communications
DSIG	Domain Special Interest Group
DSL	Digital subscriber line
DTF	Domain Task Force (LSR)
DTMF	Dual Tone Multi Frequency
DTV	Digital television

DVB	Digital video broadcasting

E

ECJ	Court of Justice of the European Communities
ECMA	European Computer Manufacturers Association
EDI	Electronic Data Interchange
EDIFACT	Electronic Data Interchange for Administration Commerce and Transport
EESSI	European Electronic Signatures Standardisation Initiative
EFTA	European Free Trade Association
eGIF	E-Government Interoperability Framework (U.K.)
EIA	Electronics Industry Association
EICTA	European Information and Communication Technology Industry Association
EJB	Enterprise Java Beans
EMOLS	Emergency Management Online Locator System (NYC)
EPA	Environmental Protection Agency
EPDP	Enterprise Product Development Process Council
ERCIM	European Research Consortium for Informatics and Mathematics
ESAP	eEurope Action Plan
ESO	European Standards Organization
ESRI	Environmental Systems Research Institute
ETSI	European Telecommunications Standards Institute
European Court of Justice	Court of Justice of the European Communities
EWOS	European Workshop for Open Systems

F

FCC	Federal Communications Commission
FCSDO	Formal communications standards development organizations
FDDI	Fiber Distributed Data Interface
FEMA	Federal Emergency Management Agency
FRAND	Fair, reasonable and non-discriminatory
FS-VDSL	Full Service very high speed Digital Subscriber Line

FSAN   Full Service Access Network
FSF   Free Software Foundation
FUD   Fear, uncertainty, and doubt

G

GEML   Gene Expression Markup Language
GILT   Globalization Internationalization, Localization, and Translation
GIS   Geographic information systems
GM   General Motors Corporation
GMAC   General Motors Acceptance Corporation
GMI2004 Global MSF Interoperability demonstration
GML   Geography Markup Language
GNU   "GNU's Not Unix!" (Free Software Foundation)
GPL   General Public License
GSM   Global system for mobile communications
GTL   Global Transport Label

H

HIMSS   Healthcare Information and Management Systems Society
HIPAA   Health Insurance Portability and Accountability Act
HPNA   Home Phoneline Networking Alliance
HTI+   Home Technology Integrator

I

IAB   Internet Architecture Board
ICSCA   International Cooperation on Standards and Conformity Assessment
ICT   Information and Communications Technologies
ICTSB   Information and Communications Technologies Standards Board
IDL   Interface Definition Language
IEC   International Electrotechnical Commission
IEEE   Institute of Electrical and Electronics Engineers
IESG   Internet Engineering Steering Group
IETF   Internet Engineering Task Force
IFK   Internationale Fragens Kommission (International Questions Commission)
IFS   Informal Forum Summit

IHA   Internet Home Alliance
IHE   Integrating the Healthcare Enterprise
IIOP   Internet Inter-ORB Protocol™
ILEC   Incumbent local exchange carriers
IMEI   Interactive Map for Emergency Information
IMT 2000 International Mobile Telecommunications 2000 standards (ITU)
INCITS International Committee for Information Technology Standards
INRIA   National Institute for Research in Computer Science and Control
IP   Internet–Protocol or Intellectual property
IRTF   Internet Research Task Force
ISO   International Organization for Standardization
ISOC   The Internet Society
ISP   Internet Service Provider
ISSS   Information Society Standardization System
ISWG   Interoperability Services Working Group
ITAs   Industry Technical Agreements
ITIC   Information Technology Industry Council
ITIL   Information Technology Infrastructure Library
ITU   International Telecommunications Union

J

JCP   Java™ Community Process
JIRA   Japan Industries Association for Radiological Systems
JTC1   Joint Technical Committee 1 (ISO/IEC)

L

LAN   Local Area Network
LAN/MAN Local/Metropolitan Area Networks
LIF   Location Interoperability Forum
LISA   Localization Industry Standards Association
LLD   Logical Data Dictionary (MISMO)
LSR   Life Sciences Research

M

MAGE   Microarray Gene Expression
MAML   Microarray Markup Language
MAN   Metropolitan Area Networks
ManTIS Manufacturing and Industrial Systems Task Force
MAP   Manufacturing Automation Protocol
MDA   Model Driven Architecture®
MEDIS-DC Medical Information System Development Centre
MEF   Metro Ethernet Switching Forum
METI   Ministry of Economy, Trade and Industry (Japan)
MfgDTF Manufacturing Domain Task Force
MGED   Open Source Microarray Gene Expression Database
MIP   Mortgage insurance premium
MISMO   Mortgage Industry Standards Maintenance Organization
MISRA   Motor Industry Software Reliability Association
MIT   Massachusetts Institute of Technology
MMS   Macromolecular Structures
MOF   Meta Object Facility™
MPLS   Multi-Protocol Label Switching (IETF)
MSAN   Multi-Service Access Node
MSF   Multiservice Switching Forum

N

N-WEST National Wireless Electronic Systems Testbed
NASED   National Association of State Election Directors
NCMS   National Center for Manufacturing Science
NEMA   National Electronic Manufacturers' Association
NGN   Next (or New) Generation Network
NIAP   National Information Assurance Partnership
NIST   National Institute of Standards and Technology
NSA   National Security Agency
NSSF   National Standardization Strategic Framework
NTSB   National Transportation Safety Board

NTTAA   National Technology Transfer Advancement Act
NVLAP   National Voluntary Laboratory Accreditation Program (NIST)

O

OASIS   Organization for the Advancement of Structured Information Standards
OEM   Office of Emergency Management (NYC)
OGC   Open GIS Consortium
OMA   Open Mobile Alliance
OMB   Office of Management and Budget
OMG   Object Management Group
ONM   Office of New Media (NYC)
OPES   Open Pluggable Edge Services (IETF)
OSCAR   Open Standards for Container/Content Allowing Re-use
OSI   Open Systems Interconnect
OSS   Open Source Software
OTA   Congressional Office of Technology Assessment

P

P3P   Platform for Privacy Preferences (W3C)
PAS   Publicly Available Specification Process
PCB   Printed circuit boards
PDES   Product Data Exchange Specification, Inc.
PDF   Portable Document Format
PDM   Product Data Management system
PICMG   PCI Industrial Computer Manufacturers Group
PKI   Public Key Infrastructure
PMI   Private mortgage insurance
POTS   Public switched telephone network
PPC   Pay per click
Project 1157 MEDIX project (IEEE)
PSAP   Public Safety Answering Point
PSTN   Public switched telephone network

Q

QoS   Quality of service

R

RAND   Reasonable and Nondiscriminatory
R&D   Research and development

RF	Royalty Free
RFC	Request for Comments (IETF)
RFID	Radio Frequency Identification
RIM	Reference Implementation Model
RM-OSI	Reference Model of Open Systems Interconnection (ISO)
RMI	Remote Method Invocation
ROI	Return on investment
RRMC	Rapid Response Manufacturing Consortium (NIST)
RSNA	Radiological Society of North America
RTLS	Real Time Locating Systems

S

SAE	Society for Automotive Engineers
SBU	Strategic Business Unit
SDoC	Self-Declaration of Compliance
SDOs	Standards developing organizations
SDRC	Structural Dynamics Research Corporation
SGML	Standard Generalized Markup Language
SIP	Session Initiatian Protocol
SMB	Server Message Block
SMDS	Switched Multimegabit Data Service
SNOMED	Systematized Nomenclature of Medicine (CAP)
SOA	GM Service Oriented Architecture
SPDL	Standard Page Description Language
SQL	Structured Query Language
SSM	Strategic Standardization Management (GM)
SSOs	Standards Setting Organizations
SSRC	Strategic Standards, Regulations, and Conformity Assessment Enterprise Council (John Deere)
STAR	Standards for Technology in Automotive Retail
STEP	STandard for the Exchange of Product Model Data

T

TABD	Trans-Atlantic Business Dialogue
TBTA	Technical Barriers to Trade Agreement
TCC	Trade Compliance Center
TCN	The Credit Network
TDLA	Technology License and Distribution Agreement

TDMA	Time division multiple access
TIA	Telecommunications Industry Association
TMF	TeleManagement Forum
TMX	Translation Memory eXchange
TOP	Technical Office Protocol
TOPS	Technical Operations Council
TRIPS	Trade–Related Intellectual Property Rights (WTO)
TTA	Telecommunications Technology Association
TTC	Telecommunications Technology Committee

U

UL	Underwriter's Laboratories
UML	Unified Modeling Language™
UNECE	United Nations Economic Commission for Europe
UNEs	Unbundled network elements
URLA	Universal Residential Loan Application
USASI	United States of America Standards Institute (ANSI)
USTR	United States Trade Representative

V

VAR	Value Added Reseller
VDSL	Very high speed digital subscriber line
VIN	Vehicle identification number
VITA	VMEbus International Trade Association
VoIP	Voices over IP

W

W3C	World Wide Web Consortium
WAP	Wireless Application Protocol
WEEB	Western European EDIFACT Board
Wi-Fi	Wireless fidelity
WiMAX	Worldwide Interoperability for Microwave Access Forum
WTO	World Trade Organization

X

XMI	XML Metadata Interchange
XML	eXtensible Markup Language

Index

and European Union, 52, 110
patents on, 41, 53, 158
Global Transport Label, 276
Glynias, Manuel, 319, 330
GM. *See* General Motors Corporation
GMAC. *See* General Motors Acceptance Corporation
GMI2004. *See* Global MSF Interoperability demonstration
GML. *See* Geography Markup Language
GM Service Oriented Architecture, 275
GM Smart Auction, 275
Gnome (OSS software), 261
GNU compression utility, 318 (n 12)
GNU General Public License, 23, 25, 28 (n16), 255, 264 (nn 1,2)
Goodden, Richard, 272, 287–292, 357
Goodman, Nat, 324
Google, 303, 311, 316, 317 (n 3)
Gosling, James, 7
"Got Milk®" marketing campaign, 6
governance structures, 17–19
government and standards, 10, 15–28, 77–144, 274, 283
geospatial standards, 235, 238, 239, 240
impact on trade, 51–52
responsibilities, 40, 42, 48, 58–59
GPL. *See* GNU General Public License
Grant Media, LLC, 303–318
the graveyard, 184, 188
"ground truth", 317 (n 1)
GSM. *See* global system for mobile communications
GTL. *See* Global Transport Label
GUI, 35
Guide 2 (ISO/IEC), 156
gzip compression, 309–310, 318 (n 12)

H

hackers, 260
"harmonized standards", 84
Hatfield, Dale N., 78, 137–144, 357
Hatori, Kenichi, 179
HAZMAT, 349, 350
Healthcare DTF, 324
Healthcare Information and Management Systems Society, 343
health informatics, 341–345
Health Insurance Portability and Accountability Act, 121
"heating centers", 290
Hebner, Robert E., 77, 103–114, 357
Help American Vote Act of 2002, 120
heterogeneity, 13

Hewlett-Packard Company, 24, 156, 157, 182, 187, 209–213
high volume/high margin markets. *See* monopolies
high volume/low margin markets. *See* commodity markets
Hill, John, 47–49, 357
HIMSS. *See* Healthcare Information and Management Systems Society
HIPAA. *See* Health Insurance Portability and Accountability Act
Hitotsubashi University, 175
HL7 consortium, 342, 343, 344–345
homeland security, 93
Home Phoneline Networking Alliance, 301
Home Technology Integrator, 276
homogeneity, 13
Hoover, Herbert, 20
HPNA. *See* Home Phoneline Networking Alliance
HTI+. *See* Home Technology Integrator
HTML, 38, 45 (n15), 205, 229, 309–310, 320
HTTP, 38, 229, 349
Hurricane Evacuation, 290, 291
hyperlinks, 205

I

IAB. *See* Internet Architecture Board
IBM, 24, 152, 156, 204, 262, 289
research and development, 200–201
ICAD, 152 (n3)
ICSCA. *See* International Cooperation on Standards and Conformity Assessment
ICTSB. *See* Standards Board (ICT)
IDC, 182
IDL. *See* Interface Definition Language
IEC. *See* International Electrotechnical Commission
IEC Publication 83, 67
IEEE. *See* Institute of Electrical and Electronics Engineers
IEEE 802, 110–111, 250
802.11, 112
802.11 card, 44 (n3), 280, 301, 302
802.16, 112
IESG. *See* Internet Engineering Steering Group
IETF. *See* Internet Engineering Task Force
IFK. *See* Internationale Fragens Kommission
IFS. *See* Informal Forum Summit
IHA. *See* Internet Home Alliance
IHE. *See* Integrating the Healthcare Enterprise
IIOP. *See* Internet Inter-ORB Protocol™
ILEC. *See* incumbent local exchange carriers
IMEI. *See* Interactive Map for Emergency Information

Jarman, Rick, 149
Java™, 10, 146, 155–167, 261, 289
   and life sciences, 319, 320, 321
   in New York City, 291
   portable technology, 8, 205
Java™ Community Process, 222, 226, 227
JCP. *See* Java™ Community Process
JEDEC Solid State Technology Association legal case, 205
JIRA. *See* Japan Industries Association for Radiological Systems
John Deere, 271, 281–285
Johnson, Larry L., 145, 147–153, 358
"joined-up thinking", 237
Joint Development Agreements, 250, 251, 252
Joint Technical Committee 1 (ISO/IEC), 45 (n16), 159–160, 170, 246, 299
   and Java™, 156, 158
   text presentation metafile, 267
Joint Technical Committee for Health Informatics, 342
JPEG, 172
JTC1. *See* Joint Technical Committee 1 (ISO/IEC)
Justice Department. *See* Department of Justice

K

Kalil, Thomas, 236
Kamlani, Deepak, 182, 199–208, 358
Kanoodle, 308, 316
Kant, Immanuel, 201, 208 (n2)
Kato, Hisashi, 179
KDE (OSS software), 261
Keio University, 42, 45 (n14)
Kempf, James, 6, 71–75, 358
Kennard, William, 138
kernels, 229
Ketchell, John, 36
Knowledge Technology International, 152 (n3)
Konnerth, Karl, 324
Kozuka, Souichirou, 179
Krechmer, Ken, 6, 51–60, 359–359
Kremen, Gary, 303–318, 359
Kristofferson, Kris, 263
Kuhn, Thomas, 164
Kultti, K., 164

L

LAN. *See* Local Area Network
LandAmerica Info1, 332
LandSafe, 332
Lane, Bob, 282
LAN/MAN Standards Committee. *See* Local/Metropolitan Area Networks Standards Committee

Laserwriter (Apple), 266–267
Leidner, Alan, 272, 287–292, 359
Lentz, Becky, 134
León, Darryl, 330
Lessig, Lawrence, 125, 138, 142
leverage, 199, 257, 274
Lexinomics, LLC, 319–330
liabilities, 339
Liberty Alliance, 275, 297
licensing software, 158, 166
LIF. *See* Location Interoperability Forum
lifecycles, 183, 185, 196
   . *See also* product life cycle
Life Sciences Research, 319–330
life science standards, 271
lifetime of a standard, 13
Liikanen, Erkki, 77, 79–81, 359
Lindows (OSS software), 261
Linux, 25, 35, 194, 205
   development of, 23–24, 257
   and Windows operating system, 263
Linux/open-source business model, 112
Linux Standards Base, 261, 262
Lion Bioscience Inc., 319–330
LISA. *See* Localization Industry Standards Association
"live and die", 318 (n 16)
LLD. *See* Logical Data Dictionary (MISMO)
Local Area Network, 38, 43–44 (n3)
local industry, 103
Localization Industry Standards Association, 278
Local/Metropolitan Area Networks Standards Committee, 110, 112
location based services, 350
Location Interoperability Forum, 296, 301
Lockheed Martin Energy Systems, 152 (n3)
"lock-in" effects, 8, 9, 11, 105–106
Lofgren, Zoe, 78, 99–102, 359–360
Logical Data Dictionary (MISMO), 336
Lotus vs. Borland legal case, 162
Lotus vs. Paperback legal case, 162
"Low Voltage Directive", 83–84, 85
low volume/high margin markets. *See* niche markets
low volume/low margin markets. *See* the graveyard
LSR. *See* Life Sciences Research
Lucash, Gesmer and Updegrove, 182, 209–213, 215–220

M

M114 brick, 53
Macintosh (Apple), 320
MacNeal-Schwendler Corporation, 152 (n3)
Macromolecular Structures, 327

Systematized Nomenclature of Medicine (CAP), 343

United Nations, 55

United Nations Economic Commission for Europe, 87

United States. *See* individual names of departments or agencies

United States of America Standards Institute, 21
. *See also* American National Standards Institute

United States Pharmacopial Convention, 20

United States Trade Representative, 95, 97

United Technologies Corporation, 152 (n3)

universal plugs and sockets, 67–68

Universal Residential Loan Application, 336

University of California legal case, 145

University of Colorado, 6, 51–60, 78, 137–144

University of Helsinki, 23

University of Michigan, 184

University of Texas at Austin, 77, 103–114

University of Tokyo, 179

UNIX® System, 44 (n10), 229, 289, 310, 319, 320
  and Linux, 23–24
  marketplace, 10, 12
  probability, 8

Updegrove, Andrew, 182, 209–213, 215–220, 363

URL, 304, 305, 306

URLA. *See* Universal Residential Loan Application

U.S.. *See* individual names of departments or agencies

USASI. *See* United States of America Standards Institute

USB 1 and 2, 280

U.S. Congress, 78, 99–102

U.S. Constitution, 99

U.S. Defense Department, 296

users, 116, 126–127, 129, 229–234, 273

U.S. government and standards, 107–108

U.S. Government Federal Enterprise Architecture, 240

U.S. House of Representatives, 78, 99–102, 107

U.S. National Standards Strategy (ANSI), 96, 101, 105, 108–109, 111

USTR. *See* United States Trade Representative

Uthurusamy, Ramasamy, 271, 273–280, 363

utilization of standards, 10–13

V

validation, 122

Value Added Reseller, 260

value as strategic choice, 190

value chain, 192, 309

value delivery system, 192

VAR. *See* Value Added Reseller

Vardakas, Evangelos, 77, 83–92, 363

variety reduction, 193–194, 196

VAX/VMS, 11

VDSL. *See* Very high speed Digital Subscriber Line

Veeck legal case, 101

vehicle identification number, 277

Vehicle Services Interface, 278

vendors, 22, 216, 236, 295, 299
. *See also* suppliers

Verhulst, Stefaan, 134

vernier caliper, 27–28 (n13)

Very high speed Digital Subscriber Line, 302

video conferencing, 205

Vienna Agreement, 108, 244

VIN. *See* vehicle identification number

viruses, 348

Visa®, 316

VITA. *See* VMEbus International Trade Association

VMEbus standards, 185–186, 186–187

VMEbus International Trade Association, 183-188

Voice over IP, 294, 302

VoIP. *See* Voice over IP

voluntary standards, 21, 26 (n1)

Voss, Hartmut, 330

W

W3C. *See* World Wide Web Consortium

"walled gardens", 52

WAP. *See* Wireless Application Protocol

Warnock, John, 266

Watanabe, Toshiya, 179

Watson, Thomas, 44 (n6)

wealth creation, 192

Web services, 235

WEEB. *See* Western European EDIFACT Board

Weiss, Martin, 45 (n27)

Werbach, Kevin, 138

West, Joel, 45 (n27)

Western Electric, 141

Western European EDIFACT Board, 342

Wi-Fi. *See* wireless fidelity

wild cats in portfolio matrix, 256

Williamson, Harold, 19

Wilson, Harold, 199

Wilson, Woodrow, 181

WiMAX Forum. *See* Worldwide Interoperability for Microwave Access Forum

Windows operating systems, 145, 163, 205, 261, 320
  2000, 263, 289
  NT, 262

"Wintel", 194

Wired (magazine), 105

wireless access protocol, 302

Wireless Application Protocol, 42, 194, 296